101 PROJECTS
FOR THE
Z80™

Other TAB books by Frank P. Tedeschi:

No. 1060 *303 Dynamic Electronic Circuits*
No. 1133 *The Active Filter Handbook*
No. 1333 *101 Microprocessor Software and Hardware Projects* (with Gary Kueck)

101 PROJECTS
FOR THE
Z80™

BY FRANK P. TEDESCHI & ROBERT COLON

TAB **TAB BOOKS Inc.**
BLUE RIDGE SUMMIT, PA. 17214

Portions of Chapters 1 through 8 appeared in slightly different
form in the *Mostek 1981 Microcomputer Data Book*; copyright © 1981 by
Mostek Corporation. Reprinted by permission of Mostek Corporation.

FIRST EDITION
FIRST PRINTING

Library of Congress Cataloging in Publication Data

Tedeschi, Frank P.
101 projects for the Z80.

Includes index.
1. Zilog Model Z-80 (Computer)—Laboratory manuals.
2. Computer interfaces—Laboratory manuals.
I. Colon, Robert. II. Title. III. Title: One hundred
one projects for Z-eighty. IV. Title: One hundred and
one projects for Z-eighty.
QA76.8.Z54T43 1983   001.64   82-19285
ISBN 0-8306-0491-X
ISBN 0-8306-1491-5 (pbk.)

Contents

10. INTERMEDIATE SOFTWARE PROJECTS 237

11. TELETYPE WRITER PROJECTS 298

12. OSCILLOSCOPE PROJECTS

313

13. MISCELLANEOUS PROJECTS

336

Introduction

This book is for everyone who wants to understand the fundamentals of microcomputer programming and interfacing by performing projects rather than reading and writing programs. Each time microprocessor programming is mentioned a particular set of instructions (programming material), technical data, and hardware must be defined. In preparing this book, we used the SD-Z80 minicomputer trainer. Information for purchasing the trainer is given in Chapter 1. Chapters 2, 3, 4, 5, 6, 7, and 8 provide hardware information, technical data, and the instruction set of the SD-Z80 trainer.

The projects in Chapters 1, 9, 10, 11, 12, and 13 are software and hardware oriented. This feature is not offered in most microprocessor project books. However, a number of software-only projects are offered for the software purist.

The first chapter includes hardware modifications to the basic SD-Z80 minicomputer that are needed to work the projects in Chapters 10, 11, 12, and 13. The electronics buff will enjoy wiring and assembling power supplies and switches to expand the SD-Z80 trainer.

Chapter 9 illustrates basic software projects performable on the basic SD-Z80 microcomputer without modifications. The programs illustrate addition, subtraction, multiplication, bit testing, parity checking, and rotation in assembly language.

Chapter 10 includes projects that can be performed on the basic SD-Z80 minicomputer and projects that need additional hardware as outlined in Chapter 1. The programs illustrate memory copy, division, combination lock, number guess game, a game called 21, random number generator, seven segment movable displays, clocks, D/A conversion, and many more enjoyable projects.

Chapter 11 requires interface between the SD-Z80 and a teletypewriter (TTY). Purchasing information is given which requires one toll free phone call to RCA and purchase of the TTY at a surprisingly low cost. The TTY can be used as an inexpensive printer in expanding your microcomputer system. The programs employed with the TTY include data design projects for your enjoyment.

Chapter 12 shows you how to interface the SD-Z80 with an oscilloscope. Interfacing projects include stationary and moving data designs displayed on the oscilloscope.

Chapter 13 includes five projects that interface the SD-Z80 with electronic circuitry to simulate electronic dice, random number generator, twenty-four-hour clock, stop clock, and a metronome.

Chapter 1

SD-Z80 System Microcomputer and Hardware Projects

Everyone in today's society has been or will be affected by a computer. The electronic hobbyist must know about computers especially microprocessors, microcomputers, and microcomputer systems. This book will help the electronics buff understand the workings of a microprocessor by allowing him to build a microcomputer employing the Z80 microprocessor, experimenting with microprocessor programs, and interfacing with peripheral devices that will develop a small microcomputer system.

The term microprocessor has been used loosely among people in the electronic field. A microprocessor is usually a single chip containing the digital logic of a central processing unit (CPU) plus other logic directing the flow of data in, out, and around the CPU (Fig. 1-1). The Z80 CPU is employed throughout this book, and an explanation of how the Z80 CPU chip functions is given.

The basic microcomputer we will be using is the Z80 Starter System, referred to as the SD-Z80.

The programs furnished in this book can be used with the basic SD-Z80. The programs are written at a fundamental level, intermediate level, and game level. In addition, there are programs that require an expansion of the SD-Z80, along with external hardware and/or instrumentation. The advanced programs include teletypewriter (TTY) communication between the SD-Z80 and a TTY, oscilloscope displays, and sound effect circuits. The advanced programming illustrates the concept of building a microprocessor into a microcomputer system through programming and hardware development. This technique is not usually illustrated in most literature, which generally only illustrates programming without hardware discussing in detail hardware interfacing with programming.

For the projects in this book, you need the SD-Z80 Starter Kit (Fig. 1-2). It is available from your favorite

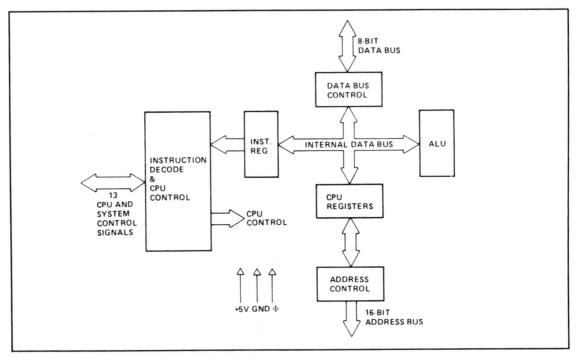

Fig. 1-1. Z80-CPU block diagram. (Courtesy of MOSFET.)

Fig. 1-2. Z80 Basic Starter Kit. (Courtesy of Donald Pavlovich.)

electronic store or from SD Systems, P.O. Box 28810, Dallas, TX 75228; telephone (214) 271-4667. The SD-Z80 contains the parts needed for you to build a complete Z80 microcomputer system on a single board and execute all of the basic software projects and most of the intermediate software projects given in later chapters. To execute the gaming projects, teletypewriter (TTY) communications projects, oscilloscope displays, and other advanced programs you will need to assemble additional hardware. Instructions for assembling the hardware required are furnished at the appropriate time. The SD-Z80 Starter Kit shown in finished form in Fig. 1-2.

You can assemble SD-Z80 Starter Kit in three to six hours, depending upon your skill and experience at building electronic projects. Only a 5-volt dc power source capable of delivering 1.3 amperes is needed to make the computer operate, using its built-in display and keyboard. However, a larger current capacity supply is necessary to operate the advanced programs presented in this book. We recommend that you use a 2-ampere supply. Instructions for assembling a 5-volt, 2-ampere dc supply are given in Project 1.

- High performance 2 MHz Z80 CPU
- Z80 Instruction Set
- Z80-PIO (programmable input/output circuit)
- Audio Cassette Interface
- EPROM Programmer (erasable programmable ROM)
- Z80-CTC (clock timer circuit)
- Wirewrap area for custom designed circuits

If you wish to interface a TTY to the SD-Z80, you will also need a −10 volt dc power supply, whose construction is shown in Project 66. You may expand both memory and I/O by adding more RAM, ROM, and Z80-SIO (serial input/output) devices in the space provided for that purpose. Projects for building the hardware needed to expand the SD-Z80 into a microcomputer system for executing the programs follow.

PROJECT 1: SD-Z80 CUSTOM DC POWER SUPPLY

The +5 V, 1.3 ampere dc power supply needed to operate the SD-Z80 Kit and projects given later is shown in Fig. 1-3. Once the power supply has been assembled, adjust potentiometer R8 so that the output voltage is +5V. Then connect the power supply to the SD-Z80 at the left side of the kit marked +5V for the PLUS side of the supply and connect the MINUS side of the supply to the terminal marked GND.

After the power supply has been connected to the trainer, measure the output of the power supply and adjust R8 so that the output of the dc supply is +5V. Now press the reset key and the minus sign character ('−') should appear on the left side of the display. If it doesn't appear, then return to the SD-Z80 reader's manual for further instructions.

PROJECT 2: LED ASSEMBLY FOR OUT PORT A AND IN PORT B

The SD-Z80 Starter Kit must be modified to execute the programs in later chapters. Figure 1-4 shows the top view of the SD-Z80 Kit. In this section we will show you the modifications that need to be made in order to wire and install 16 LEDs and their driver circuits.

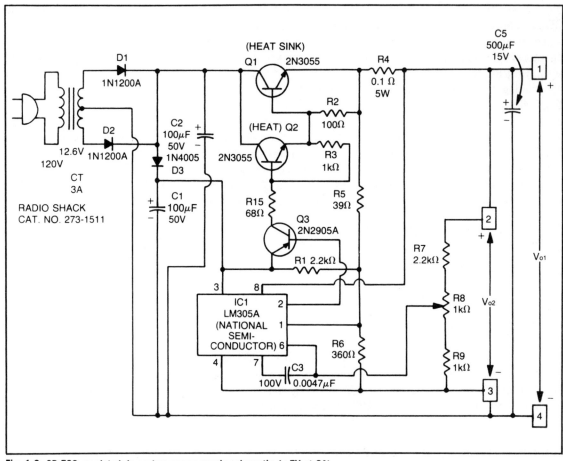

Fig. 1-3. SD-Z80 regulated dc custom power supply schematic (+5V at 2A).

Figure 1-5 illustrates the necessary wiring of the 16 LEDs to their driver circuits. Also, included on the wiring diagram is the parts list for the wiring project. Besides the 16 LEDs, 16 resistors (270 Ohms, ¼ W) and three ICs (SN7416), three DIP sockets must be used. Figure 1-5 includes the part numbers of the LEDs and DIP sockets from Radio Shack. The ICs can be purchased from your local Texas Instruments (TI) distributor.

Wiring of the components in Fig. 1-5 can be accommodated on the left side of the SD-Z80 Kit in the area marked "wirewrap area" (see Fig. 1-4).

PROJECT 3: DUAL-IN-LINE SWITCH ASSEMBLY

The location of the DIP switch on the SD-Z80 is in the area marked "wirewrap area" (see Fig. 1-4).

Figure 1-6 illustrates the necessary wiring of the dual-in-line package of switches to the driver circuits installed in Project 2. In other words, the ICs (SN7416) employed in Project 2 are also used in this project.

Besides the DIP switches and the ICs, 8 resistors (470 Ohms, ¼ W) must be used. Figure 1-6 includes the part numbers of the DIP switch package from Radio Shack.

Figure 1-7 is the schematic diagram of the LED assembly of the LEDs connected to PORTs PA0 through PA7 and PB0 through PB7.

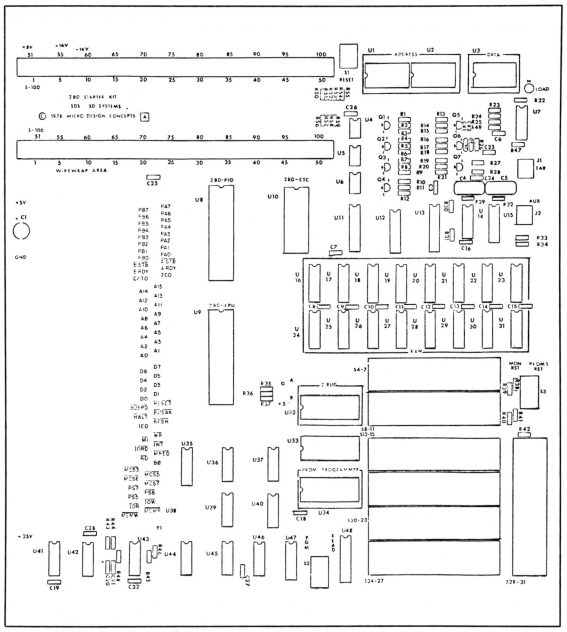

Fig. 1-4. Z80 Starter Kit assembly drawing.

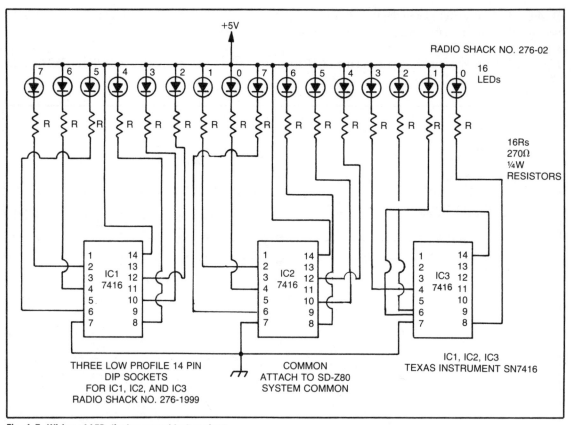

Fig. 1-5. Wiring of LED display assembly (top view).

PROJECT 4: Z80-PIO CHIP EXPANSION

The wiring diagram for the Z80-PIO chip needed for the projects later in this book is shown in Fig. 1-8. The Z80-PIO chip can be wired in the area marked "wirewrap area" (see Fig. 1-4).

The Z80-PIO chip can be purchased through your local MOSTEK distributor by asking for MOSTEK MK 3881, Z80-PIO, or from the MOSTEK Corporation, 1215 West Crosby Road, P.O. Box 169, Carrolton, TX 75006.

PROJECT 5: Z80-SIO CHIP EXPANSION

The wiring diagram for the Z80-SIO chip needed for the projects later in this book is shown in Fig. 1-9. The Z80-SIO chip can be wired in the area marked "wirewrap area" (see Fig. 1-4).

The Z80-SIO chip can be purchased through your local MOSTEK distributor by asking for MOSTEK MK 3884, Z80-SIO, or from MOSTEK Corporation, 1215 West Crosby Road, P.O. Box 169, Carrolton, TX 75006.

PROJECT 6: PROTO-BOARD EXPERIMENTATION AREA

The optional Proto-Board (Fig. 1-10) can be used for the wiring of discrete component circuits which interface with the SD-Z80 Kit. The Proto-Board is placed next to the SD-Z80 Kit and must be wired to the +5 V SD-Z80 terminal and G (ground or common) SD-Z80 terminal.

The Proto-Board is manufactured by Continental Specialities Corp. If you cannot find the Proto-Board at your favorite electronic's store, write to Continental Specialities Corp., 70 Fulton Tr., P.O. Box 1942, New Haven, CT 06509; telephone (203) 624-3103.

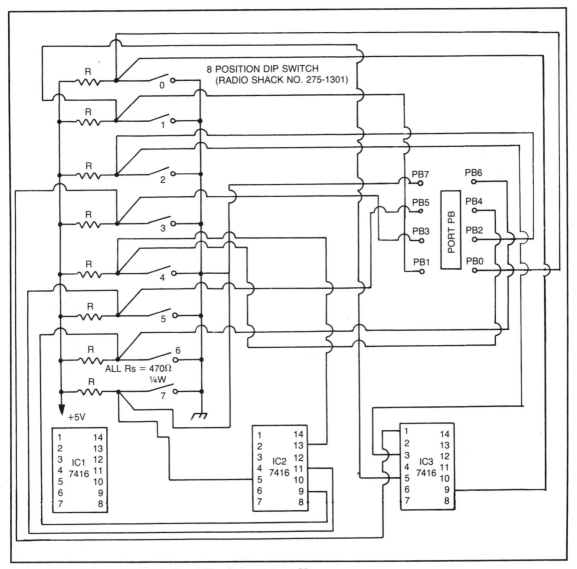

Fig. 1-6. Wiring diagram for DUAL-in line (DIP) switches and port PB.

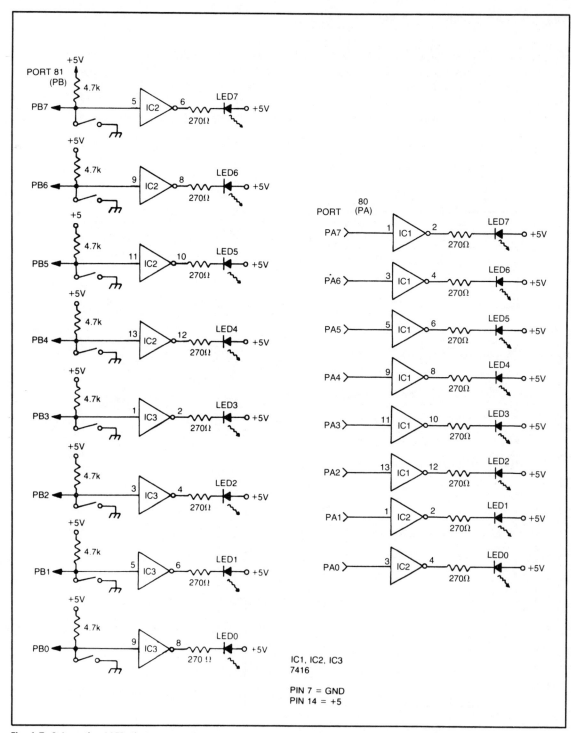

Fig. 1-7. Schematic of LED display assembly.

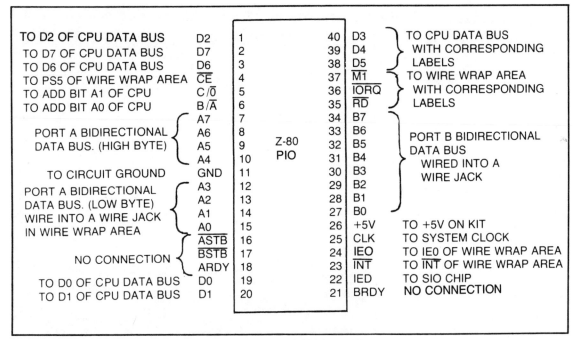

Fig. 1-8. Wiring description of the additional PIO chip onto the SD-Z80 Starter Kit.

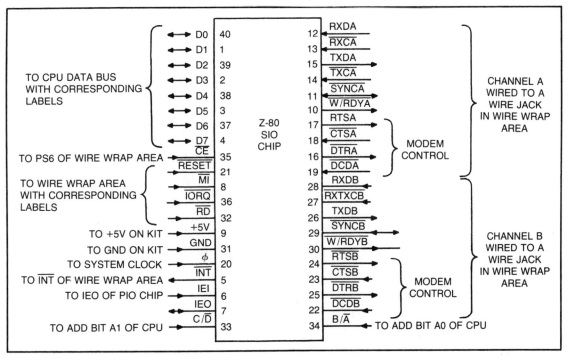

Fig. 1-9. Wiring description of the additional SIO chip onto the SD-Z80 Starter Kit.

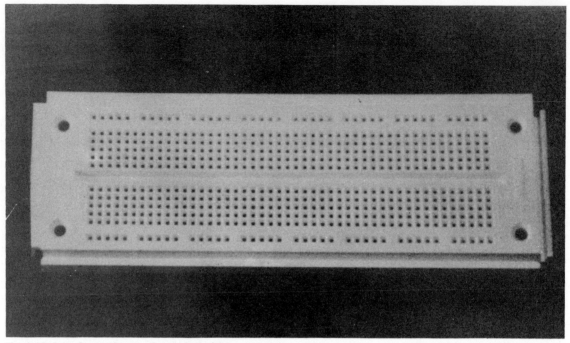

Fig. 1-10. Proto-Board. (Courtesy Donald Pavlovich.)

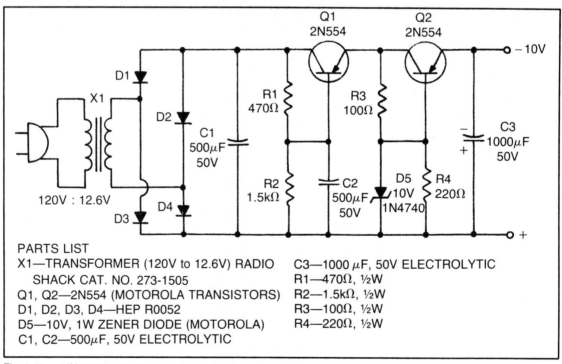

PARTS LIST

X1—TRANSFORMER (120V to 12.6V) RADIO
    SHACK CAT. NO. 273-1505
Q1, Q2—2N554 (MOTOROLA TRANSISTORS)
D1, D2, D3, D4—HEP R0052
D5—10V, 1W ZENER DIODE (MOTOROLA)
C1, C2—500μF, 50V ELECTROLYTIC

C3—1000 μF, 50V ELECTROLYTIC
R1—470Ω, ½W
R2—1.5kΩ, ½W
R3—100Ω, ½W
R4—220Ω, ½W

Fig. 1-11. −10V custom power supply for the teletypewriter (TTY).

10

PROJECT 7: TELETYPEWRITER CUSTOM DC POWER SUPPLY

For the teletypewriter (TTY) projects, you must use the power supply shown in Fig. 1-11. Figure 1-10 shows a picture of the Proto-Board you may use to assemble your teletypewriter power supply. When the power supply is assembled, check the output of the supply to insure that a – 10V output is obtained. Do not connect the power supply to the TTY until after you have read Chapter 11.

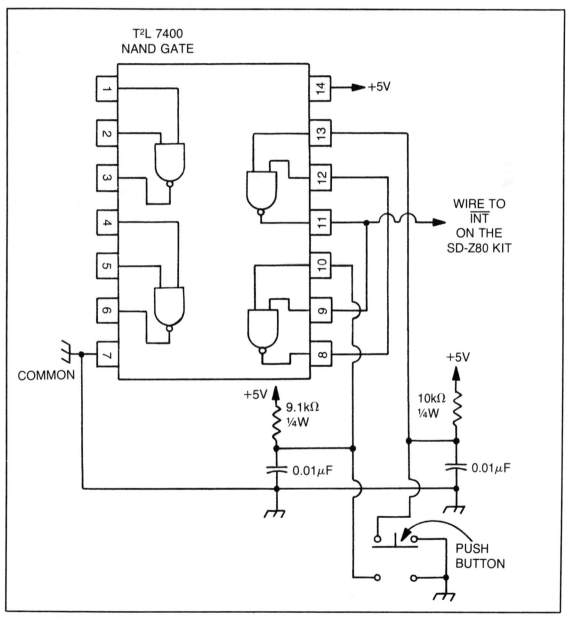

Fig. 1-12. Wiring diagram for interrupt button with debounce circuit.

PROJECT 8: RAM EXPANSION

In order to expand the RAM memory capabilities of the SD-Z80 Kit you can purchase eight 21LO2 RAM chips from your favorite electronic store. In addition, you should purchase eight 16 pin sockets which hold the RAM chips.

If you look at Fig. 1-4 you will see the spaces for additional RAM marked U16, U17, U18, U19, U20, U21, U22, and U23. First you install the 16 pin sockets by soldering the sockets to the traces provided on the bottom side of the Starter Kit, and then finally the RAM chips.

PROJECT 9: INTERRUPT BUTTON AND DEBOUNCE CIRCUIT

In order to execute the game projects and the projects requiring interrupt routines you will need an interrupt push-button. The wiring of the push-button to the SD-Z80 Kit and a debounce circuit is shown in Fig. 1-12. Parts for this circuit can be purchased at electronics supply stores.

Chapter 2

Information for the
Z80 Central Processing Unit

The term "microcomputer" has been used to describe virtually every type of small computing device designed within the last few years. This term has been applied to everything from simple "microprogrammed" controllers constructed out of TTL MSI up to low end minicomputers with a portion of the CPU constructed out of TTL LSI "bit slices." However, the major impact of the LSI technology within the last few years has been with MOS LSI. With this technology, it is possible to fabricate complete and very powerful computer systems with only a few MOS LSI components.

The Mostek Z80 family of components is a significant advancement in the state-of-the-art microcomputers. These components can be configured with any type of standard semiconductor memory to generate computer systems with an extremely wide range of capabilities. For example, as few as two LSI circuits and three standard TTL MSI packages can be combined to form a simple controller. With additional memory and I/O devices a computer can be constructed with capabilities that only a minicomputer could previously deliver. This wide range of computational power allows standard modules to be constructed by a user that can satisfy the requirements of an extremely wide range of applications.

The major reason for MOS LSI domination of the microcomputer market is the low cost of these few LSI components. For example, MOS LSI microcomputers have already replaced TTL logic in such applications as terminal controllers, peripheral device controllers, traffic signal controllers, point of sale terminals, intelligent terminals and test systems. In fact the MOS LSI microcomputer is finding its way into almost every product that now uses electronics and it is even replacing many mechanical systems such as weight scales and automobile controls.

The MOS LSI microcomputer market is already well established and new products using them are being developed at an extraordinary rate. The Mostek Z80 component set has been designed to fit into this market through the following factors:

1. The Z80 is fully software compatible with the popular 8080A CPU offered from several sources. Existing designs can be easily converted to include the Z80 as a superior alternative.
2. The Z80 component set is superior in both software and hardware capabilities to any other 8-bit microcomputer system on the market. These capabilities provide the user with significantly lower hardware and software development costs while also allowing him to obtain additional features in his system.
3. A complete development and OEM system product line including full software support is available to enable the user to easily develop new products.

Microcomputer systems are extremely simple to construct using Z80 components. Any such system consists of three parts:

1. CPU (central processing unit)
2. Memory
3. Interface circuits to peripheral devices

The CPU is the heart of the system. Its function is to obtain instructions from the memory and perform the desired operations. The memory is used to contain instructions and in most cases data that is to be processed. For example, a typical instruction sequence may be to read data from a specific peripheral device, store it in a location in memory, check the parity and write it out to another peripheral device. Note that the Mostek component set includes the CPU and various general purpose I/O device controllers, as well as a wide range of memory devices. Thus, all required components can be connected together in a very simple manner with virtually no other external logic. The user's effort then becomes primarily one of software development. That is, the user can concentrate on describing his problem and translating it into a series of instructions that can be loaded into the microcomputer memory. Mostek is dedicated to making this step of software generation as simple as possible. A good example of this is our assembly language in which a simple mnemonic is used to represent every instruction that the CPU can perform. This language is self documenting in such a way that from the mnemonic the user can understand exactly what the instruction is doing without constantly checking back to a complex cross-listing.

Z80-CPU ARCHITECTURE

A block diagram of the internal architecture of the Z80-CPU is shown in Fig. 1-1 The diagram shows all of the major elements in the CPU and it should be referred to throughout the following description.

CPU REGISTERS

The Z80-CPU contains 208 bits of R/W memory that are accessible to the programmer. Figure 2-1 illustrates how this memory is configured into eighteen 8-bit registers and four 16-bit registers. All Z80 registers are implemented using static RAM. The registers include two sets of six general purpose registers that may be used individually as 8-bit registers or in pairs as 16-bit registers. There are also two sets of accumulator and flag registers.

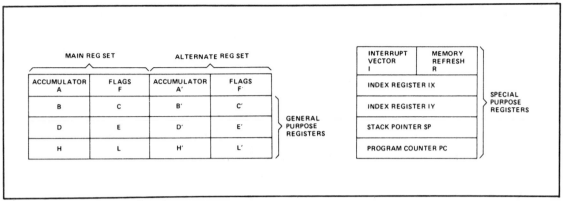

Fig. 2-1. Z80-CPU register configuration.

Special Purpose Registers

Program Counter (PC). The program counter holds the 16-bit address of the current instruction being fetched from memory. The PC is automatically incremented after its contents have been transferred to the address lines. When a program jump occurs the new value is automatically placed in the PC, overriding the incrementer.

Stack Pointer (SP). The stack pointer holds the 16-bit address of the current top of a stack located anywhere in external system RAM memory. The external stack memory is organized as a last-in first-out (LIFO) file. Data can be pushed onto the stack from specific CPU registers or popped off of the stack into specific CPU registers through the execution of PUSH and POP instructions. The data popped from the stack is always the last data pushed onto it. The stack allows simple implementation of multiple level interrupts, unlimited subroutine nesting and simplification of many types of data manipulation.

Two Index Registers (IX and IY). The two independent index registers hold a 16-bit base address that is used in indexed addressing modes. In this mode, an index register is used as a base to point to a region in memory from which data is to be stored or retrieved. An additional byte is included in indexed instructions to specify a displacement from this base. This displacement is specified as a two's complement signed integer. This mode of addressing greatly simplifies many types of programs, especially where tables of data are used.

Interrupt Page Address Register (I). The Z80-CPU can be operated in a mode where an indirect call to any memory location can be achieved in response to an interrupt. The I Register is used for this purpose to store the high order 8-bits of the indirect address while the interrupting device provides the lower 8-bits of the address. This feature allows interrupt routines to be dynamically located anywhere in memory with absolute minimal access time to the routine.

Memory Refresh Register (R). The Z80-CPU contains a memory refresh counter to enable dynamic memories to be used with the same ease as static memories. This 7-bit register is automatically incremented after each instruction fetch. The data in the refresh counter is sent out on the lower portion of the address bus along with a refresh control signal while the CPU is decoding and executing the fetched instruction. This mode of refresh is totally transparent to the programmer and does not slow down the

CPU operation. The programmer can load the R register for testing purposes, but this register is not normally used by the programmer.

Accumulator and Flag Registers

The CPU includes two independent 8-bit accumulators and associated 8-bit flag registers. The accumulator holds the results of 8-bit arithmetic or logical operations while the flag register indicates specific conditions for 8- or 16-bit operations, such as indicating whether or not the result of an operation is equal to zero. The programmer selects the accumulator and flag pair that he wishes to work with a single exchange instruction so that he may easily work with either pair.

General Purpose Registers

There are two matched sets of general purpose registers, each set containing six 8-bit registers that may be used individually as 8-bit registers or as 16-bit register pairs by the programmer. One set is called BC, DE, and HL while the complementary set is called BD', DE' and HL'. At any one time the programmer can select either set of registers to work with through a single exchange command for the entire set. In systems where fast interrupt response is required, one set of general purpose registers and an accumulator/flag register may be reserved for handling this very fast routine. Only a simple exchange command need be executed to go between the routines. This greatly reduces interrupt service time by eliminating the requirement for saving and retrieving register contents in the external stack during interrupt or subroutine processing. These general purpose registers are used for a wide range of applications by the programmer. They also simplify programming, especially in ROM based systems where little external read/write memory is available.

ARITHMETIC AND LOGIC UNIT (ALU)

The 8-bit arithmetic and logical instructions of the CPU are executed in the ALU. Internally the ALU communicates with the registers and the external data bus on the internal data bus. The type of functions performed by the ALU include:

Add	Left or right shifts or rotates (arithmetic and logical)
Subtract	Increment
Logical AND	Decrement
Logical OR	Set bit
Logical Exclusive OR	Reset bit
Compare	Test bit

INSTRUCTION REGISTER AND CPU CONTROL

As each instruction is fetched from memory, it is placed in the instruction register and decoded. The control section performs this function and then generates and supplies all of the control signals necessary to read or write data from or to the registers, controls the ALU and provides all required external control signals.

Z80-CPU PIN DESCRIPTION

The Z80-CPU is packaged in an industry standard 40 pin Dual In-Line Package. The I/O pins are shown in Fig. 2-2 and the function of each is described below.

A_0-A_{15} (**Address Bus**). Tri-state output, active high. A_0-A_{15} constitute a 16-bit address bus. The address bus provides the address for memory (up to 64K bytes) data exchanges and for I/O device data exchanges. I/O addressing uses the 8 lower address bits to allow the user to directly select up to 256 input or 256 output ports. A_0 is the least significant address bit. During refresh time, the lower 7 bits contain a valid refresh address.

D_0-D_7 (**Data Bus**). Tri-state input/output, active high. D_0-D_7 constitute an 8-bit bidirectional data bus. The data bus is used for data exchanges with memory and I/O devices.

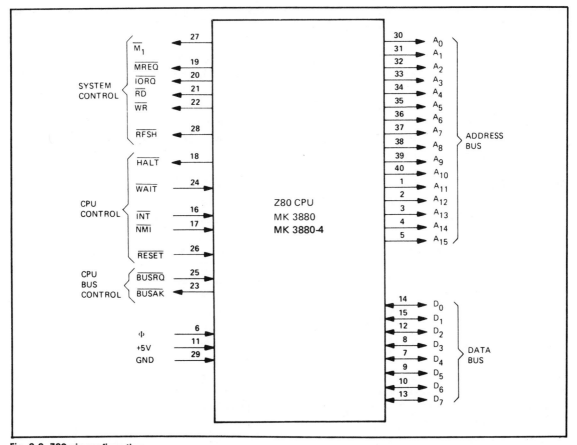

Fig. 2-2. Z80 pin configuration.

17

$\overline{M_1}$ **(Machine Cycle one).** Output, active low. $\overline{M_1}$ indicates that the current machine cycle is the OP code fetch cycle of an instruction execution. Note that during execution of 2-byte op-codes, $\overline{M_1}$ is generated as each op code byte is fetched. These two byte op-codes always begin with CBH, DDH, EDH, or FDH. $\overline{M_1}$ also occurs with $\overline{IORQ}$ to indicate an interrupt acknowledge cycle.

$\overline{MREQ}$ **(Memory Request).** Tri-state output, active low. The memory request signal indicates that the address bus holds a valid address for a memory read or memory write operation.

$\overline{IORQ}$ **(Input/Output Request).** Tri-state output, active low. The $\overline{IORQ}$ signal indicates that the lower half of the address bus holds a valid I/O address for a I/O read or write operation. An $\overline{IORQ}$ signal is also generated with an M_1 signal when an interrupt is being acknowledged to indicate that an interrupt response vector can be placed on the data bus. Interrupt Acknowledge operations occur during M_1 time while I/O operations never occur during M_1 time.

$\overline{RD}$ **(Memory Read).** Tri-state output, active low. $\overline{RD}$ indicates that the CPU wants to read data from memory or an I/O device. The addressed I/O device or memory should use this signal to gate data onto the CPU data bus.

$\overline{WR}$ **(Memory Write).** Tri-state output, active low. $\overline{WR}$ indicates that the CPU data bus holds valid data to be stored in the addressed memory or I/O device.

$\overline{RFSH}$ **(Refresh).** Output, active low. $\overline{RFSH}$ indicates that the lower 7 bits of the address bus contain a refresh address for dynamic memories and current $\overline{MREQ}$ signal should be used to do a refresh read to all dynamic memories. A_7 is a logic zero and the upper 8 bits of the Address Bus contains the I Register.

$\overline{HALT}$ **(Halt state).** Output, active low. $\overline{HALT}$ indicates that the CPU has executed a HALT software instruction and is awaiting either a non maskable or a maskable interrupt (with the mask enabled) before operation can resume. While halted, the CPU executes NOP's to maintain memory refresh activity.

$\overline{WAIT}$* **(Wait).** Input, active low. $\overline{WAIT}$ indicates to the Z80-CPU that the addressed memory or I/O devices are not ready for a data transfer. The CPU continues to enter wait states for as long as this signal is active. This signal allows memory or I/O devices of any speed to be synchronized to the CPU.

$\overline{INT}$ **(Interrupt Request).** Input, active low. The Interrupt Request signal is generated by I/O devices. A request will be honored at the end of the current instruction if the internal software controlled interrupt enable flip-flop (IFF) is enabled and if the $\overline{BUSRQ}$ signal is not active. When the CPU accepts the interrupt, an acknowledge signal ($\overline{IORQ}$ during M_1 time) is sent out at the beginning of the next instruction cycle. The CPU can respond to an interrupt in three different modes that are described in detail later in the book.

$\overline{NMI}$. Input, negative edge triggered. The nonmaskable interrupt request line has a higher priority than $\overline{INT}$ and is always recognized at the end of the current instruction, independent of the status of the interrupt enable flip-flop. $\overline{NMI}$ automatically forces the Z80-CPU to restart to location 0066_H. The program counter is automatically saved in the external stack so that the user can return to the program that was interrupted. Note that continuous WAIT cycles can prevent the current instruction from ending, and that a $\overline{BUSRQ}$ will override a $\overline{NMI}$.

18

$\overline{\text{RESET}}$. Input, active low. $\overline{\text{RESET}}$ forces the program counter to zero and initializes the CPU. The CPU initialization includes:

1. Disable the interrupt enable flip-flop
2. Set Register I = 00_H
3. Set Register R = 00_H
4. Set Interrupt Mode 0

During reset time, the address bus and data bus go to a high impedance state and all control output signals go to the inactive state. No refresh occurs.

$\overline{\text{BUSRQ}}$ (Bus Request). Input, active low. The bus request signal is used to request the CPU address bus, data bus and tri-state output control signals to go to a high impedance state so that other devices can control these buses. When $\overline{\text{BUSRQ}}$ is activated, the CPU will set these buses to a high impedance state as soon as the current CPU machine cycle is terminated.

$\overline{\text{BUSAK}}$* (Bus Acknowledge). Output, active low. Bus acknowledge is used to indicate to the requesting device that the CPU address bus, data bus and tri-state control bus signals have been set to their high impedance state and the external device can now control these signals.

Φ. Single phase system clock.

CPU TIMING

The Z80-CPU executes instructions by stepping through a very precise set of a few basic operations. These include:

Memory read or write
I/O device read or write
Interrupt acknowledge

All instructions are merely a series of these basic operations. Each of these basic operations can take from three to six clock periods to complete or they can be lengthened to synchronize the CPU to the speed of external devices. The basic clock periods are referred to as T states and the basic operations are referred to as M (for machine) cycles. Figure 2-3 illustrates how a typical instruction will be merely a series of specific M and T cycles. Notice that this instruction consists of three machine cycles (M1, M2 and M3). The first machine cycle of any instruction is a fetch cycle which is four, five or six T states long (unless lengthened by the wait signal which will be fully described in the next section). The fetch cycle (M1) is used to fetch the OP code of the next instruction to be executed. Subsequent machine cycles move data between the CPU and memory or I/O devices and they may have anywhere from three to five T cycles (again they may be lengthened by wait states to synchronize the external devices to the CPU). The following paragraphs describe the timing which occurs within any of the basic machine cycles.

All CPU timing can be broken down into a few simple timing diagrams as shown in Figs. 2-4 through 2-14.

---

*While the Z80-CPU is in either a $\overline{\text{WAIT}}$ state or a Bus Acknowledge condition, Dynamic Memory Refresh will not occur.

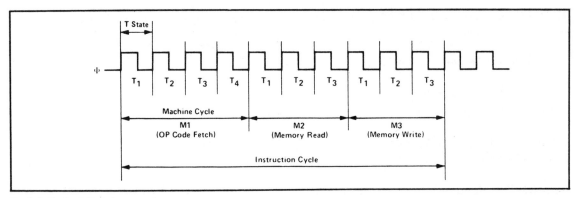

Fig. 2-3. Basic CPU timing example.

These diagrams show the following basic operations with and without wait states (wait states are added to synchronize the CPU to slow memory or I/O devices).

Instruction OP code fetch (M1 cycle)
Memory data read or write cycles
I/O read or write cycles
Bus Request/Acknowledge Cycle
Interrupt Request/Acknowledge Cycle
Non maskable Interrupt Request/Acknowledge Cycle
Exit from a HALT instruction

Instruction Fetch

Figure 2-4 shows the timing during an M1 cycle (OP code fetch). Notice that the PC is placed on the address bus at the beginning of the M1 cycle. One half clock time later the $\overline{\text{MREQ}}$ signal goes active. At this time the address to the memory has had time to stabilize so that the falling edge of $\overline{\text{MREQ}}$ can be used directly as a chip enable clock to dynamic memories. The $\overline{\text{RD}}$ line also goes active to indicate that the memory read data should be enabled onto the CPU data bus. The CPU samples the data from the memory on the data bus with the rising edge of the clock of state T3 and this same edge is used by the CPU to turn off the $\overline{\text{RD}}$ and $\overline{\text{MREQ}}$ signals. Thus the data has already been sampled by the CPU before the RD signal becomes inactive. Clock state T3 and T4 of a fetch cycle are used to refresh dynamic memories. (The CPU uses this time to decode and execute the fetched instruction so that no other operation could be performed at this time). During T3 and T4 the lower 7 bits of the address bus contain a memory refresh address and the $\overline{\text{RFSH}}$ signal becomes active to indicate that a refresh read of all dynamic memories should be accomplished. Notice that a $\overline{\text{RD}}$ signal is not generated during refresh time to prevent data from different memory segments from being gated onto the data bus. The $\overline{\text{MREQ}}$ signal during refresh time should be used to perform a refresh read of all memory elements. The refresh signal can not be used by itself since the refresh address is only guaranteed to be stable during $\overline{\text{MREQ}}$ time.

Figure 2-5 illustrates how the fetch cycle is delayed if the memory activates the $\overline{\text{WAIT}}$ line. During T2 and every subsequent Tw, the CPU samples the $\overline{\text{WAIT}}$ line with the falling edge of Φ. If the $\overline{\text{WAIT}}$ line is active at this time, another wait state will be entered during the following cycle. Using this technique the read cycle can be lengthened to match the access time of any type of memory device.

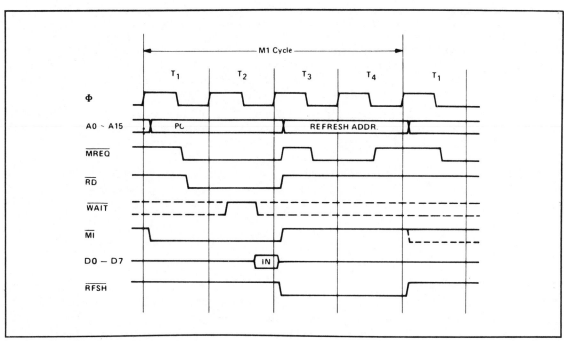

Fig. 2-4. Instruction op code fetch.

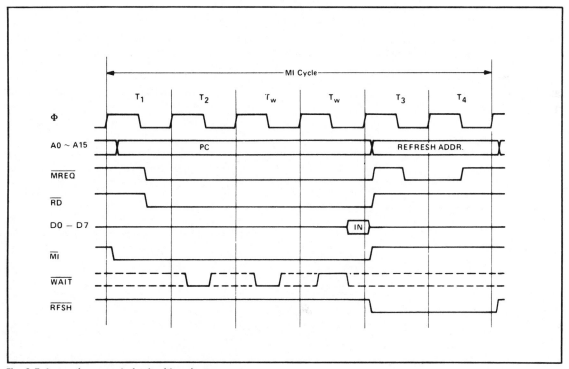

Fig. 2-5. Instruction op code fetch with wait states.

21

Memory Read or Write

Figure 2-6 illustrates the timing of memory read or write cycles other than an OP code fetch (M1 cycle). These cycles are generally three clock periods long unless wait states are requested by the memory via the $\overline{WAIT}$ signal. The $\overline{MREQ}$ signal and the $\overline{RD}$ signal are used the same as in the fetch cycle. In the case of a memory write cycle, the $\overline{MREQ}$ also becomes active when the address bus is stable so that it can be used directly as a chip enable for dynamic memories. The $\overline{WR}$ line is active when data on the data bus is stable so that it can be used directly as a R/W pulse to virtually any type of semiconductor memory. Furthermore the $\overline{WR}$ signal goes inactive one half T state before the address and data bus contents are changed so that the overlap requirements for virtually any type of semiconductor memory type will be met.

Figure 2-7 illustrates how a $\overline{WAIT}$ request signal will lengthen any memory read or write operation. This operation is identical to that previously described for a fetch cycle. Notice in this figure that a separate read and a separate write cycle are shown in the same figure although read and write cycles can never occur simultaneously.

Input or Output Cycles

Figure 2-8 illustrates an I/O read or I/O write operation. Notice that during I/O operations a single wait state is automatically inserted. The reason for this is that during I/O operations, the time from when the $\overline{IORQ}$ signal goes active until the CPU must sample the $\overline{WAIT}$ line is very short and without this extra state sufficient time does not exist for an I/O port to decode its address and activate the $\overline{WAIT}$ line if a wait is required. Also, without this wait state it is difficult to design MOS I/O devices that can operate at full CPU speed. During this wait state time the $\overline{WAIT}$ request signal is sampled. During a read I/O operation, the RD line is used to enable the addressed port onto the data bus just as in the case of a memory read. For I/O write operations, the $\overline{WR}$ line is used as a clock to the I/O port, again with sufficient overlap timing automatically provided so that the rising edge may be used as a data clock.

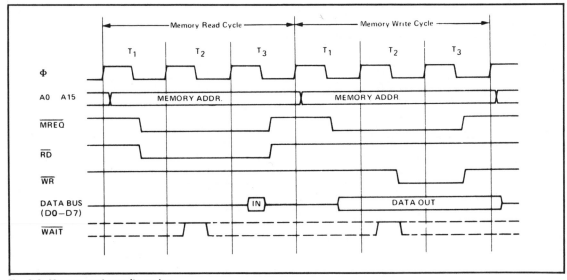

Fig. 2-6. Memory read or write cycles.

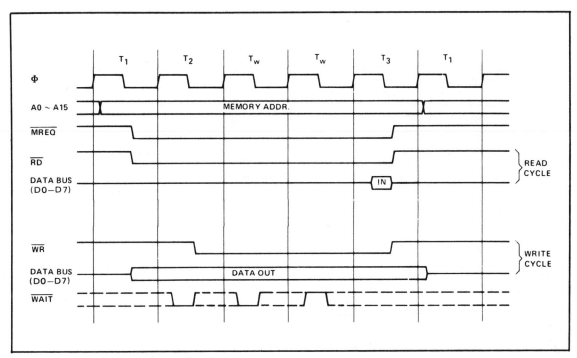

Fig. 2-7. Memory read or write cycles with wait states.

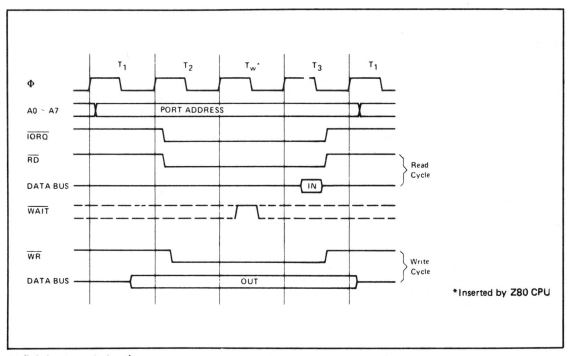

Fig. 2-8. Input or output cycles.

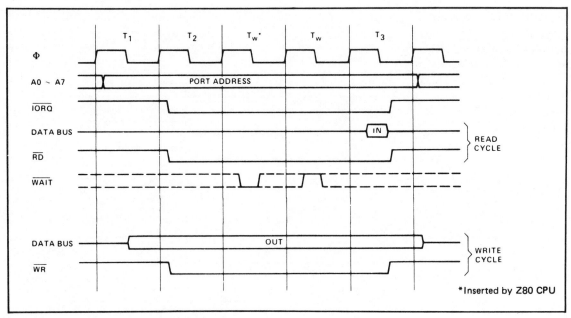

Fig. 2-9. Input or output cycles with wait states.

Figure 2-9 illustrates how additional wait states may be added with the $\overline{\text{WAIT}}$ line. The operation is identical to that previously described.

Bus Request/Acknowledge Cycle

Figure 2-10 illustrates the timing for a Bus Request/Acknowledge cycle. The $\overline{\text{BUSRQ}}$ signal is sampled by the CPU with the rising edge of the last clock period of any machine cycle. If the $\overline{\text{BUSRQ}}$ signal is active,

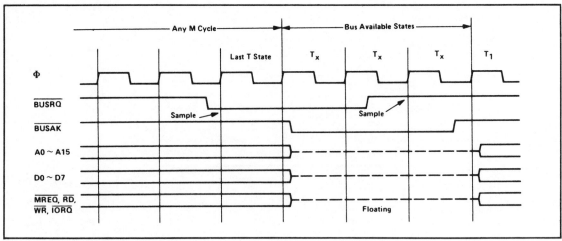

Fig. 2-10. Bus request/acknowledge cycle.

the CPU will set its address, data and tri-state control signals to the high impedance state with the rising edge of the next clock pulse. At that time any external device can control the buses to transfer data between memory and I/O devices. (This is generally known as Direct Memory Access [DMA] using cycle stealing). The maximum time for the CPU to respond to a bus request is the length of a machine cycle and the external controller can maintain control of the bus for as many clock cycles as is desired. Note, however, that if very long DMA cycles are used, and dynamic memories are being used, the external controller must also perform the refresh function. This situation only occurs if very large blocks of data are transferred under DMA control. Also note that during a bus request cycle, the CPU cannot be interrupted by either a $\overline{\text{NMI}}$ or an $\overline{\text{INT}}$ signal.

Interrupt Request/Acknowledge Cycle

Figure 2-11 illustrates the timing associated with an interrupt cycle. The interrupt signal ($\overline{\text{INT}}$) is sampled by the CPU with the rising edge of the last clock at the end of any instruction. The signal will not be accepted if the internal CPU software controlled interrupt enable flip-flop is not set or if the $\overline{\text{BUSRQ}}$ signal is active. When the signal is accepted a special M1 cycle is generated. During this special M1 cycle the $\overline{\text{IORQ}}$ signal becomes active (instead of the normal $\overline{\text{MREQ}}$) to indicate that the interrupting device can place an 8-bit vector on the data bus. Notice that two wait states are automatically added to this cycle. These states are added so that a ripple priority interrupt scheme can be easily implemented. The two wait states allow sufficient time for the ripple signals to stabilize and identify which I/O device must insert the response vector. Refer to Chapter 3 for details on how the interrupt response vector is utilized by the CPU.

Figure 2-12 illustrates how additional wait states can be added to the interrupt response cycle. Again the operation is identical to that previously described.

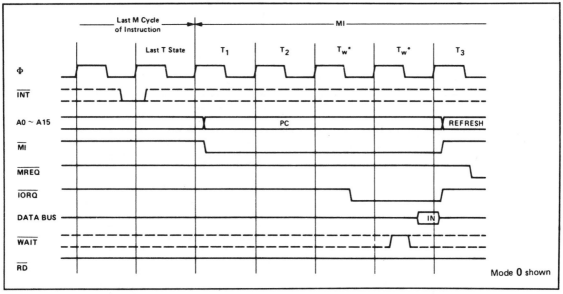

Fig. 2-11. Interrupt request/acknowledge cycle.

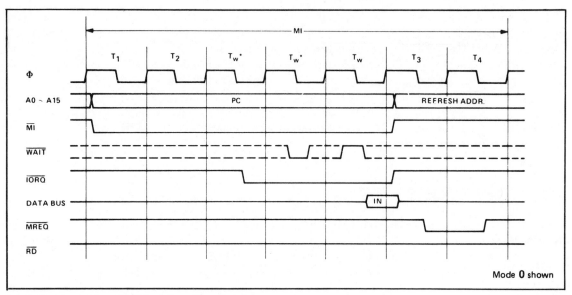

Fig. 2-12. Interrupt request/acknowledge with wait states.

Nonmaskable Interrupt Response

Figure 2-13 illustrates the request/acknowledge cycle for the non-maskable interrupt. A pulse on the NMI input sets an internal NMI latch which is tested by the CPU at the end of every instruction. This NMI latch is sampled at the same time as the interrupt line, but this line has priority over the normal interrupt and it can not be disabled under software control. Its usual function is to provide immediate response to important signals such as an impending power failure. The CPU response to a non maskable interrupt is

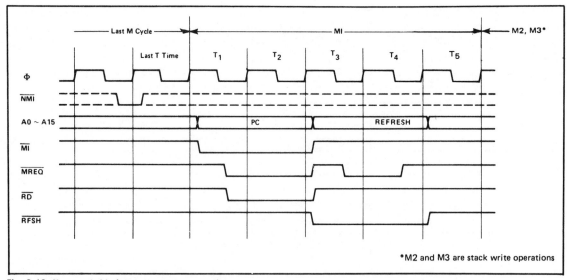

Fig. 2-13. Non-maskable interrupt request operation.

26

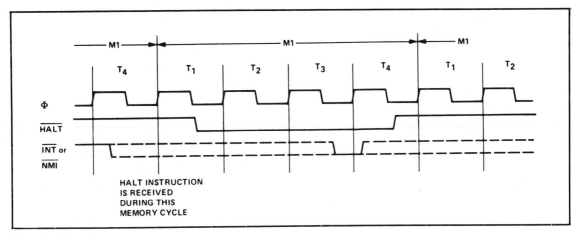

Fig. 2-14. Halt exit.

similar to a normal memory read operation. The only difference being that the content of the data bus is ignored while the processor automatically stores the PC in the external stack and jumps to location 0066H. The service routine for the non maskable interrupt must begin at this location if this interrupt is used.

Halt Exit

Whenever a software halt instruction is executed the CPU begins executing NOP's until an interrupt is received (either a non-maskable or a maskable interrupt while the interrupt flip-flop is enabled). The two interrupt lines are sampled with the rising clock edge during each T4 state as shown in Fig. 2-14. If a non-maskable interrupt has been received or a maskable interrupt has been received and the interrupt enable flip-flop is set, then the halt state will be exited on the next rising clock edge. The following cycle will then be an interrupt acknowledge cycle corresponding to the type of interrupt that was received. If both are received at this time, then the non-maskable one will be acknowledged since it was highest priority. The purpose of executing NOP instructions while in the halt state is to keep the memory refresh signals active. Each cycle in the halt state is a normal M1 (fetch) cycle except that the data received from the memory is ignored and a NOP instruction is forced internally to the CPU. The halt acknowledge signal is active during this time to indicate that the processor is in the halt state.

Chapter 3

Z80 CPU Instruction Set

The Z80-CPU can execute 158 different instruction types including all 78 of the 8080A CPU instructions. The instructions can be broken down into the following major groups:

- Load and Exchange
- Block Transfer and Search
- Arithmetic and Logical
- Rotate and Shift
- Bit Manipulation (set, reset, test)
- Jump, Call and Return
- Input/Output
- Basic CPU Control

The load instructions move data internally between CPU registers or between CPU registers and external memory. All of these instructions must specify a source location from which the data is to be moved and a destination location. The source location is not altered by a load instruction. Examples of load group instructions include moves between any of the general purpose registers such as move the data to Register B from Register C. This group also includes load immediate to any CPU register or to any external memory location. Other types of load instructions allow transfer between CPU registers and memory locations. The exchange instructions can trade the contents of two registers.

A unique set of block transfer instructions is provided in the Z80. With a single instruction a block of memory of any size can be moved to any other location in memory. This set of block moves is extremely valuable when large strings of data must be processed. The Z80 block search instructions are also valuable for this type of processing. With a single instruction, a block of external memory of any desired length can be searched for any 8-bit character. Once the character is found the instruction automatically terminates. Both the block transfer and the block search instructions can be interrupted during their execution so as to not occupy the CPU for long periods of time.

The arithmetic and logical instructions operate on data stored in the accumulator and other general purpose CPU registers or external memory locations. The results of the operations are placed in the accumulator and the appropriate flags are set according to the result of the operation. An example of an arithmetic operation is adding the accumulator to the contents of an external memory location. The results of the addition are placed in the accumulator. This group also includes 16-bit addition and subtraction between 16-bit CPU registers.

The bit manipulation instructions allow any bit in the accumulator, any general purpose register or any external memory location to be set, reset or tested with a single instruction. For example, the most significant bit of register H can be reset. This group is especially useful in control applications and for controlling software flags in general purpose programming.

The jump, call and return instructions are used to transfer between various locations in the user's program. This group uses several different techniques for obtaining the new program counter address from specific external memory locations. A unique type of jump is the restart instruction. This instruction actually contains the new address as a part of the 8-bit OP code. This is possible since only 8 separate addresses located in page zero of the external memory may be specified. Program jumps may also be achieved by loading register HL, IX or IY directly into the PC, thus allowing the jump address to be a complex function of the routine being executed.

The input/output group of instructions in the Z80 allow for a wide range of transfers between external memory locations or the general purpose CPU registers, and the external I/O devices. In each case, the port number is provided on the lower 8 bits of the address bus during any I/O transaction. One instruction allows this port number to be specified by the second byte of the instruction while other Z80 instructions allow it to be specified as the content of the C register. One major advantage of using the C register as a pointer to the I/O device is that it allows different I/O ports to share common software driver routines. This is not possible when the address is part of the OP code if the routines are stored in ROM. Another feature of these input instructions is that they set the flag register automatically so that additional operations are not required to determine the state of the input data (for example its parity). The Z80-CPU includes single instructions that can move blocks or data (up to 256 bytes) automatically to or from any I/O port directly to any memory location. In conjunction with the dual set of general purpose registers, these instructions provide for fast I/O block transfer rates. The value of this I/O instruction set is demonstrated by the fact that the Z80-CPU can provide all required floppy disk formatting (i.e., the CPU provides the preamble, address, data and enables the CRC codes) on double density floppy disk drives on an interrupt driven basis.

Finally, the basic CPU control instructions allow various options and modes. This group includes instructions such as setting or resetting the interrupt enable flip-flop or setting the mode of interrupt response.

ADDRESSING MODES

Most of the Z80 instructions operate on data stored in internal CPU registers, external memory or in the I/O ports. Addressing refers to how the address of this data is generated in each instruction. This section gives a brief summary of the types of addressing used in the Z80 while subsequent sections detail the type of addressing available for each instruction group.

Immediate. In this mode of addressing the byte following the OP code in memory contains the actual operand.

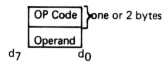

Examples of this type of instruction would be to load the accumulator with a constant, where the constant is the byte immediately following the OP code.

Immediate Extended. This mode is merely an extension of immediate addressing in that the two bytes following the op codes are the operand.

<table>
<tr><td>OP Code</td><td>one or 2 bytes</td></tr>
<tr><td>Operand</td><td>low order</td></tr>
<tr><td>Operand</td><td>high order</td></tr>
</table>

Examples of this type of instruction would be to load the HL register pair (16-bit register) with 16 bits (2 bytes) of data.

Modified Page Zero Addressing. The Z80 has a special single byte call instruction to any of 8 locations in memory. This instruction (which is referred to as a restart) sets the PC to an effective address in page zero. The value of this instruction is that it allows a single byte to specify a complete 16-bit address where commonly called subroutines are located thus saving memory space.

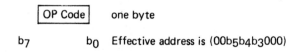

Relative Addressing. Relative addressing uses one byte of data following the OP code to specify a displacement from the existing program to which a program jump can occur. This displacement is a signed two's complement number that is added to the address of the OP code of the following instruction.

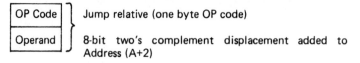

30

The value of relative addressing is that it allows jumps to nearby locations while only requiring two bytes of memory space. For most programs, relative jumps are by far the most prevalent type of jump due to the proximity of related program segments. Thus, these instructions can significantly reduce memory space requirements. The signed displacement can range between +127 and −128 from A + 2. This allows for a total displacement of +129 to −126 from the jump relative OP code address. Another major advantage is that it allows for relocatable code.

Extended Addressing. Extended Addressing provides for two bytes (16 bits) of address to be included in the instruction. This data can be an address to which a program can jump or it can be an address where an operand is located.

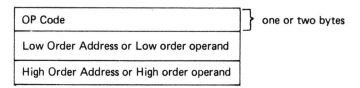

Extended addressing is required for a program to jump from any location in memory to any other location or load and store data in any memory location.

When extended addressing is used to specify the source of destination address of an operand, the notation (nn) will be used to indicate the content of memory at nn, where nn is the 16-bit address specified in the instruction. This means that the two bytes of address nn are used as a pointer to a memory location. The use of the parentheses always means that the value enclosed within them is used as a pointer to a memory location. For example, (1200) refers to the contents of memory at location 1200.

Indexed Addressing. In this type of addressing, the byte of data following the OP code contains a displacement which is added to one of the two index registers (the OP code specifies which index register is used) to form a pointer to memory. The contents of the index register are not altered by this operation.

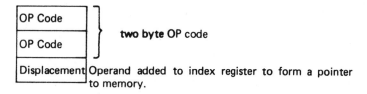

An example of an indexed instruction would be to load the contents of the memory location (Index Register + Displacement) into the accumulator. The displacement is a signed two's complement number. Indexed addressing greatly simplifies programs using tables of data since the index register can point to the start of any table. Two index registers are provided since very often operations require two or more tables. Indexed addressing also allows for relocatable code.

The two index registers in the Z80 are referred to as IX and IY. To indicate indexed addressing the notation:

$$(Ix+d) \text{ or } (IY+d)$$

is used. Here d is the displacement specified after the OP code. The parentheses indicate that this value is used as a pointer to external memory.

Register Addressing. Many of the Z80 OP codes contain bits of information that specify which CPU register is to be used for operation. An example of register addressing would be to load the data in register B into register C.

Implied Addressing. Implied addressing refers to operations where the OP code automatically implies one or more CPU registers as containing the operands. An example is the set of arithmetic operations where the accumulator is always implied to be the destination of the results.

Register Indirect Addressing. This type of addressing specifies a 16-bit CPU register pair (such as HL) to be used as a pointer to any location in memory. This type of instruction is very powerful and it is used in a wide range of applications.

An example of this type of instruction would be to load the accumulator with the data in the memory location pointed to by the HL register contents. Indexed addressing is actually a form of register indirect addressing except that a displacement is added with indexed addressing. Register indirect addressing allows for very powerful but simple to implement memory accesses. The block and search commands in the Z80 are extensions of this type of addressing where automatic register incrementing, decrementing and comparing has been added. The notation for indicating register indirect addressing is to put parentheses around the name of the register that is to be used as the pointer. For example, the symbol

(HL)

specifies that the contents of the HL register are to be used as a pointer to a memory location. Often register indirect addressing is used to specify 16-bit operands. In this case, the register contents point to the lower order portion of the operand while the register contents are automatically incremented to obtain the upper portion of the operand.

Bit Addressing. The Z80 contains a large number of bit set, reset and test instructions. These instructions allow any memory location or CPU register to be specified for a bit operation through one of three previous addressing modes (register, register indirect and indexed) while three bits in the OP code specify which of the eight bits is to be manipulated.

Addressing Mode Combinations

Many instructions include more than one operand (such as arithmetic instructions or loads). In these cases, two types of addressing may be employed. For example, load can use immediate addressing to specify the source and register indirect or indexed addressing to specify the source and register indirect or indexed addressing to specify the destination.

INSTRUCTION OP CODES

This section describes each of the Z80 instructions and provides tables listing the OP codes for every instruction. In each of these tables the shaded OP codes are identical to those offered in the 8080A CPU. Also shown is the assembly language mnemonic that is used for each instruction. All instruction OP codes are listed in hexadecimal notation. Single byte OP codes require two hex characters while double byte OP codes require four hex characters. The conversion from hex to binary is repeated here for convenience.

Hex	Binary	Decimal	Hex	Binary	Decimal
0 =	0000	= 0	8 =	1000	= 8
1 =	0001	= 1	9 =	1001	= 9
2 =	0010	= 2	A =	1010	= 10
3 =	0011	= 3	B =	1011	= 11
4 =	0100	= 4	C =	1100	= 12
5 =	0101	= 5	D =	1101	= 13
6 =	0110	= 6	E =	1110	= 14
7 =	0111	= 7	F =	1111	= 15

Z80 instruction mnemonics consist of an OP code and zero, one or two operands. Instructions in which the operand is implied have no operand. Instructions which have only one logical operand or those in which one operand is invariant (such as the Logical OR instruction) are represented by a one operand mnemonic. Instructions which may have two varying operands are represented by two operand mnemonics.

Load and Exchange

Table 3-1 defines the OP code for all of the 8-bit load instructions implemented in the Z80-CPU. Also shown in this table is the type of addressing used for each instruction. The source of the data is found on the top horizontal row while the destination is specified by the left hand column. For example, load register C from register B uses the OP code 48H. In all of the tables the OP code is specified in hexadecimal notation and the 48H (=0100 1000 binary) code is fetched by the CPU from the external memory during M1 time, decoded and then the register is automatically performed by the CPU.

The assembly language mnemonic for this entire group is LD, followed by the destination followed by the source (LD DEST., SOURCE). Note that several combinations of addressing modes are possible. For example, the source may use register addressing and the destination may be register indirect, such as load the memory location pointed to by register HL with the contents of register D. The OP code for this operation would be 72. The mnemonic for this load instruction would be as follows: LD (HL), D.

The parentheses around the HL means that the contents of HL are used as a pointer to a memory location. In all Z80 load instruction mnemonics the destination is always listed first, with the source following. The Z80 assembly language has been defined for ease of programming. Every instruction is self-documenting and programs written in Z80 language are easy to maintain.

Note in Table 3-1 that some load OP codes that are available in the Z80 use two bytes. This is an efficient method of memory utilization since, 8, 16, 24 or 32 bit instructions are implemented in the Z80. Thus often

Table 3-1. 8-Bit Load Group.

		SOURCE															
		IMPLIED		REGISTER							REG INDIRECT			INDEXED		EXT. ADDR.	IMME.
		I	R	A	B	C	D	E	H	L	(HL)	(BC)	(DE)	(IX + d)	(IY + d)	(nn)	n
DESTINATION — REGISTER	A	ED 57	ED 5F	7F	78	79	7A	7B	7C	7D	7E	0A	1A	DD 7E d	FD 7E d	3A n n	3E n
	B			47	40	41	42	43	44	45	46			DD 46 d	FD 46 d		06 n
	C			4F	48	49	4A	4B	4C	4D	4E			DD 4E d	FD 4E d		0E n
	D			57	50	51	52	53	54	55	56			DD 56 d	FD 56 d		16 n
	E			5F	58	59	5A	5B	5C	5D	5E			DD 5E d	FD 5E d		1E n
	H			67	60	61	62	63	64	65	66			DD 66 d	FD 66 d		26 n
	L			6F	68	69	6A	6B	6C	6D	6E			DD 6E d	FD 6E d		2E n
DESTINATION — REG INDIRECT	(HL)			77	70	71	72	73	74	75							36 n
	(BC)			02													
	(DE)			12													
DESTINATION — INDEXED	(IX+d)			DD 77 d	DD 70 d	DD 71 d	DD 72 d	DD 73 d	DD 74 d	DD 75 d							DD 36 d n
	(IY+d)			FD 77 d	FD 70 d	FD 71 d	FD 72 d	FD 73 d	FD 74 d	FD 75 d							FD 36 d n
DESTINATION — EXT. ADDR	(nn)			32 n n													
DESTINATION — IMPLIED	I			ED 47													
	R			ED 4F													

utilized instructions such as arithmetic or logical operations are only 8-bits which results in better memory utilization than is achieved with fixed instruction sizes such as 16-bits.

All load instructions using indexed addressing for either the source or destination location actually use three bytes of memory with the third byte being the displacement d. For example a load register E with the operand pointed to by IX with an offset of +8 would be written: LD E, (IX + 8)

The instruction sequence for this in memory would be:

Address A	DD	OP Code
A+1	5F	
A+2	08	Displacement operand

The two extended addressing instructions are also three byte instructions. For example the instruction to load the accumulator with the operand in memory location 6F32H would be written:

LD A, (6F 32H)

and its instruction sequence would be:

Address A	3A	OP Code
A+1	32	low order address
A+2	6F	high order address

Notice that the low order portion of the address is always the first operand.

The load immediate instructions for the general purpose 8-bit registers are two-byte instructions. The instruction load register H with the value 36H would be written:

LD H, 36H

and its sequence would be:

Address A	26	OP Code
A+1	36	Operand

Loading a memory location using indexed addressing for the destination and immediate addressing for the source requires four bytes. For example:

LD (IIX -15), 21H

would appear as:

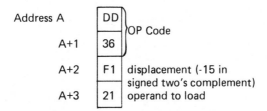

Address A	DD	OP Code
A+1	36	
A+2	F1	displacement (-15 in signed two's complement)
A+3	21	operand to load

Notice that with any indexed addressing the displacement always follows directly after the OP code.

Table 3-2 specifies the 16-bit load operations. This table is very similar to the previous one. Notice that the extended addressing capability covers all register pairs. Also notice that register indirect operations specifying the stack pointer are the PUSH and POP instruction. The mnemonic for these instructions is "PUSH" and "POP". These differ from the other 16-bit loads in that the stack pointer is automatically decremented and incremented as each byte is pushed onto or popped from the stack respectively. For example the instruction:

PUSH AF

is a single byte instruction with the OP code of F5H. When this instruction is executed the following sequence is generated:

Decrement SP
LD (SP) A
Decrement SP
LD (SP), F

Thus the external stack now appears as follows:

(SP)	F	Top of stack
(SP+1)	A	
.	.	
.	.	
	°	

The POP instruction is the exact reverse of a PUSH. Notice that all PUSH and POP instructions utilize a 16-bit operand and the high order is always pushed first and popped last. That is a:

Table 3-2. 16 Bit Load Group 'LD' 'Push' and 'Pop.'

		SOURCE								IMM. EXT.	EXT. ADDR.	REG. INDIR.
		REGISTER								nn	(nn)	(SP)
DESTINATION		AF	BC	DE	HL	SP	IX	IY				
REGISTER	AF											F1
	BC									01 n n	ED 4B n n	C1
	DE									11 n n	ED 5B n n	D1
	HL									21 n n	2A n n	E1
	SP				F9		DD F9	FD F9		31 n n	ED 7B n n	
	IX									DD 21 n n	DD 2A n n	DD E1
	IY									FD 21 n n	FD 2A n n	FD E1
EXT. ADDR.	(nn)		ED 43 n n	ED 53 n n	22 n n	ED 73 n n	DD 22 n n	FD 22 n n				
REG. IND. (PUSH INSTRUCTIONS →)	(SP)	F5	C5	D5	E5		DD E5	FD E5				

POP INSTRUCTIONS ↑

NOTE: The Push & Pop Instructions adjust the SP after every execution

36

PUSH BC is PUSH B then C
PUSH DE is PUSH D then E
PUSH HL is PUSH H then L
Pop HL is POP L then H

The instruction using extended immediate addressing for the source obviously requires 2 bytes of data following the OP code. For example:

LD DE, 0659H

will be:

Address A	11	OP Code
A+1	59	Low order operand to register E
A+2	06	High order operand to register D

In all extended immediate or extended addressing modes, the low order byte always appears first after the OP code.

Table 3-3 lists the 16-bit exchange instructions implemented in the Z80. OP code 08H allows the programmer to switch between the two pairs of accumulator flag registers while D9H allows the programmer to switch between the duplicate set of six general purpose registers. These OP codes are only one byte in length to absolutely minimize the time necessary to perform the exchange so that the duplicate banks can be used to effect very fast interrupt response times.

Block Transfer and Search

Table 3-4 lists the extremely powerful block transfer instructions. All of these instructions operate with three registers.

Table 3-3. Exchanges 'EX' and 'EXX.'

		IMPLIED ADDRESSING				
		AF'	BC',DE' & HL'	HL	IX	IY
IMPLIED	AF	08				
	BC, DE & HL		D9			
	DE			EB		
REG. INDIR.	(SP)			E3	DD E3	FD E3

37

Table 3-4. Block Transfer Group.

DESTINATION			SOURCE REG. INDIR. (HL)	
DESTINATION	REG. INDIR.	(DE)	ED A0	'LDI' – Load (DE)◄——(HL) Inc HL & DE, Dec BC
DESTINATION	REG. INDIR.	(DE)	**ED A0**	'LDIR,' – Load (DE)◄——(HL) Inc HL & DE, Dec BC, Repeat until BC = 0
DESTINATION	REG. INDIR.	(DE)	**ED B0**	'LDD' – Load (DE)◄——(HL) Dec HL & DE, Dec BC
DESTINATION	REG. INDIR.	(DE)	ED B8	'LDDR' – Load (DE)◄——(HL) Dec HL & DE, Dec BC, Repeat until BC = 0

Reg HL points to source
Reg DE points to destination
Reg BC is byte counter

HL points to the source location.
DE points to the destination location.
BC is a byte counter.

After the programmer has initialized these three registers, any of these four instructions may be used. The LDI (Load and Increment) instruction moves one byte from the location pointed to by HL to the location pointed to by DE. Register pairs HL and DE are then automatically incremented and are ready to point to the following locations. The byte counter (register pair BC) is also decremented at this time. This instruction is valuable when blocks of data must be moved but other types of processing are required between each move. The LDIR (Load, Increment and Repeat) instruction is an extension of the LDI instruction. The same load and increment operation is repeated until the byte counter reaches the count of zero. Thus, this single instruction can move any block of data from one location to any other.

Note that since 16-bit registers are used, the size of the block can be up to 64K bytes (1K = 1024) long and it can be moved from any location in memory to any other location. Furthermore the blocks can be overlapping since there are absolutely no constraints on the data that is used in the three register pair.

The LDD and LDDR instructions are very similar to the LDI and LDIR. The only difference is that register pairs HL and DE are decremented after every mode so that a block transfer starts from the highest address of the designated block rather than the lowest.

Table 3-5 specifies the OP codes for the four search instructions. The first, CPI (compare and increment) compares the data in the accumulator, with the contents of the memory location pointed to by register HL. The result of the compare is stored in one of the flag bits and the HL register pair is then incremented and the byte counter (register pair BC) is decremented.

The instruction CPIR is merely an extension of the CPI instruction in which the compare is repeated until either a match is found or the byte counter (register pair BC) becomes zero. Thus, this single instruction can search the entire memory for any 8-bit character.

Table 3-5. Block Search Group.

```
      SEARCH
      LOCATION

      ┌──────────┐
      │ REG.     │
      │ INDIR.   │
      ├──────────┤
      │ (HL)     │
      ├──────────┬─────────────────────────────────────┐
      │ ED       │ 'CPI'                                │
      │ A1       │ Inc HL, Dec BC                       │
      ├──────────┼─────────────────────────────────────┤
      │ ED       │ 'CPIR', Inc HL, Dec BC              │
      │ B1       │ repeat until BC = 0 or find match    │
      ├──────────┼─────────────────────────────────────┤
      │ ED       │                                      │
      │ A9       │ 'CPD' Dec HL & BC                    │
      ├──────────┼─────────────────────────────────────┤
      │ ED       │ 'CPDR' Dec HL & BC                   │
      │ B9       │ Repeat until BC = 0 or find match    │
      └──────────┴─────────────────────────────────────┘

      HL points to location in memory
         to be compared with accumulator
         contents
      BC is byte counter
```

The CPD (Compare and Decrement) and CPDR (Compare, Decrement and Repeat) are similar instructions, their only difference being that they decrement HL after every compare so that they search the memory in the opposite direction. (The search is started at the highest location in the memory block.)

It should be emphasized again that these block transfer and compare instructions are extremely powerful in string manipulation applications.

Arithmetic and Logic

Table 3-6 lists all of the 8-bit arithmetic operations that can be performed with the accumulator, also listed are the increment (INC) and decrement (DEC) instructions. In all of these instructions, except INC and DEC, the specified 8-bit operation is performed between the data in the accumulator and the source data specified in the table. The result of the operation is placed in the accumulator with the exception of compare (CP) that leaves the accumulator unaffected. All of these operations affect the flag register as a result of the specified operation. INC and DEC instructions specify a register or a memory location as both source and destination of the result. When the source operand is addressed using the index registers the displacement must follow directly. With immediate addressing the actual operand will follow directly. For example the instruction:

AND 07H

Table 3-6. 8 Bit Arithmetic and Logic.

	SOURCE										
	REGISTER ADDRESSING							REG. INDIR.	INDEXED		IMMED.
	A	B	C	D	E	H	L	(HL)	(IX+d)	(IY+d)	n
'ADD'	87	80	81	82	83	84	85	86	DD 86 d	FD 86 d	C6 n
ADD w CARRY 'ADC'	8F	88	89	8A	8B	8C	8D	8E	DD 8E d	FD 8E d	CE n
SUBTRACT 'SUB'	97	90	91	92	93	94	95	96	DD 96 d	FD 96 d	D6 n
SUB w CARRY 'SBC'	9F	98	99	9A	9B	9C	9D	9E	DD 9E d	FD 9E d	DE n
'AND'	A7	A0	A1	A2	A3	A4	A5	A6	DD A6 d	FD A6 d	E6 n
'XOR'	AF	A8	A9	AA	AB	AC	AD	AE	DD AE d	FD AE d	EE n
'OR'	B7	B0	B1	B2	B3	B4	B5	B6	DD B6 d	FD B6 d	F6 n
COMPARE 'CP'	BF	B8	B9	BA	BB	BC	BD	BE	DD BE d	FD BE d	FE n
INCREMENT 'INC'	3C	04	0C	14	1C	24	2C	34	DD 34 d	FD 34 d	
DECREMENT 'DEC'	3D	05	0D	15	1D	25	2D	35	DD 35 d	FD 35 d	

would appear as:

Address A	E6	OP Code
A+1	07	Operand

Assuming that the accumulator contained the value F3H the result of 03H would be placed in the accumulator:

Acc before operation	1111 0011 = F3H
Operand	0000 0111 = 07H
Result to Acc	0000 0011 = 03H

The Add Instruction (ADD) performs a binary add between the data in the source location and the data in the accumulator. The subtract (SUB) does a binary subtraction. When the add with carry is specified (ADC) or the subtract with carry (SBC), then the carry flag is also added or subtracted respectively. The flags and decimal adjust instruction (DAA) in the Z80 allow arithmetic operations for:

multiprecision packed BCD numbers

multiprecision signed or unsigned binary numbers

multiprecision two's complement signed numbers

Other instructions in this group are logical and (AND), logical (OR), exclusive or (XOR) and compare (CP).

There are five general purpose arithmetic instructions that operate on the accumulator or carry flag. These five are listed in Table 3-7. The decimal adjust instruction can adjust for subtraction as well as addition, thus making BCD arithmetic operations simple. Note that to allow for this operation the flag N is used. This flag is set if the last arithmetic operation was a subtract. The negate accumulator (NEG) instruction forms the two's complement of the number in the accumulator. Finally notice that a reset carry instruction is not included in the Z80 since this operation can be easily achieved through other instructions such as a logical AND of the accumulator with itself.

Table 3-8 lists all of the 16-bit arithmetic operations between 16-bit registers. There are five groups of instructions including add with carry and subtract with carry. ADC and SBC affect all of the flags. These two groups simplify address calculation operations or other 16-bit arithmetic operations.

Rotate and Shift

A major capability of the Z80 is its ability to rotate or shift data in the accumulator, any general purpose register, or any memory location. All of the rotate and shift OP codes are shown in Table 3-9. Also included in the Z80 are arithmetic and logical shift operations. These operations are useful in an extremely wide range of applications including integer multiplication and division. Two BCD digit rotate instructions (RRD and RLD) allow a digit in the accumulator to be rotated with the two digits in a memory location pointed to by register pair HL. These instructions allow for efficient BCD arithmetic.

Table 3-7. General Purpose AF Operations.

Decimal Adjust Acc, 'DAA'	27
Complement Acc, 'CPL'	2F
Negate Acc, 'NEG' (2's complement)	ED 44
Complement Carry Flag, 'CCF'	3F
Set Carry Flag, 'SCF'	37

Table 3-8. 16 Bit Arithmetic.

			SOURCE					
DESTINATION			BC	DE	HL	SP	IX	IY
	'ADD'	HL	09	19	29	39		
		IX	DD 09	DD 19		DD 39	DD 29	
		IY	FD 09	FD 19		FD 39		FD 29
	ADD WITH CARRY AND SET FLAGS 'ADC'	HL	ED 4A	ED 5A	ED 6A	ED 7A		
	SUB WITH CARRY AND SET FLAGS 'SBC'	HL	ED 42	ED 52	ED 62	ED 72		
	INCREMENT 'INC.		03	13	23	33	DD 23	FD 23
	DECREMENT 'DEC'		0B	1B	2B	3B	DD 2B	FD 2B

Table 3-9. Rotates and Shifts.

Source and Destination	A	B	C	D	E	H	L	(HL)	(IX + d)	(IY + d)
'RLC'	CB 07	CB 00	CB 01	CB 02	CB 03	CB 04	CB 05	CB 06	DD CB d 06	FD CB d 06
'RRC'	CB 0F	CB 08	CB 09	CB 0A	CB 0B	CB 0C	CB 0D	CB 0E	DD CB d 0E	FD CB d 0E
'RL'	CB 17	CB 10	CB 11	CB 12	CB 13	CB 14	CB 15	CB 16	DD CB d 16	FD CB d 16
'RR'	CB 1F	CB 18	CB 19	CB 1A	CB 1B	CB 1C	CB 1D	CB 1E	DD CB d 1E	FD CB d 1E
'SLA'	CB 27	CB 20	CB 21	CB 22	CB 23	CB 24	CB 25	CB 26	DD CB d 26	FD CB d 26
'SRA'	CB 2F	CB 28	CB 29	CB 2A	CB 2B	CB 2C	CB 2D	CB 2E	DD CB d 2E	FD CB d 2E
'SRL'	CB 3F	CB 38	CB 39	CB 3A	CB 3B	CB 3C	CB 3D	CB 3E	DD CB d 3E	FD CB d 3E
'RLD'								ED 6F		
'RRD'								ED 67		

TYPE OF ROTATE OR SHIFT

	A
RLCA	07
RRCA	0F
RLA	17
RRA	1F

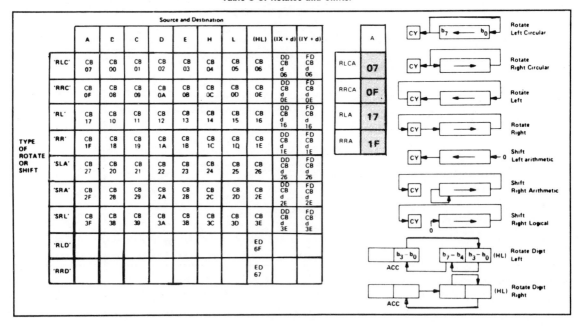

Rotate Left Circular
Rotate Right Circular
Rotate Left
Rotate Right
Shift Left arithmetic
Shift Right Arithmetic
Shift Right Logical
Rotate Digit Left
Rotate Digit Right

42

BIT MANIPULATION

The ability to set, reset and test individual bits in a register or memory location is needed in almost every program. These bits may be flags in a general purpose software routine, indications of external control conditions or data packed into memory locations to make memory utilization more efficient.

The Z80 has the ability to set, reset and test any bit in the accumulator, any general purpose register or any memory location with a single instruction. Table 3-10 lists the 240 instructions that are available for this purpose. Register addressing can specify the accumulator or any general purpose register on which the operation is to be performed. Register indirect and indexed addressing are available to operate on external memory locations. Bit test operations set the zero flag (Z) if the tested bit is a zero.

Jump, Call, and Return

Table 3-11 lists all of the jump, call and return instructions implemented in the Z80 CPU. A jump is a branch in a program where the program counter is loaded with the 16-bit value as specified by one of the three available addressing modes (Immediate Extended, Relative or Register Indirect). Notice that the jump group has several different conditions that can be specified to be met before the jump will be made. If these conditions are not met, the program merely continues with the next sequential instruction. The conditions are all dependent on the data in the flag register. The immediate extended addressing is used to jump to any location in the memory. This instruction requires three bytes (two to specify the 16-bit address) with the low order address byte first followed by the high order address byte.

For example, an unconditional Jump to memory location 3E32H would be:

Address A	C3	OP Code
A+1	32	Low order address
A+2	3E	High order address

The relative jump instruction uses only two bytes, the second byte is a signed two's complement displacement from the existing PC. This displacement can be in the range of +129 to −126 and is measured from the address of the instruction OP code.

Three types of register indirect jumps are also included. These instructions are implemented by loading the register pair HL or one of the index registers IX or IY directly into the PC. This capability allows for program jumps to be a function of previous calculations.

A call is a special form of a jump where the address of the byte following the call instruction is pushed onto the stack before the jump is made. A return instruction is the reverse of a call because the data on the top of the stack is popped directly into the PC to form a jump address. The call and return instructions allow for simple subroutine and interrupt handling. Two special return instructions have been included in the Z80 family of components. The return from interrupt instruction (RETI) and the return from non-maskable interrupt (RETN) are treated in the CPU as an unconditional return identical to the OP code C9H. The difference is that (RETI) can be used at the end of an interrupt routine and all Z80 peripheral chips will

	BIT	REGISTER ADDRESSING							REG. INDIR.	INDEXED	
		A	B	C	D	E	H	L	(HL)	(IX+d)	(IY+d)
TEST 'BIT'	0	CB 47	CB 40	Cd 41	CB 42	CB 43	CB 44	CB 45	CB 46	DD CB d 46	FD CB d 46
	1	CB 4F	CB 48	CB 49	CB 4A	CB 4B	CB 4C	CB 4D	CB 4E	DD CB d 4E	FD CB d 4E
	2	CB 57	CB 50	CB 51	CB 52	CB 53	CB 54	CB 55	CB 56	DD CB d 56	FD CB d 56
	3	CB 5F	CB 58	CB 59	CB 5A	CB 5B	CB 5C	CB 5D	CB 5E	DD CB d 5E	FD CB d 5E
	4	CB 67	CB 60	CB 61	CB 62	CB 63	CB 64	CB 65	CB 66	DD CB d 66	FD CB d 66
	5	CB 6F	CB 68	CB 69	CB 6A	CB 6B	CB 6C	CB 6D	CB 6E	DD CB d 6E	FD CB d 6E
	6	CB 77	CB 70	CB 71	CB 72	CB 73	CB 74	GB 75	CB 76	DD CB d 76	FD CB d 76
	7	CB 7F	CB 78	CB 79	CB 7A	CB 7B	CB 7C	CB 7D	CB 7E	DD CB d 7E	FD CB d 7E
RESET BIT 'RES'	0	CB 87	CB 80	CB 81	CB 82	CB 83	CB 84	CB 85	CB 86	DD CB d 86	FD CB d 86
	1	CB 8F	CB 88	CB 89	CB 8A	CB 8B	CB 8C	CB 8D	CB 8E	DD CB d 8E	FD CB d 8E
	2	CB 97	CB 90	CB 91	CB 92	CB 93	CB 94	CB 95	CB 96	DD CB d 96	FD CB d 96
	3	CB 9F	CB 98	CB 99	CB 9A	CB 9B	CB 9C	CB 9D	CB 9E	DD CB d 9E	FD CB d 9E
	4	CB A7	CB A0	CB A1	CB A2	CB A3	CB A4	CB A5	CB A6	DD CB d A6	FD CB d A6
	5	CB AF	CB A8	CB A9	CB AA	CB AB	CB AC	CB AD	CB AE	DD CB d AE	FD CB d AE
	6	CB B7	CB B0	CB B1	CB B2	CB B3	CB B4	CB B5	CB B6	DD CB d B6	FD CB d B6
	7	CB BF	CB B8	CB B9	CB BA	CB BB	CB BC	CB BD	CB BE	DD CB d BE	FD CB d BE
SET BIT 'SET'	0	CB C7	CB C0	CB C1	CB C2	CB C3	CB C4	CB C5	CB C6	DD CB d C6	FD CB d C6
	1	CB CF	CB C8	CB C9	CB CA	CB CB	CB CC	CB CD	CB CE	DD CB d CE	FD CB d CE
	2	CB D7	CB D0	CB D1	CB D2	CB D3	CB D4	CB D5	CB D6	DD CB d D6	FD CB d D6
	3	CB DF	CB D8	CB D9	CB DA	CB DB	CB DC	CB DD	CB DE	DD CB d DE	FD CB d DE
	4	CB E7	CB E0	CB E1	CB E2	CB E3	CB E4	CB E5	CB E6	DD CB d E6	FD CB d E6
	5	CB EF	CB E8	CB E9	CB EA	CB EB	CB EC	CB ED	CB EE	DD CB d EE	FD CB d EE
	6	CB F7	CB F0	CB F1	CB F2	CB F3	CB F4	CB F5	CB F6	DD CB d F6	FD CB d F6
	7	CB FF	CB F8	CB F9	CB FA	CB FB	CB FC	CB FD	CB FE	DD CB d FE	FD CB d FE

Table 3-10. Bit Manipulation Group.

Table 3-11. Jump, Call and Return Group.

			CONDITION									
			UN-COND.	CARRY	NON CARRY	ZERO	NON ZERO	PARITY EVEN	PARITY ODD	SIGN NEG	SIGN POS	REG B≠0
JUMP 'JP'	IMMED. EXT.	nn	C3 n n	DA n n	D2 n n	CA n n	C2 n n	EA n n	E2 n n	FA n n	F2 n n	
JUMP 'JR'	RELATIVE	PC+e	18 e-2	38 e-2	30 e-2	28 e-2	20 e-2					
JUMP 'JP'		(HL)	E9									
JUMP 'JP'	REG. INDIR.	(IX)	DD E9									
JUMP 'JP'		(IY)	FD E9									
'CALL'	IMMED. EXT.	nn	CD n n	DC n n	D4 n n	CC n n	C4 n n	EC n n	E4 n n	FC n n	F4 n n	
DECREMENT B, JUMP IF NON ZERO 'DJNZ'	RELATIVE	PC+e										10 e-2
RETURN 'RET'	REGISTER INDIR.	(SP) (SP+1)	C9	D8	D0	C8	C0	E8	E0	F8	F0	
RETURN FROM INT 'RETI'	REG. INDIR.	(SP) (SP+1)	ED 4D									
RETURN FROM NON MASKABLE INT 'RETN'	REG. INDIR.	(SP) (SP+1)	ED 45									

recognize the execution of this instruction for proper control of nested priority interrupt handling. This instruction coupled with the Z80 peripheral devices implementation simplifies the normal return from nested interrupt. Without this feature the following software sequence would be necessary to inform the interrupting device that the interrupt routine is completed:

Disable Interrupt   Prevent interrupt before
              routine is exited.

LD A, n   Notify peripheral that service
OUT n, A   routine is complete

Enable Interrupt

Return

This seven byte sequence can be replaced with the three byte EI RETI instruction sequence in the Z80. This is important since interrupt service time often must be minimized.

To facilitate program loop control the instruction DJNZ e can be used advantageously. This two byte, relative jump instruction decrements the B register and the jump occurs if the B register has not been

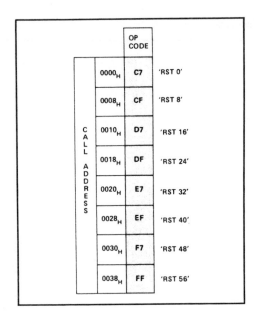

	OP CODE	
0000_H	C7	'RST 0'

Table 3-12. Restart Group.

decremented to zero. The relative displacement is expressed as a signed two's complement number. A simple example of its use might be:

Address	Instruction	Comments
N, N+1	LD B,7	; set B register to count of 7
N + 2 to N + 9	(Perform a sequence of instructions)	; loop to be performed 7 times
N + 10, N + 11	DJNZ -10	; to jump from N + 12 to N + 2
N + 12	(Next Instruction)	

Table 3-12 lists the eight OP codes for the restart instructions. This instruction is a single byte call to any of the eight addresses listed. The simple mnemonic for these eight calls is also shown. The value of this instruction is that frequently used routines can be called with this instruction to minimize memory usage.

INPUT/OUTPUT

The Z80 has an extensive set of Input and Output instruction as shown in Table 3-13 and Table 3-14. The addressing of the input or output device can be either absolute or register indirect, using the C register. Notice that in the register indirect addressing mode data can be transferred between the I/O devices and any of the internal registers. In addition eight block transfer instructions have been implemented. These instructions are similar to the memory block transfers except that they use register pair HL for a pointer to the memory source (output commands) or destination (input commands) while register B is used as a byte counter. Register C holds the address of the port for which the input or output command is desired. Since register B is eight bits in length, the I/O block transfer command handles up to 256 bytes.

In the instructions IN A, n and OUT n, A and I/O device address n appears in the lower half of the address bus (A_0-A_7) while the accumulator content is transferred in the upper half of the address bus. In all register indirect input output instructions, including block I/O transfers the content of register C is transferred to the lower half of the address bus (device address) while the content of register B is transferred to the upper half of the address bus.

CPU Control Group

Table 3-15 illustrates the six general purpose CPU control instructions. The NOP is a do-nothing instruction. The HALT instruction suspends CPU operation until a subsequent interrupt is received, while the DI and EI are used to lock out and enable interrupts. The three interrupt mode commands set the CPU into any of the three available interrupt response modes as follows. If mode zero is set the interrupting

Table 3-13. Input Group.

				PORT ADDRESS	
				IMMED.	REG. INDIR.
				n	(C)
INPUT DESTINATION	INPUT 'IN'	REG ADDRESSING	A	DB	ED 78
			B		ED 40
			C		ED 48
			D		ED 50
			E		ED 58
			H		ED 60
			L		ED 68
	'INI' — INPUT & Inc HL, Dec B	REG, INDIR	(HL)		ED A2
	'INIR'— INP, Inc HL, Dec B, REPEAT IF B≠0				ED B2
	'IND'—INPUT & Dec HL, Dec B				ED AA
	'INDR'—INPUT, Dec HL, Dec B, REPEAT IF B≠0				ED BA

BLOCK INPUT COMMANDS

Table 3-14. Output Group.

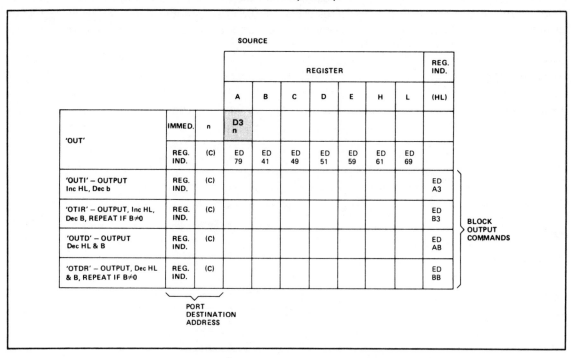

			SOURCE							
			REGISTER							REG. IND.
'OUT' / 'OUTI' etc.			A	B	C	D	E	H	L	(HL)
'OUT'	IMMED.	n	D3 n							
'OUT'	REG. IND.	(C)	ED 79	ED 41	ED 49	ED 51	ED 59	ED 61	ED 69	
'OUTI' – OUTPUT Inc HL, Dec b	REG. IND.	(C)								ED A3
'OTIR' – OUTPUT, Inc HL, Dec B, REPEAT IF B≠0	REG. IND.	(C)								ED B3
'OUTD' – OUTPUT Dec HL & B	REG. IND.	(C)								ED AB
'OTDR' – OUTPUT, Dec HL & B, REPEAT IF B≠0	REG. IND.	(C)								ED BB

BLOCK OUTPUT COMMANDS

PORT DESTINATION ADDRESS

Table 3-15. Miscellaneous CPU Control.

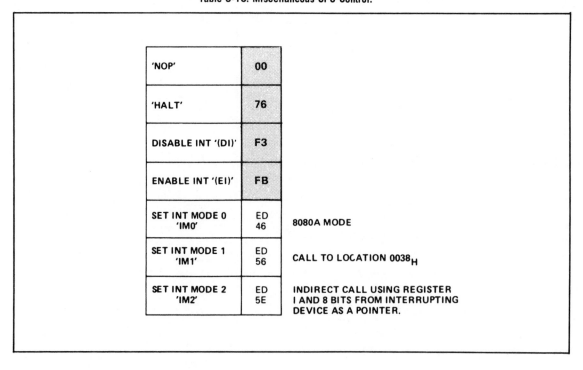

'NOP'	00	
'HALT'	76	
DISABLE INT '(DI)'	F3	
ENABLE INT '(EI)'	FB	
SET INT MODE 0 'IM0'	ED 46	8080A MODE
SET INT MODE 1 'IM1'	ED 56	CALL TO LOCATION 0038$_H$
SET INT MODE 2 'IM2'	ED 5E	INDIRECT CALL USING REGISTER I AND 8 BITS FROM INTERRUPTING DEVICE AS A POINTER.

48

device can insert any instruction on the data bus and allow the CPU to execute it. Mode 1 is a simplified mode where the CPU automatically executes a restart (RST) to location 0038H so that no external hardware is required. (The old PC content is pushed onto the stack.) Mode 2 is the most powerful in that it allows for an indirect call to any location in memory. With this mode the CPU forms a 16-bit memory address where the upper 8-bits are the content of register I and the lower 8-bits are supplied by the interrupting device. The address points of the first of two sequential bytes in a table where the address of the service routine is located. The CPU automatically obtains the starting address and performs a CALL to this address.

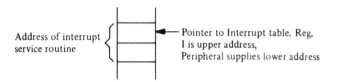

Address of interrupt service routine

Pointer to Interrupt table. Reg. I is upper address, Peripheral supplies lower address

FLAGS

Each of the two Z80-CPU Flag registers contains six bits of information which are set or reset by various CPU operations. Four of these bits are testable; that is, they are used as conditions for jump, call or return instructions. For example a jump may be desired only if a specific bit in the flag register is set. The four testable flag bits are:

1. Carry Flag (C). This flag is the carry from the highest order bit of the accumulator. For example, the carry flag will be set during an add instruction where a carry from the highest bit of the accumulator is generated. This flag is also set if a borrow is generated during a subtraction instruction. The shift and rotate instructions also affect this bit.

2. Zero Flag (Z). This flag is set if the result of the operation loaded a zero into the accumulator. Otherwise it is reset.

3. Sign Flag(S). This flag is intended to be used with signed numbers and it is set if the result of the operation was negative. Since bit 7 (MSB) represents the sign of the number (A negative number has a 1 in bit 7), this flag stores the state of bit 7 in the accumulator.

4. Parity/Overflow Flag (P/V). This dual purpose flag indicates the parity of the result in the accumulator when logical operations are performed (such as AND, A, B) and it represents overflow when signed two's complement arithmetic operations are performed. The Z80 overflow flag indicates that the two's complement number in the accumulator is in error since it has exceeded the maximum possible (+127) or is less than the minimum possible (−128) number that can be represented two's complement notation. For example consider adding:

$$
\begin{array}{rl}
+120 = & 0111\ 1000 \\
+105 = & 0110\ 1001 \\
\hline
C = 0 & 1110\ 0001 = 95 \text{ (wrong) Overflow has occurred;}
\end{array}
$$

Here the result is incorrect. Overflow has occurred and yet there is no carry to indicate an error. For this case the overflow flag would be set. Also consider the addition of two negative numbers:

$$
\begin{array}{r}
-5 \;=\; 1111\ 1011 \\
-16 \;=\; \underline{1111\ 0000} \\
C \;=1\,\overline{1110\ 1011}\; = -21\ \text{correct}
\end{array}
$$

Notice that the answer is correct but the carry is set so that this flag can not be used as an overflow indicator. In this case the overflow would not be set.

For logical operations (AND, OR, XOR) this flag is set if the parity of the result is even and it is reset if it is odd.

There are also two non-testable bits in the flag register. Both of these are used for BCD arithmetic. They are:

1. Half Carry (H). This is the BCD carry or borrow result from the least significant four bits of operation. When using the DAA (Decimal Adjust Instruction) this flag is used to correct the result of a previous packed decimal add or subtract.

2. Add/Subtract Flag (N). Since the algorithm for correcting BCD operations is different for addition or subtraction, this flag is used to specify what type of instruction was executed last so that the DAA operation will be correct for either addition or subtraction.

The Flag register can be accessed by the programmer and its format is as follows:

D7							D0
S	Z	X	H	X	P/V	N	C

X means flag is indeterminate.

Table 3-16 lists how each flag bit is affected by various CPU instructions. In this table a '·' indicates that the instruction does not change the flag, an 'X' means that the flag goes to an indeterminate state, a '0' means that it is reset, a '1' means that it is set and the symbol ↕ indicates that it is set or reset according to the previous discussion. Note that any instruction not appearing in this table does not affect any of the flags.

Table 3-16 includes a few special causes that must be described for clarity. Notice that the block search instruction sets the Z flag if the last compare operation indicated a match between the source and the accumulator data. Also, the parity flag is set if the byte counter (register pair BC) is not equal to zero. This same use of the parity flag is made with the block move instructions. Another special case is during block input or output instructions, here the Z flag is used to indicate the state of register B which is used as a byte counter. Notice that when the I/O block transfer is complete, the zero flag will be reset to a zero (i.e., B=0), while in the case of a block move command the parity flag is reset when the operation is complete. A final case is when the refresh or I register is loaded into the accumulator, the interrupt enable flip-flop is loaded into the parity flag so that the complete state of the CPU can be saved at any time.

SUMMARY OF OP CODES AND EXECUTION TIMES

The following section gives a summary of the Z80 instruction set. The instructions are logically arranged into groups as shown on Tables 3-17 through 3-27. Each table shows the assembly language mnemonic OP

Table 3-16. Summary of Flag Operation.

Instruction	S	Z		H		P/V	N	C	Comments
	D7							D0	
ADD A,s; ADC A,s	↕	↕	X	↕	X	V	0	↕	8-bit add or add with carry
SUB s; SBCA,s; CP s; NEG	↕	↕	X	↕	X	V	1	↕	8-bit subtract, subtract with carry, compare and negate accumulator
AND s	↕	↕	X	1	X	P	0	0	} Logical operations
OR s; XOR s	↕	↕	X	0	X	P	0	0	
INC s	↕	↕	X	↕	X	V	0	•	8-bit increment
DEC s	↕	↕	X	↕	X	V	1	•	8-bit decrement
ADD DD, SS	•	•	X	X	X	•	0	↕	16-bit add
ADC HL, SS	↕	↕	X	X	X	V	0	↕	16-bit add with carry
SBC HL, SS	↕	↕	X	X	X	V	1	↕	16-bit subtract with carry
RLA; RLCA; RRA; RRCA	•	•	X	0	X	•	0	↕	Rotate accumulator
RL s; RLC s; RR s; RRC s; SLA s; SRA s; SRL s	↕	↕	X	0	X	P	0	↕	Rotate and shift locations
RLD; RRD	↕	↕	X	0	X	P	0	•	Rotate digit left and right
DAA	↕	↕	X	↕	X	P	•	↕	Decimal adjust accumulator
CPL	•	•	X	1	X	•	1	•	Complement accumulator
SCF	•	•	X	0	X	•	0	1	Set carry
CCF	•	•	X	X	X	•	0	↕	Complement carry
IN r, (C)	↕	↕	X	0	X	P	0	•	Input register indirect
INI; IND; OUTI; OUTD	X	↕	X	X	X	X	1	X	} Block input and output
INIR; INDR; OTIR; OTDR	X	1	X	X	X	X	1	X	} Z = 0 if B ≠ 0 otherwise Z = 1
LDI; LDD	X	X	X	0	X	↕	0	•	} Block transfer instructions
LDIR; LDDR	X	X	X	0	X	0	0	•	} P/V = 1 if BC ≠ 0, otherwise P/V = 0
CPI; CPIR; CPD; CPDR	↕	↕	X	↕	X	↕	1	•	Block search instructions Z = 1 if A = (HL), otherwise Z = 0 P/V = 1 if BC ≠ 0, otherwise P/V = 0
LD A, I; LD A, R	↕	↕	X	0	X	IFF	0	•	The content of the interrupt enable flip-flop (IFF) is copied into the P/V flag
BIT b, s	X	↕	X	1	X	X	0	•	The state of bit b of location s is copied into the Z flag

The following notation is used in this table:

SYMBOL	OPERATION
C	Carry/link flag. C=1 if the operation produced a carry from the MSB of the operand or result.
Z	Zero flag. Z=1 if the result of the operation is zero.
S	Sign flag. S=1 if the MSB of the result is one.
P/V	Parity or overflow flag. Parity (P) and overflow (V) share the same flag. Logical operations affect this flag with the parity of the result while arithmetic operations affect this flag with the overflow of the result. If P/V holds parity, P/V=1 if the result of the operation is even, P/V=0 if result is odd. If P/V holds overflow, P/V=1 if the result of the operation produced an overflow.
H	Half-carry flag. H=1 if the add or subtract operation produced a carry into or borrow from bit 4 of the accumulator.
N	Add/Subtract flag. N=1 if the previous operation was a subtract.
	H and N flags are used in conjunction with the decimal adjust instruction (DAA) to properly correct the result into packed BCD format following addition or subtraction using operands with packed BCD format. The flag is affected according to the result of the operation.
•	The flag is unchanged by the operation.
0	The flag is reset by the operation.
1	The flag is set by the operation.
X	The flag is a "don't care".
V	P/V flag affected according to the overflow result of the operation.
P	P/V flag affected according to the parity result of the operation.
r	Any one of the CPU registers A, B, C, D, E, H, L.
s	Any 8-bit location for all the addressing modes allowed for the particular instruction.
ss	Any 16-bit location for all the addressing modes allowed for that instruction.
ii	Any one of the two index registers IX or IY.
R	Refresh counter.
n	8-bit value in range <0, 255>
nn	16-bit value in range <0, 65535>

Table 3-17. 8-Bit Load Group.

Mnemonic	Symbolic Operation	S	Z		H		P/V	N	C	Op-Code 76 543 210	Hex	No. of Bytes	No. of M Cycles	No. of T States	Comments
LD r, s	r ← s	•	•	X	•	X	•	•	•	01 r s		1	1	4	r, s Reg.
LD r, n	r ← n	•	•	X	•	X	•	•	•	00 r 110		2	2	7	000 B
										← n →					001 C
LD r, (HL)	r ← (HL)	•	•	X	•	X	•	•	•	01 r 110		1	2	7	010 D
LD r, (IX+d)	r ← (IX+d)	•	•	X	•	X	•	•	•	11 011 101	DD	3	5	19	011 E
										01 r 110					100 H
										← d →					101 L
LD r, (IY+d)	r ← (IY+d)	•	•	X	•	X	•	•	•	11 111 101	FD	3	5	19	111 A
										01 r 110					
										← d →					
LD (HL), r	(HL) ← r	•	•	X	•	X	•	•	•	01 110 r		1	2	7	
LD (IX+d), r	(IX+d) ← r	•	•	X	•	X	•	•	•	11 011 101	DD	3	5	19	
										01 110 r					
										← d →					
LD (IY+d), r	(IY+d) ← r	•	•	X	•	X	•	•	•	11 111 101	FD	3	5	19	
										01 110 r					
										← d →					
LD (HL), n	(HL) ← n	•	•	X	•	X	•	•	•	00 110 110	36	2	3	10	
LD (IX+d), n	(IX+d) ← n	•	•	X	•	X	•	•	•	11 011 101	DD	4	5	19	
										00 110 110	36				
										← d →					
										← n →					
LD (IY+d), n	(IY+d) ← n	•	•	X	•	X	•	•	•	11 111 101	FD	4	5	19	
										00 110 110	36				
										← d →					
										← n →					
LD A, (BC)	A ← (BC)	•	•	X	•	X	•	•	•	00 001 010	0A	1	2	7	
LD A, (DE)	A ← (DE)	•	•	X	•	X	•	•	•	00 011 010	1A	1	2	7	
LD A, (nn)	A ← (nn)	•	•	X	•	X	•	•	•	00 111 010	3A	3	4	13	
										← n →					
										← n →					
LD (BC), A	(BC) ← A	•	•	X	•	X	•	•	•	00 000 010	02	1	2	7	
LD (DE), A	(DE) ← A	•	•	X	•	X	•	•	•	00 G10 010	12	1	2	7	
LD (nn), A	(nn) ← A	•	•	X	•	X	•	•	•	00 110 010	32	3	4	13	
										← n →					
										← n →					
LD A, I	A ← I	↕	↕	X	0	X	IFF	0	•	11 101 101	ED	2	2	9	
										01 010 111	57				
LD A, R	A ← R	↕	↕	X	0	X	IFF	0	•	11 101 101	ED	2	2	9	
										01 011 111	5F				
LD I, A	I ← A	•	•	X	•	X	•	•	•	11 101 101	ED	2	2	9	
										01 000 111	47				
LD R, A	R ← A	•	•	X	•	X	•	•	•	11 101 101	ED	2	2	9	
										01 001 111	4F				

Notes: r, s means any of the registers A, B, C, D, E, H, L
IFF the content of the interrupt enable flip-flop (IFF) is copied into the P/V flag

Flag Notation: • = flag not affected, 0 = flag reset, 1 = flag set, X = flag is unknown,
↕ = flag is affected according to the result of the operation.

Table 3-18. 16-Bit Load Group.

Mnemonic	Symbolic Operation	S	Z		H		P/V	N	C	76 543 210	Hex	No. of Bytes	No. of M Cycles	No. of T States	Comments
LD dd, nn	dd ← nn	•	•		X	•	X	•	•	•	00 dd0 001 ← n → ← n →		3	3	10	dd Pair 00 BC 01 DE
LD IX, nn	IX ← nn	•	•		X	•	X	•	•	•	11 011 101 00 100 001 ← n → ← n →	DD 21	4	4	14	10 HL 11 SP
LD IY, nn	IY ← nn	•	•		X	•	X	•	•	•	11 111 101 00 100 001 ← n → ← n →	FD 21	4	4	14	
LD HL, (nn)	H ← (nn+1) L ← (nn)	•	•		X	•	X	•	•	•	00 101 010 ← n → ← n →	2A	3	5	16	
LD dd, (nn)	dd$_H$ ← (nn+1) dd$_L$ ← (nn)	•	•		X	•	X	•	•	•	11 101 101 01 dd1 011 ← n → ← n →	ED	4	6	20	
LD IX, (nn)	IX$_H$ ← (nn+1) IX$_L$ ← (nn)	•	•		X	•	X	•	•	•	11 011 101 00 101 010 ← n → ← n →	DD 2A	4	6	20	
LD IY, (nn)	IY$_H$ ← (nn+1) IY$_L$ ← (nn)	•	•		X	•	X	•	•	•	11 111 101 00 101 010 ← n → ← n →	FD 2A	4	6	20	
LD (nn), HL	(nn+1) ← H (nn) ← L	•	•		X	•	X	•	•	•	00 100 010 ← n → ← n →	22	3	5	16	
LD (nn), dd	(nn+1) ← dd$_H$ (nn) ← dd$_L$	•	•		X	•	X	•	•	•	11 101 101 01 dd0 011 ← n → ← n →	ED	4	6	20	
LD (nn), IX	(nn+1) ← IX$_H$ (nn) ← IX$_L$	•	•		X	•	X	•	•	•	11 011 101 00 100 010 ← n → ← n →	DD 22	4	6	20	
LD (nn), IY	(nn+1) ← IY$_H$ (nn) ← IY$_L$	•	•		X	•	X	•	•	•	11 111 101 00 100 010 ← n → ← n →	FD 22	4	6	20	
LD SP, HL	SP ← HL	•	•		X	•	X	•	•	•	11 111 001	F9	1	1	6	
LD SP, IX	SP ← IX	•	•		X	•	X	•	•	•	11 011 101 11 111 001	DD F9	2	2	10	
LD SP, IY	SP ← IY	•	•		X	•	X	•	•	•	11 111 101 11 111 001	FD F9	2	2	10	qq Pair 00 BC
PUSH qq	(SP-2) ← qq$_L$ (SP-1) ← qq$_H$	•	•		X	•	X	•	•	•	11 qq0 101		1	3	11	01 DE 10 HL
PUSH IX	(SP-2) ← IX$_L$ (SP-1) ← IX$_H$	•	•		X	•	X	•	•	•	11 011 101 11 100 101	DD E5	2	4	15	11 AF
PUSH IY	(SP-2) ← IY$_L$ (SP-1) ← IY$_H$	•	•		X	•	X	•	•	•	11 111 101 11 100 101	FD E5	2	4	15	
POP qq	qq$_H$ ← (SP+1) qq$_L$ ← (SP)	•	•		X	•	X	•	•	•	11 qq0 001		1	3	10	
POP IX	IX$_H$ ← (SP+1) IX$_L$ ← (SP)	•	•		X	•	X	•	•	•	11 011 101 11 100 001	DD E1	2	4	14	
POP IY	IY$_H$ ← (SP+1) IY$_L$ ← (SP)	•	•		X	•	X	•	•	•	11 111 101 11 100 001	FD E1	2	4	14	

Notes: dd is any of the register pairs BC, DE, HL, SP
qq is any of the register pairs AF, BC, DE, HL
(PAIR)$_H$, (PAIR)$_L$ refer to high order and low order eight bits of the register pair respectively.
e.g. BC$_L$ = C, AF$_H$ = A

Flag Notation: • = flag not affected, 0 = flag reset, 1 = flag set, X = flag is unknown,
↕ flag is affected according to the result of the operation.

Table 3-19. Exchange Group and Block Transfer and Search Group.

Mnemonic	Symbolic Operation	S	Z		H		P/V	N	C	76 543 210	Hex	No. of Bytes	No. of M Cycles	No. of T States	Comments
EX DE, HL	DE↔HL	•	•	X	•	X	•	•	•	11 101 011	EB	1	1	4	
EX AF, AF'	AF↔AF'	•	•	X	•	X	•	•	•	00 001 000	08	1	1	4	
EXX	(BC↔BC' DE↔DE' HL↔HL')	•	•	X	•	X	•	•	•	11 011 001	D9	1	1	4	Register bank and auxiliary register bank exchange
EX (SP), HL	H↔(SP+1) L↔(SP)	•	•	X	•	X	•	•	•	11 100 011	E3	1	5	19	
EX (SP), IX	IX$_H$↔(SP+1) IX$_L$↔(SP)	•	•	X	•	X	•	•	•	11 011 101 11 100 011	DD E3	2	6	23	
EX (SP), IY	IY$_H$↔(SP+1) IY$_L$↔(SP)	•	•	X	•	X	•	•	•	11 111 101 11 100 011	FD E3	2	6	23	
LDI	(DE)←(HL) DE ← DE+1 HL ← HL+1 BC ← BC-1	•	•	X	0	X	①↕	0	•	11 101 101 10 100 000	ED A0	2	4	16	Load (HL) into (DE), increment the pointers and decrement the byte counter (BC)
LDIR	(DE)←(HL) DE ← DE+1 HL ← HL+1 BC ← BC-1 Repeat until BC = 0	•	•	X	0	X	0	0	•	11 101 101 10 110 000	ED B0	2 2	5 4	21 16	If BC ≠ 0 If BC = 0
LDD	(DE)←(HL) DE ← DE-1 HL ← HL-1 BC ← BC-1	•	•	X	0	X	①↕	0	•	11 101 101 10 101 000	ED A8	2	4	16	
LDDR	(DE)←(HL) DE ← DE-1 HL ← HL-1 BC ← BC-1 Repeat until BC = 0	•	•	X	0	X	0	0	•	11 101 101 10 111 000	ED B8	2 2	5 4	21 16	If BC ≠ 0 If BC = 0
CPI	A – (HL) HL ← HL+1 BC ← BC-1	↕	②↕	X	↕	X	①↕	1	•	11 101 101 10 100 001	ED A1	2	4	16	
CPIR	A – (HL) HL ← HL+1 BC ← BC-1 Repeat until A = (HL) or BC = 0	↕	②↕	X	↕	X	①↕	1	•	11 101 101 10 110 001	ED B1	2 2	5 4	21 16	If BC ≠ 0 and A ≠ (HL) If BC = 0 or A = (HL)
CPD	A – (HL) HL ← HL-1 BC ← BC-1	↕	②↕	X	↕	X	①↕	1	•	11 101 101 10 101 001	ED A9	2	4	16	
CPDR	A – (HL) HL ← HL-1 BC ← BC-1 Repeat until A = (HL) or BC = 0	↕	②↕	X	↕	X	①↕	1	•	11 101 101 10 111 001	ED B9	2 2	5 4	21 16	If BC ≠ 0 and A ≠ (HL) If BC = 0 or A = (HL)

Notes: ① P/V flag is 0 if the result of BC-1 = 0, otherwise P/V = 1
      ② Z flag is 1 if A = (HL), otherwise Z = 0.

Flag Notation: • = flag not affected, 0 = flag reset, 1 = flag set, X = flag is unknown,
          ↕ = flag is affected according to the result of the operation.

Table 3-20. 8-Bit Arithmetic and Logical Group.

Mnemonic	Symbolic Operation	S	Z		H		P/V	N	C	76 543 210	Hex	No. of Bytes	No. of M Cycles	No. of T States	Comments
ADD A, r	A ← A + r	↕	↕	X	↕	X	V	0	↕	10 [000] r		1	1	4	r Reg.
ADD A, n	A ← A + n	↕	↕	X	↕	X	V	0	↕	11 [000] 110		2	2	7	000 B
										← n →					001 C
															010 D
ADD A, (HL)	A ← A+(HL)	↕	↕	X	↕	X	V	0	↕	10 [000] 110		1	2	7	011 E
ADD A, (IX+d)	A ← A+(IX+d)	↕	↕	X	↕	X	V	0	↕	11 011 101	DD	3	5	19	100 H
										10 [000] 110					101 L
										← d →					111 A
ADD A, (IY+d)	A ← A+(IY+d)	↕	↕	X	↕	X	V	0	↕	11 111 101	FD	3	5	19	
										10 [000] 110					
										← d →					
ADC A, s	A ← A+s+CY	↕	↕	X	↕	X	V	0	↕	[001]					s is any of r, n,
SUB s	A ← A - s	↕	↕	X	↕	X	V	1	↕	[010]					(HL), (IX+d),
SBC A, s	A ← A - s - CY	↕	↕	X	↕	X	V	1	↕	[011]					(IY+d) as shown for
AND s	A ← A ∧ s	↕	↕	X	1	X	P	0	0	[100]					ADD instruction.
OR s	A ← A ∨ s	↕	↕	X	0	X	P	0	0	[110]					The indicated bits
XOR s	A ← A ⊕ s	↕	↕	X	0	X	P	0	0	[101]					replace the [000] in
CP s	A - s	↕	↕	X	↕	X	V	1	↕	[111]					the ADD set above.
INC r	r ← r + 1	↕	↕	X	↕	X	V	0	•	00 r [100]		1	1	4	
INC (HL)	(HL)←(HL)+1	↕	↕	X	↕	X	V	0	•	00 110 [100]		1	3	11	
INC (IX+d)	(IX+d) ← (IX+d)+1	↕	↕	X	↕	X	V	0	•	11 011 101	DD	3	6	23	
										00 110 [100]					
										← d →					
INC (IY+d)	(IY+d) ← (IY+d)+1	↕	↕	X	↕	X	V	0	•	11 111 101	FD	3	6	23	
										00 110 [100]					
										← d →					
DEC s	s ← s - 1	↕	↕	X	↕	X	V	1	•	[101]					s is any of r, (HL), (IX+d), (IY+d) as shown for INC. DEC same format and states as INC. Replace [100] with [101] in OP Code.

Notes: The V symbol in the P/V flag column indicates that the P/V flag contains the overflow of the result of the operation. Similarly the P symbol indicates parity. V = 1 means overflow, V = 0 means not overflow, P = 1 means parity of the result is even, P = 0 means parity of the result is odd.

Flag Notation: • = flag not affected, 0 = flag reset, 1 = flag set, X = flag is unknown.
    ↕ = flag is affected according to the result of the operation.

code, the actual OP code, the symbolic operation, the content of the flag register following the execution of each instruction, the number of bytes required for each instruction as well as the number of memory cycles and the total number of T states (external clock periods) required for the fetching and execution of each instruction. Care has been taken to make each table self-explanatory without requiring any cross reference with the text or other tables.

INTERRUPT RESPONSE

The purpose of an interrupt is to allow peripheral devices to suspend CPU operation in an orderly manner and force the CPU to start a peripheral service routine. Usually this service routine is involved with the

Table 3-21. General Purpose Arithmetic and CPU Control Groups.

Mnemonic	Symbolic Operation	Flags								Op-Code			No. of Bytes	No. of M Cycles	No. of T States	Comments
		S	Z		H		P/V	N	C	76 543 210	Hex					
AA	Converts acc, content into packed BCD following add or subtract with packed BCD operands	‡	‡	X	‡	X	P	•	‡	00 100 111	27	1	1	4	Decimal adjust accumulator
CPL	A → Ā	•	•	X	1	X	•	1	•	00 101 111	2F	1	1	4	Complement accumulator (One's complement)
NEG	A → Ā + 1	‡	‡	X	‡	X	V	1	‡	11 101 101	ED	2	2	8	Negate acc, (two's complement)
										01 000 100	44				
CCF	CY → C̄Y	•	•	X	X	X	•	0	‡	00 111 111	3F	1	1	4	Complement carry flag
SCF	CY → 1	•	•	X	0	X	•	0	1	00 110 111	37	1	1	4	Set carry flag
NOP	No operation	•	•	X	•	X	•	•	•	00 000 000	00	1	1	4	
HALT	CPU halted	•	•	X	•	X	•	•	•	01 110 110	76	1	1	4	
DI*	IFF → 0	•	•	X	•	X	•	•	•	11 110 011	F3	1	1	4	
EI*	IFF → 1	•	•	X	•	X	•	•	•	11 111 011	FB	1	1	4	
IM 0	Set interrupt mode 0	•	•	X	•	X	•	•	•	11 101 101	ED	2	2	8	
										01 000 110	46				
IM 1	Set interrupt mode 1	•	•	X	•	X	•	•	•	11 101 101	ED	2	2	8	
										01 010 110	56				
IM 2	Set interrupt mode 2	•	•	X	•	X	•	•	•	11 101 101	ED	2	2	8	
										01 011 110	5E				

Notes: IFF indicates the interrupt enable flip-flop
CY indicates the carry flip-flop.

Flag Notation: • = flag not affected, 0 = flag reset, 1 = flag set, X = flag is unknown,
‡ = flag is affected according to the result of the operation.

*Interrupts are not sampled at the end of EI or DI

exchange of data, or status and control information, between the CPU and the peripheral. Once the service routine is completed, the CPU returns to the operation from which it was interrupted.

Interrupt Enable—Disable

The Z80-CPU has two interrupt inputs, a software maskable interrupt and a non-maskable interrupt. The non-maskable interrupt (NMI) can not be disabled by the programmer and it will be accepted whenever a peripheral device requests it. This interrupt is generally reserved for very important functions that must be serviced whenever they occur, such as an impending power failure. The maskable interrupt (INT) can be selectively enabled or disabled by the programmer. This allows the programmer to disable the interrupt during periods where his program has timing constraints that do not allow it to be interrupted. In the Z80-CPU there is an enable flip-flop (called IFF) that is set or reset by the programmer using the Enable Interrupt (EI) and Disable Interrupt (DI) instructions. When the IFF is reset, an interrupt can not be accepted by the CPU.

56

Actually, for purposes that will be subsequently explained, there are two enable flip-flops, called IFF$_1$ and IFF$_2$.

| IFF$_1$ | IFF$_2$ |

Actually **disables** interrupts
from being accepted.

Temporary storage location
for IFF$_1$.

The state of IFF$_1$ is used to actually inhibit interrupts while IFF$_2$ is used as a temporary storage location for IFF$_1$. The purpose of storing the IFF$_1$ will be subsequently explained.

A reset to the CPU will force both IFF$_1$ and IFF$_2$ to the reset state so that interrupts are disabled. They can then be enabled by an EI instruction at any time by the programmer. When an EI instruction is executed, any pending interrupt request will not be accepted until after the instruction following EI has been executed. This single instruction delay is necessary for cases when the following instruction is a return

Table 3-22. 16-Bit Arithmetic Group.

Mnemonic	Symbolic Operation	Flags								Op-Code		No. of Bytes	No. of M Cycles	No. of T States	Comments	
		S	Z		H		P/V	N	C	76 543 210	Hex					
ADD HL, ss	HL ← HL+ss	•	•	X	X	X	•	0	↕	00 ss1 001		1	3	11	ss	Reg.
															00	BC
ADC HL, ss	HL ← HL+ss+CY	↕	↕	X	X	X	V	0	↕	11 101 101 01 ss1 010	ED	2	4	15	01 10	DE HL
															11	SP
SBC HL, ss	HL ← HL-ss-CY	↕	↕	X	X	X	V	1	↕	11 101 101 01 ss0 010	ED	2	4	15		
ADD IX, pp	IX ← IX + pp	•	•	X	X	X	•	0	↕	11 011 101 00 pp1 001	DD	2	4	15	pp 00 01 10 11	Reg. BC DE IX SP
ADD IY, rr	IY ← IY + rr	•	•	X	X	X	•	0	↕	11 111 101 00 rr1 001	FD	2	4	15	rr 00 01 10 11	Reg. BC DE IY SP
INC ss	ss ← ss + 1	•	•	X	•	X	•	•	•	00 ss0 011		1	1	6		
INC IX	IX ← IX + 1	•	•	X	•	X	•	•	•	11 011 101 00 100 011	DD 23	2	2	10		
INC IY	IY ← IY + 1	•	•	X	•	X	•	•	•	11 111 101 00 100 011	FD 23	2	2	10		
DEC ss	ss ← ss - 1	•	•	X	•	X	•	•	•	00 ss1 011		1	1	6		
DEC IX	IX ← IX - 1	•	•	X	•	X	•	•	•	11 011 101 00 101 011	DD 2B	2	2	10		
DEC IY	IY ← IY - 1	•	•	X	•	X	•	•	•	11 111 101 00 101 011	FD 2B	2	2	10		

Notes: ss is any of the register pairs BC, DE, HL, SP
pp is any of the register pairs BC, DE, IX, SP
rr is any of the register pairs BC, DE, IY, SP.

Flag Notation: • = flag not affected, 0 = flag reset, 1 = flag set, X = flag is unknown.
↕ = flag is affected according to the result of the operation.

Table 3-23. Rotate and Shift Group.

Mnemonic	Symbolic Operation	S	Z		H	P/V	N	C	Op-Code 76 543 210	Hex	No.of Bytes	No.of M Cycles	No.of T States	Comments
RLCA	[CY]←[7←0] A	•	•	X	0	X	•	0	↕	00 000 111	07	1	1	4	Rotate left circular accumulator
RLA	[CY]←[7←0] A	•	•	X	0	X	•	0	↕	00 010 111	17	1	1	4	Rotate left accumulator
RRCA	[7→0]→[CY] A	•	•	X	0	X	•	0	↕	00 001 111	0F	1	1	4	Rotate right circular accumulator
RRA	[7→0]→[CY] A	•	•	X	0	X	•	0	↕	00 011 111	1F	1	1	4	Rotate right accumulator
RLC r		↕	↕	X	0	X	P	0	↕	11 001 011 00 [000] r	CB	2	2	8	Rotate left circular register r
RLC (HL)		↕	↕	X	0	X	P	0	↕	11 001 011 00 [000] 110	CB	2	4	15	r Reg. 000 B 001 C
RLC (IX+d)	[CY]←[7←0] r,(HL),(IX+d),(IY+d)	↕	↕	X	0	X	P	0	↕	11 011 101 11 001 011 - d - 00 [000] 110	DD CB	4	6	23	010 D 011 E 100 H 101 L 111 A
RLC (IY+d)		↕	↕	X	0	X	P	0	↕	11 111 101 11 001 011 - d - 00 [000] 110	FD CB	4	6	23	
RL s	[CY]←[7←0]← s≡r,(HL),(IX+d),(IY+d)	↕	↕	X	0	X	P	0	↕	[010]					Instruction format and states are as shown for RLC's. To form new Op-Code replace [000] of RLC's with shown code
RRC s	[7→0]→[CY] s≡r,(HL),(IX+d),(IY+d)	↕	↕	X	0	X	P	0	↕	[001]					
RR s	[7→0]→[CY] s≡r,(HL),(IX+d),(IY+d)	↕	↕	X	0	X	P	0	↕	[011]					
SLA s	[CY]←[7←0]←0 s≡r,(HL),(IX+d),(IY+d)	↕	↕	X	0	X	P	0	↕	[100]					
SRA s	[7→0]→[CY] s≡r,(HL),(IX+d),(IY+d)	↕	↕	X	0	X	P	0	↕	[101]					
SRL s	0→[7→0]→[CY] s≡r,(HL),(IX+d),(IY+d)	↕	↕	X	0	X	P	0	↕	[111]					
RLD	A [7-4][3-0] [7-4][3-0](HL)	↕	↕	X	0	X	P	0	•	11 101 101 01 101 111	ED 6F	2	5	18	Rotate digit left and right between the accumulator and location (HL).
RRD	A [7-4][3-0] [7-4][3-0](HL)	↕	↕	X	0	X	P	0	•	11 101 101 01 100 111	ED 67	2	5	18	The content of the upper half of the accumulator is unaffected

Table 3-24. Bit Set, Reset and Test Group.

Mnemonic	Symbolic Operation	Flags								Op-Code			No. of Bytes	No.of M Cycles	No.of T States	Comments	
		S	Z		H		P/V	N	C	76 543 210	Hex						
BIT b, r	Z ← r̄_b	X	↕	X	1	X	X	0	•	11 001 011	CB	2	2	8	r	Reg.
										01 b r					000	B
BIT b, (HL)	Z ← (HL)̄_b	X	↕	X	1	X	X	0	•	11 001 011	CB	2	3	12	001	C
										01 b 110					010	D
BIT b, (IX+d)_b	Z ← (IX+d)̄_b	X	↕	X	1	X	X	0	•	11 011 101	DD	4	5	20	011	E
										11 001 011	CB				100	H
										← d →					101	L
										01 b 110					111	A
															b	Bit Tested
BIT b, (IY+d)_b	Z ← (IY+d)̄_b	X	↕	X	1	X	X	0	•	11 111 101	FD	4	5	20	000	0
										11 001 011	CB				001	1
										← d →					010	2
										01 b 110					011	3
															100	4
															101	5
															110	6
															111	7
SET b, r	r_b ← 1	•	•	X	•	X	•	•	•	11 001 011	CB	2	2	8		
										⌈11⌉ b r						
SET b, (HL)	(HL)_b ← 1	•	•	X	•	X	•	•	•	11 001 011	CB	2	4	15		
										⌈11⌉ b 110						
SET b, (IX+d)	(IX+d)_b ← 1	•	•	X	•	X	•	•	•	11 011 101	DD	4	6	23		
										11 001 011	CB					
										← d →						
										⌈11⌉ b 110						
SET b, (IY+d)	(IY+d)_b ← 1	•	•	X	•	X	•	•	•	11 111 101	FD	4	6	23		
										11 001 011	CB					
										← d →						
										⌈11⌉ b 110						
RES b, s	s_b ← 0 s ≡ r, (HL), (IX+d), (IY+d)	•	•	X	•	X	•	•	•	⌈10⌉					To form new Op-Code replace ⌈11⌉ of SET b, s with ⌈10⌉. Flags and time states for SET instruction	

Notes: The notation s_b indicates bit b (0 to 7) or location s.

Flag Notation: • = flag not affected, 0 = flag reset, 1 = flag set, X = flag is unknown,
↕ = flag is affected according to the result of the operation.

instruction and interrupts must not be allowed until the return has been completed. The EI instruction sets both IFF_1 and IFF_2 to the enable state. When an interrupt is accepted by the CPU, both IFF_1 and IFF_2 are automatically reset, inhibiting further interrupts until the programmer wishes to issue a new EI instruction. Note that for all of the previous cases, IFF_1 and IFF_2 are always equal.

The purpose of IFF_2 is to save the status of IFF_1 when a non-maskable interrupt occurs. When a non-maskable interrupt is accepted, IFF_1 is reset to prevent further interrupts until reenabled by the programmer. Thus, after a non-maskable interrupt has been accepted maskable interrupts are disabled but the previous state of IFF_1 has been saved so that the complete state of the CPU just prior to the non-maskable interrupt can be restored at any time. When a Load Register A with Register I (LD A, I)

Table 3-25. Jump Group.

Mnemonic	Symbolic Operation	S	Z		H		P/V	N	C	76 543 210	Hex	No. of Bytes	No. of M Cycles	No. of T States	Comments
JP nn	PC ← nn	•	•	X	•	X	•	•	•	11 000 011	C3	3	3	10	
										← n →					
										← n →					
JP cc, nn	If condition cc is true PC ← nn, otherwise continue	•	•	X	•	X	•	•	•	11 cc 010		3	3	10	
										← n →					
										← n →					
JR e	PC ← PC + e	•	•	X	•	X	•	•	•	00 011 000	18	2	3	12	
										← e-2 →					
JR C, e	If C = 0, continue	•	•	X	•	X	•	•	•	00 111 000	38	2	2	7	If condition not met
										← e-2 →					
	If C = 1, PC ← PC+e											2	3	12	If condition is met
JR NC, e	If C = 1, continue	•	•	X	•	X	•	•	•	00 110 000	30	2	2	7	If condition not met
										← e-2 →					
	If C = 0, PC ← PC+e											2	3	12	If condition is met
JR Z, e	If Z = 0 continue	•	•	X	•	X	•	•	•	00 101 000	28	2	2	7	If condition not met
										← e-2 →					
	If Z = 1, PC ← PC+e											2	3	12	If condition is met
JR NZ, e	If Z = 1, continue	•	•	X	•	X	•	•	•	00 100 000	20	2	2	7	If condition not met
										← e-2 →					
	If Z = 0, PC ← PC+e											2	3	12	If condition is met
JP (HL)	PC ← HL	•	•	X	•	X	•	•	•	11 101 001	E9	1	1	4	
JP (IX)	PC ← IX	•	•	X	•	X	•	•	•	11 011 101	DD	2	2	8	
										11 101 001	E9				
JP (IY)	PC ← IY	•	•	X	•	X	•	•	•	11 111 101	FD	2	2	8	
										11 101 001	E9				
DJNZ, e	B ← B-1 If B = 0, continue	•	•	X	•	X	•	•	•	00 010 000	10	2	2	8	If B = 0
										← e-2 →					
	If B ≠ 0, PC ← PC+e											2	3	13	If B ≠ 0

cc	Condition
000	NZ non zero
001	Z zero
010	NC non carry
011	C carry
100	PO parity odd
101	PE parity even
110	P sign positive
111	M sign negative

Notes: e represents the extension in the relative addressing mode.

e is a signed two's complement number in the range <126, 129>

e-2 in the op-code provides an effective address of pc+e as PC is incremented by 2 prior to the addition of e.

Flag Notation: • = flag not affected, 0 = flag reset, 1 = flag set, X = flag is unknown,
‡ = flag is affected according to the result of the operation.

Table 3-26. Call and Return Group.

Mnemonic	Symbolic Operation	S	Z		H		P/V	N	C	Op-Code 76 543 210	Hex	No. of Bytes	No.of M Cycles	No.of T States	Comments
CALL nn	$(SP-1) \leftarrow PC_H$ $(SP-2) \leftarrow PC_L$ $PC \leftarrow nn$	•	•	X	•	X	•	•	•	11 001 101 ← n → ← n →	CD	3	5	17	
CALL cc, nn	If condition cc is false continue, otherwise same as CALL nn	•	•	X	•	X	•	•	•	11 cc 100 ← n → ← n →		3 3	3 5	10 17	If cc is false If cc is true
RET	$PC_L \leftarrow (SP)$ $PC_H \leftarrow (SP+1)$	•	•	X	•	X	•	•	•	11 001 001	C9	1	3	10	
RET cc	If condition cc is false continue, otherwise same as RET	•	•	X	•	X	•	•	•	11 cc 000		1 1	1 3	5 11	If cc is false If cc is true
RETI	Return from interrupt	•	•	X	•	X	•	•	•	11 101 101 01 001 101	ED 4D	2	4	14	
RETN[1]	Return from non maskable interrupt	•	•	X	•	X	•	•	•	11 101 101 01 000 101	ED 45	2	4	14	
RST p	$(SP-1) \leftarrow PC_H$ $(SP-2) \leftarrow PC_L$ $PC_H \leftarrow 0$ $PC_L \leftarrow p$	•	•	X	•	X	•	•	•	11 t 111		1	3	11	

cc	Condition	
000	NZ	non zero
001	Z	zero
010	NC	non carry
011	C	carry
100	PO	parity odd
101	PE	parity even
110	P	sign positive
111	M	sign negative

t	p
000	00H
001	08H
010	10H
011	18H
100	20H
101	28H
110	30H
111	38H

[1] RETN loads $IFF_2 \leftarrow IFF_1$

Flag Notation: • = flag not affected, 0 = flag reset, 1 = flag set, X = flag is unknown,
‡ = flag is affected according to the result of the operation.

Table 3-27. Input and Output Group.

Mnemonic	Symbolic Operation	S	Z		H		P/V	N	C	76 543 210	Hex	No.of Bytes	No.of M Cycles	No.of T States	Comments
IN A, (n)	A ← (n)	•	•	X	•	X	•	•	•	11 011 011 ← n →	DB	2	3	11	n to $A_0 \sim A_7$ Acc to $A_8 \sim A_{15}$
IN r, (C)	r ← (C) if r = 110 only the flags will be affected	↕	↕	X	↕	X	P	0	•	11 101 101 01 r 000	ED	2	3	12	C to $A_0 \sim A_7$ B to $A_8 \sim A_{15}$
INI	(HL) ← (C) B ← B - 1 HL ← HL + 1	X	↕ ①	X	X	X	X	1	X	11 101 101 10 100 010	ED A2	2	4	16	C to $A_0 \sim A_7$ B to $A_8 \sim A_{15}$
INIR	(HL) ← (C) B ← B - 1 HL ← HL + 1 Repeat until B = 0	X	1	X	X	X	X	1	X	11 101 101 10 110 010	ED B2	2 / 2	5 (If B ≠ 0) / 4 (If B = 0)	21 / 16	C to $A_0 \sim A_7$ B to $A_8 \sim A_{15}$
IND	(HL) ← (C) B ← B - 1 HL ← HL - 1	X	↕ ①	X	X	X	X	1	X	11 101 101 10 101 010	ED AA	2	4	16	C to $A_0 \sim A_7$ B to $A_8 \sim A_{15}$
INDR	(HL) ← (C) B ← B - 1 HL ← HL - 1 Repeat until B = 0	X	1	X	X	X	X	1	X	11 101 101 10 111 010	ED BA	2 / 2	5 (If B ≠ 0) / 4 (If B = 0)	21 / 16	C to $A_0 \sim A_7$ B to $A_8 \sim A_{15}$
OUT (n), A	(n) ← A	•	•	X	•	X	•	•	•	11 010 011	D3	2	3	11	n to $A_0 \sim A_7$ Acc to $A_8 \sim A_{15}$
OUT (C), r	(C) ← r	•	•	X	•	X	•	•	•	11 101 101 01 r 001	ED	2	3	12	C to $A_0 \sim A_7$ B to $A_8 \sim A_{15}$
OUTI	B ← B - 1 (C) ← (HL) HL ← HL + 1	X	↕ ①	X	X	X	X	1	X	11 101 101 10 100 011	ED A3	2	4	16	C to $A_0 \sim A_7$ B to $A_8 \sim A_{15}$
OTIR	B ← B - 1 (C) ← (HL) HL ← HL + 1 Repeat until B = 0	X	1	X	X	X	X	1	X	11 101 101 10 110 011	ED B3	2 / 2	5 (If B ≠ 0) / 4 (If B = 0)	21 / 16	C to $A_0 \sim A_7$ B to $A_8 \sim A_{15}$
OUTD	(C) ← (HL) B ← B - 1 HL ← HL - 1	X	↕ ①	X	X	X	X	1	X	11 101 101 10 101 011	ED AB	2	4	16	C to $A_0 \sim A_7$ B to $A_8 \sim A_{15}$
OTDR	(C) ← (HL) B ← B - 1 HL ← HL - 1 Repeat until B = 0	X	1	X	X	X	X	1	X	11 101 101 10 111 011	ED BB	2 / 2	5 (If B ≠ 0) / 4 (If B = 0)	21 / 16	C to $A_0 \sim A_7$ B to $A_8 \sim A_{15}$

Notes: ① If the result of B - 1 is zero the Z flag is set, otherwise it is reset.

Flag Notation: • = flag not affected, 0 = flag reset, 1 = flag set, X = flag is unknown, ↕ = flag is affected according to the result of the operation.

instruction or a Load Register A with Register R (LD, A, R) instruction is executed, the state of IFF_2 is copied into the parity flag where it can be tested or stored.

A second method of restoring the status of IFF_1 is through the execution of a Return From Non-Maskable Interrupt (RETN) instruction. Since this instruction indicates that the nonmaskable interrupt service routine is complete, the contents of IFF_2 are now copied back into IFF_1, so that the status of IFF_1 just prior to the acceptance of the non-maskable interrupt will be restored automatically.

Figure 3-1 is a summary of the effect of different instructions on the two enable flip-flops. Figures 3-2, 3-3, and 3-4 illustrate the starting address table for the interrupt service routine, interrupt request acknowledge cycle, and how the $\overline{\text{INT}}$, $\overline{\text{NMI}}$ & $\overline{\text{BUSRQ}}$ interact, respectively.

CPU Response

Non-Maskable. A non-maskable interrupt will be accepted at all times by the CPU. When this occurs, the CPU ignores the next instruction that it fetches and instead does a restart to location 0066H. Thus, it behaves exactly as if it had received a restart instruction but, it is to a location that is not one of the 8 software restart locations. A restart is merely a call to a specific address in page 0 memory.

Maskable. The CPU can be programmed to respond to the maskable interrupt in any one of three possible modes.

Mode 0. This mode is identical to the 8080A interrupt response mode. With this mode, the interrupting device can place any instruction on the data bus and the CPU will execute it. Thus, the interrupting device provides the next instruction to be executed instead of the memory. Often this will be a restart instruction since the interrupting device only need supply a single-byte instruction. Alternatively, any other instruction such as a 3 byte call to any location in memory could be executed by issuing a restart to the 3 byte op code.

The number of clock cycles necessary to execute this instruction is 2 more than the normal number for the instruction. This occurs since the CPU automatically adds 2 wait states to an interrupt response cycle to allow sufficient time to implement an external daisy-chain for priority control. After the application of RESET the CPU will automatically enter interrupt Mode 0.

ACTION	IFF₁	IFF₂	
CPU RESET	0	0	
DI	0	0	
EI	1	1	
LD A, I	•	•	IFF₂→PARITY FLAG
LD A, R	•	•	IFF₂→PARITY FLAG
ACCEPT NMI	0	•	
RETN	IFF₂	•	IFF₂→IFF₁
ACCEPT INT	0	0	
RETI	•	•	"•" INDICATES NO CHANGE

Fig. 3-1. Interrupt enable/disable flip-flops.

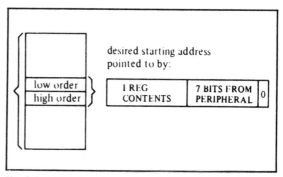

Fig. 3-2. Interrupt service routine starting address table.

63

Mode 1. When this mode has been selected by the programmer, the CPU will respond to an interrupt by executing a restart to location 0038H. Thus, the response is identical to that for a nonmaskable interrupt except that the call location is 0038H instead of 0066H. Another difference is that the number of cycles required to complete the restart instruction is 2 more than normal due to the two added wait states.

Mode 2. This mode is the most powerful interrupt response mode. With a single 8-bit byte from the user an indirect call can be made to any memory location.

With this mode the programmer maintains a table of 16-bit starting addresses for every interrupt service routine. This table may be located anywhere in memory. When an interrupt is accepted, a 16-bit pointer must be formed to obtain the desired interrupt service routine-starting address from the table. The upper 8 bits of this pointer is formed from the contents of the I register. The I register must have been previously loaded with the desired value by the programmer, i.e., LD I, A. Note that a CPU reset clears the I register so that it is initialized to zero. The lower eight bits of the pointer must be supplied by the interrupting device. Actually, only 7 bits are required from the interrupting device as the least bit must be a zero. This is required since the pointer is used to get two adjacent bytes to form a complete 16 bit routine starting address and the addresses must always start in even locations.

The first byte in the table is the least significant (low order) portion of the address. The programmer must obviously fill this table in with the desired addresses before any interrupts are to be accepted.

Note that this table can be changed at any time by the programmer (if it is stored in Read/Write Memory) to allow different peripherals to be serviced by different service routines.

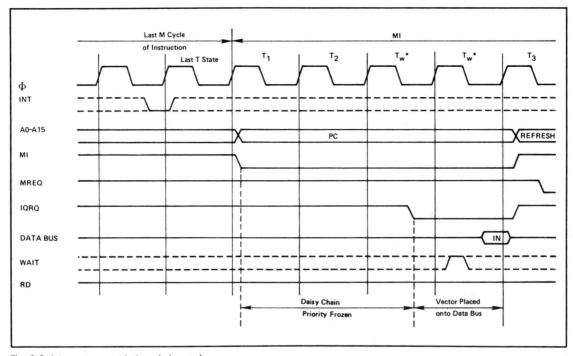

Fig. 3-3. Interrupt request/acknowledge cycle.

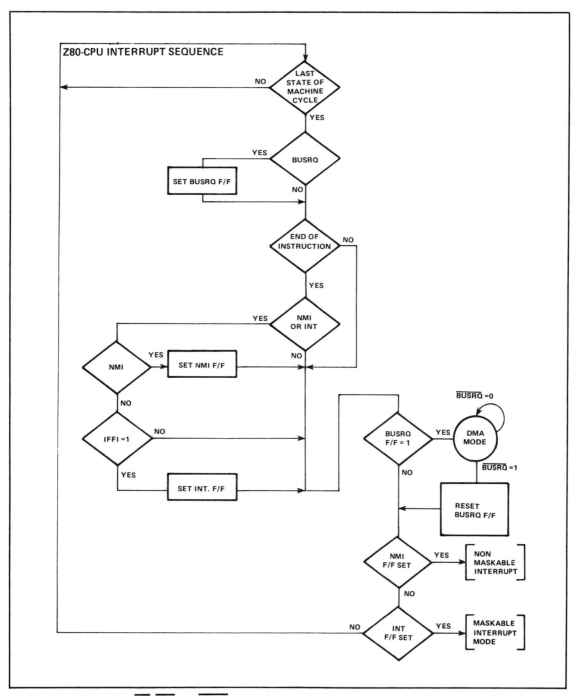

Fig. 3-4. Interrelationship of INT, NMI, and BUSRQ. The following flowchart details the relationship of three control inputs to the Z80-CPU. Note the following from the flowchart. (1) INT and NMI are always acted on at the end of an instruction. (2) BUSRQ is acted on at the end of a machine cycle. (3) While the CPU is in the DMA MODE, it will not respond to active inputs on INT or NMI. (4) These three inputs are acted on in the following order of priority: a) BUSRQ b) NMI c) INT.

Once the interrupting device supplies the lower portion of the pointer, the CPU automatically pushes the program counter onto the stack, obtains the starting address from the table and does a jump to this address. This mode of response requires 19 clock periods to complete (7 to fetch the lower 8 bits from the interrupting device, 6 to save the program counter, and 6 to obtain the jump address).

Note that the Z80 peripheral devices all include a daisy-chain priority interrupt structure that automatically supplies the programmed vector to the CPU during interrupt acknowledge. Refer to the Z80-PIO, Z80-SIO and Z80-CTC chapters for details.

Z80 Interrupt Acknowledge Summary

Peripheral Device Requests Interrupt. Any device requesting an interrupt can pull the wired-or line $\overline{INT}$ low.

CPU Acknowledges Interrupt. Priority status is frozen when $\overline{M1}$ goes low during the Interrupt Acknowledge sequence. Propagation delays down the IEI/IEO daisy chain must be settled out when $\overline{IORQ}$ goes low. If IEI is HIGH, an active peripheral device will place its interrupt vector on the data bus when $\overline{IORQ}$ goes low. That peripheral then releases its hold in $\overline{INT}$ allowing interrupts from a higher priority device. Lower priority devices are inhibited from placing their vector on the data bus or Interrupting because IEO is low on the active device.

Interrupt Is Cleared. An active peripheral device (IEI=1, IEO=0) monitors OP code fetches for an RETI (ED 4D) instruction which tells the peripheral that its interrupt service routine is over. The peripheral device then re-activates its internal Interrupt structure as well as raising its IEO line to enable lower priority devices.

Chapter 4

Z80-CPU Implementation

HARDWARE EXAMPLES

This chapter is intended to serve as a basic introduction to implementing systems with the Z80 CPU.

Minimum System

Figure 4-1 is a diagram of a very simple Z80 system. Any Z80 system must include the following five elements:

1. Five volt power supply
2. Oscillator
3. Memory devices
4. I/O circuits
5. CPU

Since the Z80-CPU only requires a single 5 volt supply, most small systems can be implemented using only this single supply.

The oscillator can be very simple since the only requirement is that it be a 5-volt square wave. For systems not running at full speed, a simple RC oscillator can be used. When the CPU is operated near the highest possible frequency, a crystal oscillator is generally required because the system timing will not tolerate

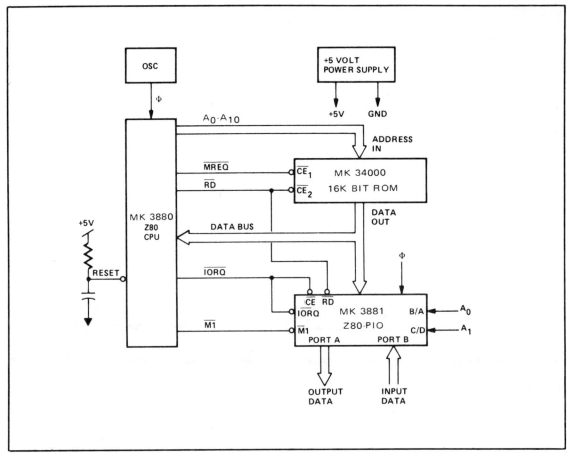

Fig. 4-1. Minimum Z80 computer system.

the drift or jitter that an RC network will generate. A crystal oscillator can be made from inverters and a few discrete components or monolithic circuits are widely available.

The external memory can be any mixture of standard RAM, ROM, or PROM. In this simple example we have shown a single 16K bit ROM (2K bytes) being utilized as the entire memory system. For this example we have assumed that the Z80 internal register configuration contains sufficient Read/Write storage so that external RAM memory is not required.

Every computer system requires I/O circuits to allow it to interface to the "read world." In this simple example it is assumed that the output is an 8 bit control vector and the input is an 8 bit status word. The input data could be gated onto the data bus using any standard tri-state driver while the output data could be latched with any type of standard TTL latch. For this example we have used a Z80-PIO for the I/O circuit. This single circuit attaches to the data bus as shown and provides the required 16 bits of TTL compatible I/O. (Refer to the Z80-PIO manual for details on the operation of this circuit.) Notice in this example that with only three LSI circuits, a simple oscillator and a single 5 volt power supply, a powerful computer has been implemented.

68

Adding RAM

Most computer systems require some amount of external Read/Write memory for data storage and to implement a "stack." Figure 4-2 illustrates how 256 bytes of static memory can be added to the previous example. In this example the memory space is assumed to be organized as follows:

In this diagram the address space is described in hexidecimal notation. For this example, address bit A_{11} separates the ROM space from the RAM space so that it can be used for the chip select function. For larger amounts of external ROM or RAM, a simple TTL decoder will be required to form the chip selects.

MEMORY SPEED CONTROL

For many applications, it may be desirable to use slow memories to reduce costs. The $\overline{\text{WAIT}}$ line on the CPU allows the Z80 to operate with any speed memory. The memory access time requirements are most severe during the M1 cycle instruction fetch. All other memory accesses have an additional one-half of a clock cycle to be completed. For this reason it may be desirable in some applications to add one wait state to the M1 cycle so that slower memories can be used. Figure 4-3 is an example of a simple circuit that will accomplish this task. This circuit can be changed to add a single wait state to any memory access as shown in Fig. 4-4.

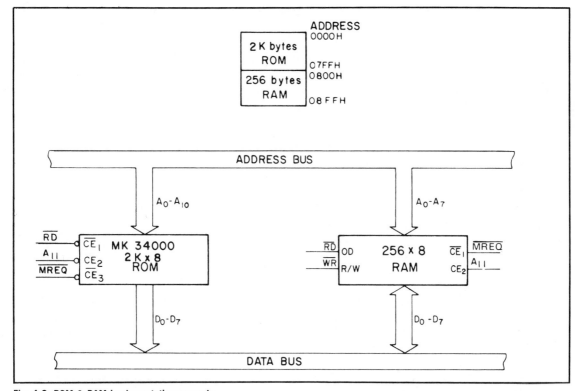

Fig. 4-2. ROM & RAM implementation example.

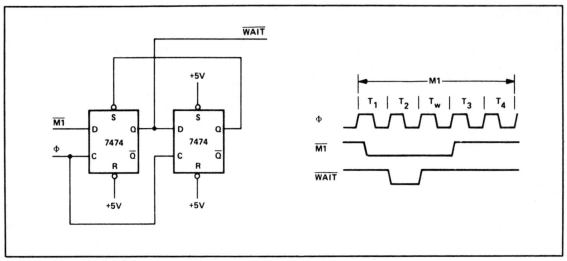

Fig. 4-3. Adding one wait state to an M1 cycle.

Interfacing Dynamic Memories

This section is intended only to serve as a brief introduction to interfacing dynamic memories. Each individual dynamic RAM has varying specifications that will require minor modifications to the description given here and no attempt will be made in this document to give details for any particular RAM.

Figure 4-5 illustrates the logic necessary to interface 8K bytes of dynamic RAM using 16-pin 4K dynamic memories. This Figure assumes that the RAMs are the only memory in the system so that A_{12} is used to select between the two pages of memory. During refresh time, all memories in the system must be read. The CPU provides the proper refresh address on lines A_0 through A_6. To add additional memory to the system it is necessary to only replace the two gates that operate on A_{12} with a decoder that operates on all required address bits. For larger systems, buffering for the address and data bus is also generally required.

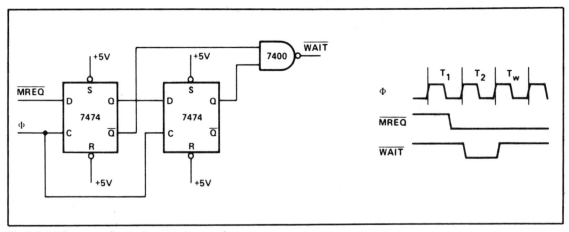

Fig. 4-4. Adding one wait state to any memory cycle.

70

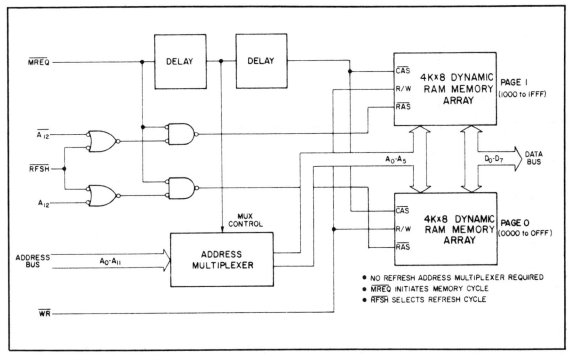

Fig. 4-5. Interfacing dynamic RAMS.

An application note entitled "Z80 Interfacing Techniques for Dynamic RAM" is available from your MOSTEK representative which describes dynamic RAM design techniques.

Z80-CPU Design Considerations: Clock Circuitry

Proper Z80 clock circuitry design is of paramount importance when designing a Z80 system. Parameters such as clock rise and fall times, min./max. clock high and low times, and max clock over and under shoot should be closely adhered to. Violation of these specs will result in unreliable and unpredictable CPU/peripheral behavior. Several manufacturers offer a wide variety of combination oscillator/drivers housed in 14 pin DIP packages. The following is a suggested source of reliable oscillators/drivers currently available.

Vendor	Function	Part No.
Motorola	Oscillator /Driver	K1160 series
Motorola	Oscillator	K1114
MF Electronics	Oscillator	MF1114
Hybrid House	Driver	HH3006A

Figure 4-6 illustrates a schematic recommended for driving the Z80 CPU, as well as other Z80 peripherals. This configuration meets the 30 ns rise and fall time while driving up to a 150 pf. load. Note the divide by two input flip-flop to provide a 50 percent duty cycle clock. This stage may be omitted if the oscillator is guaranteed to be within the specifications.

71

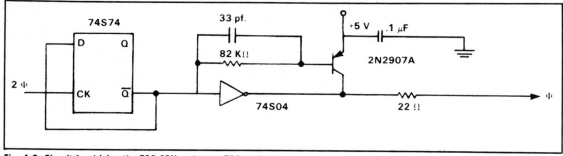

Fig. 4-6. Circuit for driving the Z80 CPU and other Z80 peripherals.

Reset Circuitry

The Z80-CPU has the characteristic that if the $\overline{\text{RESET}}$ input goes low during T2 or T4 of a cycle that the MREQ signal will go to an indeterminate state for one T-State approximately 3 T-States later. If there are dynamic memories in the system this action could cause an aborted or short access of the dynamic RAM which could cause destruction of data within the RAM. If the contents of RAM are of no concern after $\overline{\text{RESET}}$, then this characteristic is no problem as the CPU always resets properly. If RAM contents must be preserved, then the falling edge of the $\overline{\text{RESET}}$ input must be synchronized by the falling edge of $\overline{\text{M1}}$.

The circuitry of Fig. 4-7 does this synchronization as well as providing a one-shot to limit the duration of the CPU $\overline{\text{RESET}}$ pulse. The CPU $\overline{\text{RESET}}$ signal must be a pulse even though the EXTERNAL RESET

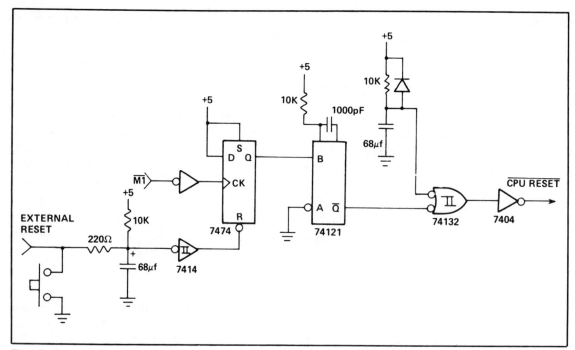

Fig. 4-7. Manual and power—on reset circuit.

button is held closed to avoid suspending the CPU refresh of dynamic RAM for a time long enough to destroy data in the RAM.

Address Latching

In order to guarantee proper operation of the Z80-CPU with dynamic RAMs the upper 4 bits of the address should be latched as shown in Fig. 4-8. This action is required because the Z80-CPU does not guarantee that the Address Bus will hold valid before the rising edge of MREQ on an OP Code Fetch.

This action does not directly affect dynamic memories because they latch addresses internally. The problem comes from the address decoder which generates $\overline{\text{RAS}}$. If the address lines which drive the decoder are allowed to change while $\overline{\text{MREQ}}$ is low, then a "glitch" can occur on the $\overline{\text{RAS}}$ line or lines, which may have the effect of destroying one row of data within the dynamic RAM.

SOFTWARE IMPLEMENTATION

Several different approaches are possible in developing software for the Z80 (Fig. 4-10). First of all, assembly language or a high-level language may be used as the source language. These languages may then be translated into machine language on a commercial time sharing facility using a cross-assembler or cross-compiler or, in the case of assembly language, the translation can be accomplished on a Z80 Development System using a resident assembler. Finally, the resulting machine code can be debugged either on a time-sharing facility using a Z80 simulator or on a Z80 Development System which uses a Z80-CPU directly.

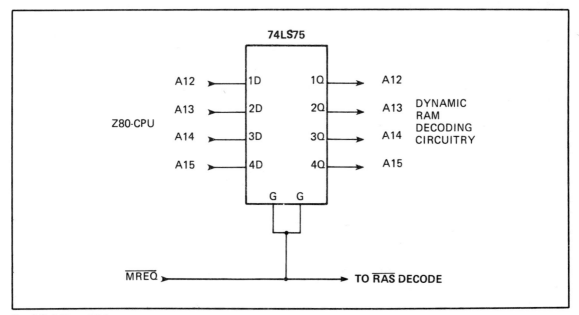

Fig. 4-8. Address latch.

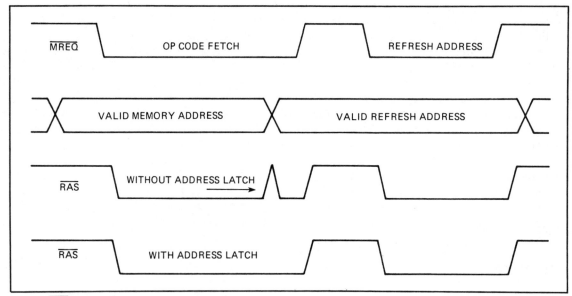

Fig. 4-9. $\overline{\text{RAS}}$ timing with and without address latch.

In selecting a source language, the primary factors to be considered are clarity and ease of programming vs. code efficiency. A high level language with its machine independent constraints is typically better for formulating and maintaining algorithms, but the resulting machine code is usually somewhat less efficient than what can be written directly in assembly language. These tradeoffs can often be balanced by combining high level language and assembly language routines, identifying those portions of a task which must be optimized and writing them as assembly language subroutines.

Deciding whether to use a resident or cross-assembler is a matter of available and short-term vs. long-term expense. While the initial expenditure for a development system is higher than that for a time-sharing terminal, the cost of an individual assembly using a resident assembler is negligible while the same operation on a time-sharing system is relatively expensive and in a short time this cost can equal the total cost of a development system.

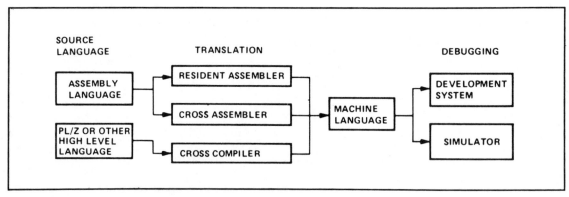

Fig. 4-10. Software generation techniques.

74

Debugging on a development system vs. a simulator is also a matter of availability and expense combined with operational fidelity and flexibility. As with the assembly process, debugging is less expensive on a development system than on a simulator available through time-sharing. In addition, the fidelity of the operating environment is preserved through real-time execution on a Z80-CPU and by connecting the I/O and memory components which will actually be used in the production system. The only advantage to the use of a simulator is the range of criteria which may be selected for such debugging procedures as tracing and setting breakpoints. This flexibility exists because a software simulation can achieve any degree of complexity in its interpretation of machine instructions while development system procedures have hardware limitations such as the capacity of the real-time storage module, the number of breakpoint registers and the pin configuration of the CPU. Despite such hardware limitations, debugging on a development system is typically more productive than on a simulator because of the direct interaction that is possible between the programmer and the authentic execution of his program.

SOFTWARE FEATURES

The Z80 instruction set provides the user with a large and flexible repetoire of operations with which to formulate control of the Z80-CPU.

The primary, auxiliary and index registers can be used to hold the arguments of arithmetic and logical operations, or to form memory addresses, or as fast-access storage for frequently used data.

Information can be moved directly from register to register; from memory to memory; from memory to registers; or from registers to memory. In addition, register contents and register/memory contents can be exchanged without using temporary storage. In particular, the contents of primary and auxiliary registers can be completely exchanged by executing only two instructions. EX and EXX. This register exchange procedure can be used to separate the set of working registers between different logical procedures or to expand the set of available registers in a single procedure.

Storage and retrieval of data between pairs of registers and memory can be controlled on a last-in first-out basis through PUSH and POP instructions which utilize a special stack pointer register, SP. This stack register is available both to manipulate data and to automatically store and retrieve addresses for subroutine linkage. When a subroutine is called, for example, the address following the CALL instruction is placed on the top of the push-down stack pointed to by SP. When a subroutine returns to the calling routine, the address on the top of the stack is used to set the program counter for the address of the next instruction. The stack pointer is adjusted automatically to reflect the current "top" stack position during PUSH, POP, CALL and RET instructions. This stack mechanism allows pushdown data stacks and subroutine calls to be nested to any practical depth because the stack area can potentially be as large as memory space.

The sequence of instruction execution can be controlled by six different flags (carry, zero, sign, parity/overflow, add-subtract, half-carry) which reflect the results of arithmetic, logical, shift and compare instructions. After the execution of an instruction which sets a flag, that flag can be used to control a conditional jump or return instruction. These instructions provide logical control following the manipulation of single bit, eight-bit byte (or) sixteen-bit data quantities.

A full set of logical operations, including AND, OR, XOR (exclusive—OR), CPL (NOR) and NEG (two's complement) are available for Boolean operations between the accumulator and 1) all other eight-bit registers, 2) memory locations or 3) immediate operands.

In addition, a full set of arithmetic and logical shifts in both directions are available which operate on the contents of all eight-bit primary registers or directly on any memory location. The carry flag can be included or simply set by these shift instructions to provide both the testing of shift results and to link register/register or register/memory shift operations.

EXAMPLES OF SPECIAL Z80 INSTRUCTIONS

Let us assume that a string of data in memory starting at location "DATA" is to be moved into another area of memory starting at location "BUFFER" and that the string length is 737 bytes. This operation can be accomplished as follows:

OPCODE	OPERAND	COMMENT
LD	HL, DATA	;START ADDRESS OF DATA STRING.
LD	DE, BUFFER	;START ADDRESS OF TARGET BUFFER.
LD	BC, 737	;LENGTH OF DATA STRING.
LDIR		;MOVE STRING — TRANSFER MEMORY ;POINTED TO BY HL INTO MEMORY ;LOCATION POINTED TO BY DE, INCREMENT ;HL AND DE, DECREMENT BC, PROCESS ; UNTIL BC=0.

For this operation 11 bytes are required and each byte of data is moved in 21 clock cycles.

Let's assume that a string in memory starting at location "DATA" is to be moved into another area of memory starting at location "BUFFER" until an ASCII $ character (used as string delimiter) is found. Let's also assume that the maximum string length is 132 characters. The operation can be performed as follows:

LABEL	OP CODE	OPERAND	COMMENT
	LD	HL, DATA	;STARTING ADDRESS OF DATA STRING.
	LD	DE, BUFFER	;STARTING ADDRESS OF TARGET BUFFER.
	LD	BC, 132	;MAXIMUM STRING LENGTH.
LOOP:	LD	A, '$'	;STRING DELIMITER CODE.
	CP	(HL)	;COMPARE MEMORY CONTENTS WITH DE-;LIMITER.
	JR	Z, END—$	;GO TO END IF CHARACTERS EQUAL.
	LDI		;MOVE CHARACTER (HL) TO (DE). ;INCREMENT HL AND DE, DECREMENT BC.
END:	JP	PE,LOOP	;GO TO "LOOP" IF MORE CHARACTERS. ;OTHERWISE, FALL THROUGH. ;NOTE: P/V FLAG IS USED ;TO INDICATE THAT REGISTER BC WAS ;DECREMENTED TO ZERO.

For this operation 19 bytes are required.

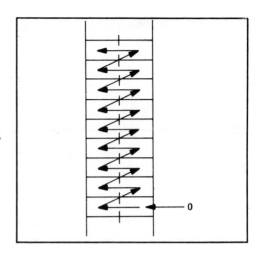

Fig. 4-11. BCD data shifting. 11 bytes are required for this operation.

Let us assume that a 16-digit decimal number represented in packed BCD format (two BCD digits/byte) has to be shifted as shown in the Fig. 4-11 in order to mechanize BCD multiplication or division. The operation can be accomplished as follows:

LABEL	OPCODE	OPERAND	COMMENT
	LD	HL, DATA	;ADDRESS OF FIRST BYTE.
	LD	B, COUNT	;SHIFT COUNT.
	XOR	A	;CLEAR ACCUMULATOR.
ROTAT:	RLD		;ROTATE LEFT LOW ORDER DIGIT IN ACC
			;WITH DIGITS IN (HL).
	INC	HL	;ADVANCE MEMORY POINTER.
	DJNZ	ROTAT—$	;DECREMENT B AND GO TO ROTAT IF
			;B IS NOT ZERO, OTHERWISE FALL THROUGH.

For this operation, 11 bytes are required.

Let us assume that one number is to be subtracted from another and a) that they are both in packed BCD format, b) that they are of equal but varying length, and c) that the result is to be stored in the location of the minuend. The operation can be accomplished as follows:

LABEL	OPCODE	OPERAND	COMMENT
	LD	HL, ARG1	;ADDRESS OF MINUEND.
	LD	DE, ARG2	;ADDRESS OF SUBTRAHEND.
	LD	B, LENGTH	;LENGTH OF TWO ARGUMENTS.
	AND	A	;CLEAR CARRY FLAG.
SUBDEC:	LD	A, (DE)	;SUBTRAHEND TO ACC.
	SBC	A, (HL)	;SUBTRACT (HL) FROM ACC.
	DAA		;ADJUST RESULT TO DECI-MAL CODED VALUE.
	LD	(HL), A	;STORE RESULT.
	INC	HL	;ADVANCE MEMORY POINTERS.
	INC	DE	
	DJNZ	SUBDEC—$	;DECREMENT B AND GO TO "SUBDEC" IF B
			;NOT ZERO, OTHERWISE FALL THROUGH.

For this operation, 17 bytes are required.

EXAMPLES OF PROGRAMMING TASKS

The following program sorts an array of numbers each in the range <0,255> into ascending order using a standard exchange sorting algorithm.

01/22/76   11:14:37   BUBBLE LISTING

LABEL	OP CODE	OPERAND	COMMENT
1	; *** STANDARD EXCHANGE (BUBBLE) SORT ROUTINE ***		
2	;		
3	; AT ENTRY: HL CONTAINS ADDRESS OF DATA.		
4	; C CONTAINS NUMBER OF ELEMENTS TO BE SORTED.		
5	; (1<C<256)		
6	;		
7	; AT EXIT: DATA SORTED IN ASCENDING ORDER.		
8	;		
9	; USE OF REGISTERS.		
10	;		
11	; REGISTER CONTENTS.		
12	;		
13	; A		TEMPORARY STORAGE FOR CALCULATIONS.
14	; B		COUNTER FOR DATA ARRAY.
15	; C		LENGTH OF DATA ARRAY.
16	; D		FIRST ELEMENT IN COMPARISON.
17	; E		SECOND ELEMENT IN COMPARISON.
18	; H		FLAG TO INDICATE EXCHANGE.
19	; L		UNUSED.
20	; IX		POINTER INTO DATA ARRAY.
21	; IY		UNUSED.
22	;		

ADDRESS	DATA	LABEL	OP CODE	OPERAND	COMMENT
0000	222600	23 SORT:	LD	(DATA), HL	;SAVE DATA ADDRESS.
0003	CB84	24 LOOP:	RES	FLAG, H	;INITIALIZE EXCHANGE FLAG.
0005	41	25	LD	B,C	;INITIALIZE LENGTH COUNTER.
0006	05	26	DEC	B	;ADJUST FOR TESTING.
0007	DD2A2600	27	LD	IX, (DATA)	;INITIALIZE ARRAY POINTER.
000B	DD7E00	28 NEXT:	LD	A,(IX+0)	;FIRST ELEMENT IN COMPARISON.
000E	57	29	LD	D, A	;TEMPORARY STORAGE FOR ELEMENT.
000F	DD5E01	30	LD	E, (IX+1)	;SECOND ELEMENT IN COMPARISON.
0012	93	31	SUB	E	;COMPARISON FIRST TO SECOND.
0013	3008	32	JR	NC,NOEX-$	;IF FIRST>SECOND, NO JUMP.
0015	DD7300	33	LD	(IX), E	;EXCHANGE ARRAY ELEMENTS.
0018	DD7201	34	LD	(IX+1), D	
001B	CBC4	35	SET	FLAG H	;RECORD EXCHANGE OCCURRED.
001D	DD23	36 NOEX:	INC	IX	;POINT TO NEXT DATA ELEMENT.
001F	10EA	37	DJNZ	NEXT-$	;COUNT NUMBER OF COMPARISONS; ;REPEAT IF MORE DATA PAIRS.
0021	CB44	39	BIT	FLAG, H	;DETERMINE IF EXCHANGE OCCURRED.

ADDRESS	DATA	LABEL		OP CODE	OPERAND	COMMENT
0023	20DE	40		JR	NZ, LOOP-$	;CONTINUE IF DATA UNSORTED.
0025	C9	41		RET		;OTHERWISE, EXIT.
		42	;			
0026		43	FLAG:	EQU	0	;DESIGNATION OF FLAG BIT.
0026		44	DATA:	DEFS	2	;STORAGE FOR DATA ADDRESS.
		45		END		

The following program multiplies two unsigned 16-bit integers and leaves the result in the HL register pair.

01/22/76   11:32:36   MULTIPLY LISTING

ADDRESS	DATA	LABEL		OP CODE	OPERAND	COMMENT
0000		1	MULT:;	UNSIGNED SIXTEEN BIT INTEGER MULTIPLY.		
		2	;	ON ENTRANCE: MULTIPLIER IN HL.		
		3	;	MULTIPLICAND IN DE.		
		4	;			
		5	;	ON EXIT: RESULT IN HL.		
		6	;			
		7	;	REGISTERS USES:		
		8	;			
		9	;			
		10	;	H HIGH ORDER PARTIAL RESULT.		
		11	;	L LOW ORDER PARTIAL RESULT.		
		12	;	D HIGH ORDER MULTIPLICAND.		
		13		E LOW ORDER MULTIPLICAND.		
		14	;	B COUNTER FOR NUMBER OF SHIFTS.		
		15	;	C HIGH ORDER BITS OF MULTIPLIER.		
		16	;	A LOW ORDER BITS OF MULTIPLIER.		
		17	;			
0000	0610	18		LD	B,16;	NUMBER OF BITS—INITIALIZE.
0002	4A	19		LD	C,D;	MOVE MULTIPLIER.
0003	7B	20		LD	A,E;	
0004	EB	21		EX	DE,HL;	MOVE MULTIPLICAND.
0005	210000	22		LD	HL,0;	CLEAR PARTIAL RESULT.
0008	CB39	23	MLOOP:	SRL	C;	SHIFT MULTIPLIER RIGHT.
000A	1F	24		RR	A;	LEAST SIGNIFICANT BIT IS IN CARRY.
000B	3001	26		JR	NC, NOADD-$	IF NO CARRY' SKIP THE ADD.
000D	19	27		ADD	HL,DE;	ELSE ADD MULTIPLICAND TO PARTIAL RESULT.
000E	EB	29	NOADD:	EX	DE,HL;	SHIFT MULTIPLICAND LEFT
000F	29	30		ADD	HL,HL;	BY MULTIPLYING IT BY TWO.
0010	EB	31		EX	DE,HL;	
0011	10F5	32		DJNZ	MLOOP-$;	REPEAT UNTIL NO MORE BITS.
0013	C9	33		RET;		
		34		END;		

Z80 INSTRUCTION BREAKDOWN BY MACHINE CYCLE

This section tabulates each Z80 instruction type and breaks each instruction down into its machine cycles

79

and corresponding T-States. The different standard machine cycles (OP Code Fetch, Memory Read, Port Read, etc.) are described in Chapter 2. This chart will allow the system designer to predict what the Z80 will do on each clock cycle during the execution of a given instruction. The instruction types are listed together by functions and in the same order as the Tables in Chapter 3. Table 4-1 shows the instruction breakdown by machine cycle for all instruction types.

The best way to learn how to use these tables is to look at a few examples. The first example is to register exchange instructions (LD r, s) where r,s can be any of the following CPU Registers: B,C,D,E,H,L, or A. The instruction breakdown table shows this instruction to have one machine cycle (M1) four T-States long (number in parenthesis) which is an OP Code Fetch. Referring to Figs. 2-5 and 2-6 one sees the standard form for an OP Code Fetch and the state of the CPU bus during these four T-States. Taking the next instruction shown (LD r, n) which loads one of the previous registers with data or immediate value "n" one finds the breakdown to be a four T-State OP Code Fetch followed by a three T-State Operand Data Read. An Operand Data Read takes the form of the Standard Memory Read shown in Figs. 2-7 and 2-8.

After these two simple examples, a more complex one is in order. The LD r, (IX+d) is the first double byte OP Code shown and executes as follows: First there are two M1 cycles (and related memory refreshes) followed by an Operand Data Read of the displacement "d". Next M3 consists of a five T-State Internal Operation which is the calculation of the Indexed address (IX+d). The last machine cycle (M4) consists of a Memory Read of the data continued in address IX+d and the loading of register "r" with that data.

The LD dd, (nn) instruction loads an internal 16-bit register pair with the contents of the memory location specified in the Operand Bytes of the instruction. This instruction is four bytes long (two bytes of OP Code + two bytes of Operand Address). As shown, there are two M1 cycles to fetch the OP Code and then two Machine Cycles to read the Operand Addresses, low order byte first. Machine cycle 4 is a read of memory to obtain the data for the low order register (e.g., C of BC, E of DE and L of HL) followed by a read of the data for the high order register.

The first instruction to use the Stack Register is the PUSH qq instruction which executes as follows: Machine cycle 1 is extended by one cycle and the Stack Pointer is decremented in the extra T-State to point to an empty location on the Stack. Machine cycle 2 is a write of the high byte of the referenced register to the address contained in the Stack Pointer. The Stack Pointer is again decremented and a write of the low byte of the referenced register is made to the Stack in Machine Cycle 3. Note that the Stack Pointer is left pointing to the last data referenced on the Stack. The block transfer instructions such as LDI and LDIR are very similar. LDI is 16 T-States long and is composed of a double byte OP Code Fetch (two memory refreshes) followed by a memory read and a memory write. The memory write is 5 T-States long to allow updating of the block length counter —BC. The repetitive form of this instruction (LDIR) has an additional Machine Cycle (M4) of 5 T-States to allow decrementing of the Program Counter by two (PC-2) which results in refetching of the OP Code (LDIR). Each movement of data by this instruction is 21 T-States long (except the last) and the refetching of the OP Codes results in memory refresh occurring as well as the sampling of interrupts and BUSRQ.

The NMI Interrupt sequence is 11 T-States long with the first M1 being a dummy OP Code Fetch of 5 T-States long. The Program Counter is not advanced, the OP Code on the data bus is ignored and an internal Restart is done to address 66H. The following two Machine Cycles are a write of the Program Counter to the Stack.

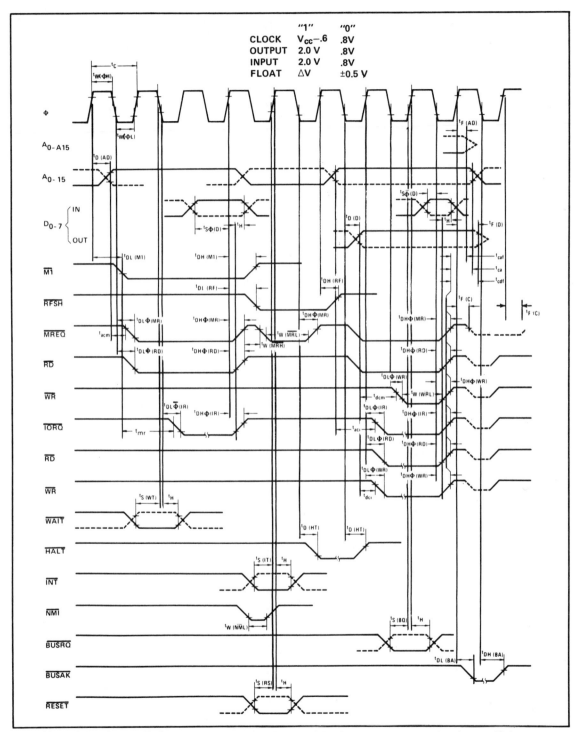

	"1"	"0"
CLOCK	$V_{cc}-.6$	.8V
OUTPUT	2.0 V	.8V
INPUT	2.0 V	.8V
FLOAT	ΔV	±0.5 V

Fig. 4-12. Ac timing diagram. Timing measurements are made at the following voltages, unless otherwise specified.

Table 4-1. Z80 Breakdown by Machine Code.

INSTRUCTION TYPE	BYTES	MACHINE CYCLE				
		M1	M2	M3	M4	M5
LD r, s	1	OCF (4)				
LD r, n	2	OCF (4)	OD (3)			
LD r, (HL)	1	OCF (4)	MR (3)			
LD (HL), r	1	OCF (4)	MW (3)			
LD r, (IX+d)	3	OCF (4)/OCF (4)	OD (3)	IO (5)	MR (3)	
LD (IX+d), r	3	OCF (4)/OCF (4)	OD (3)	IO (5)	MW (3)	
LD (HL), n	2	OCF (4)	OD (3)	MW (3)		
LD A, (BC DE)	1	OCF (4)	MR (3)			
LD (BC DE), A		OCF (4)	MW (3)			
LD A, (nn)	3	OCF (4)	ODL (3)	ODH (3)	MR (3)	
LD (nn), A		OCF (4)	ODL (3)	ODH (3)	MW (3)	
LD A, I/R LD I/R, A	2	OCF (4)/OCF(5)				
LD dd, nn	3	OCF (4)	ODL (3)	ODH (3)		
LD IX, nn	4	OCF (4)/OCF (4)	ODL (3)	ODH (3)		
LD HL, (nn)	3	OCF (4)	ODL (3)	ODH (3)	MRL (3)	MRH (3)
LD (nn), HL		OCF (4)	ODL (3)	ODH (3)	MWL (3)	MWH (3)
LD dd, (nn)	4	OCF (4)/OCF (4)	ODL (3)	ODH (3)	MRL (3)	MRH (3)
LD (nn), dd		OCF (4)/OCF (4)	ODL (3)	ODH (3)	MWL (3)	MWH (3)
LD IX, (nn)		OCF (4)/OCF (4)	ODL (3)	ODH (3)	MRL (3)	MRH (3)
LD (nn), IX		OCF (4)/OCF (4)	ODL (3)	ODH (3)	MWL (3)	MWH (3)
LD SP, HL	1	OCF (6)				
LD SP, IX	2	OCF (4)/OCF (6)				
PUSH qq	1	OCF (5) SP-1 →	SWH (3) SP-1 →	SWL (3) →		
PUSH IX	2	OCF (4)/OCF (5) SP-1 →	SWH (3) SP-1 →	SWL (3) →		
POP qq	1	OCF (4)	SRH (3) SP+1 →	SRL (3) →	SP+1 →	
POP IX	2	OCF (4)/OCF (4)	SRH (3) SP+1 →	SRL (3) →	SP+1 →	
EX DE, HL	1	OCF (4)				
EX AF, AF'	1	OCF (4)				

INSTRUCTION TYPE	BYTES	M1	M2	M3	M4	M5
EXX	1	OCF (4)				
EX (SP), HL	1	OCF (4)	SRL (3) SP+1 →	SRH (4)	SWH (3) SP-1	SWL (5) →
EX (SP), IX	2	OCF (4)/OCF (4)	SRL (3) SP+1 →	SRH (4)	SWH (3) SP-1	SWL (5) →
LDI LDD CPI CPD	2	OCF (4)/OCF (4)	MR (3)	MW (5)		
LDIR LDDR CPIR CPDR	2	OCF (4)/OCF (4)	MR (3)	MW (5)	IO (5)* *only if BC ≠ 0	
ALU A, r ADD ADC SUB SBC AND OR XOR CP	1	OCF (4)				
ALU A, n	2	OCF (4)	OD (3)			
ALU A, (HL)	1	OCF (4)	MR (3)			
ALU A, (IX+d)	3	OCF (4)/OCF (4)	OD (3)	IO (5)	MR (3)	
DEC INC r	1	OCF (4)				
DEC INC (HL)	1	OCF (4)	MR (4)	MW (3)		
DEC INC (IX+D)	2	OCF (4)/OCF (4)	OD (3)	IO (5)	MR (4)	MW (3)
DAA CPL CCF SCF NOP HALT DI EI	1	OCF (4)				
NEG IMO IM1 IM2	2	OCF (4)/OCF (4)				

(continued on page 84)

Table. 4-1. Z80 Instruction Breakdown by Machine Code (continued from page 83).

INSTRUCTION TYPE	BYTES	MACHINE CYCLE				
		M1	M2	M3	M4	M5
ADD HL, ss	1	OCF (4)	IO (4)	IO (3)		
ADC HL, ss SBC HL, ss ADD IX, pp	2	OCF (4)/OCF (4)	IO (4)	IO (3)		
INC ss DEC ss	1	OCF (6)				
DEC IX INC IX	2	OCF (4)/OCF (6)				
RLCA RLA RRCA RRA	1	OCF (4)				
RLC r RL RRC RR SLA SRA SRL	2	OCF (4)/OCF (4)				
RLC (HL) RL RRC RR SLA SRA SRL	2	OCF (4)/OCF (4)	MR (4)	MW (3)		
RLC (IX+d) RL RRC RR SLA SRA SRL	4	OCF (4)/OCF (4)	OD (3)	IO (5)	MR (4)	MW (3)
RLD RRD	2	OCF (4)/OCF (4)	MR (3)	IO (4)	MW (3)	
BIT b, r SET RES	2	OCF (4)/OCF (4)				

		MACHINE CYCLE				
INSTRUCTION TYPE	BYTES	M1	M2	M3	M4	M5
BIT b, (HL)	2	OCF (4)/OCF (4)	MR (4)			
SET b, (HL) RES	2	OCF (4)/OCF (4)	MR (4)	MW (3)		
BIT b, (IX+d)	4	OCF (4)/OCF (4)	OD (3)	IO (5)	MR (4)	
SET b, (IX+d) RES	4	OCF (4)/OCF (4)	OD (3)	IO (5)	MR (4)	MW (3)
JP nn JP cc, nn	3	OCF (4)	ODL (3)	ODH (3)		
JR e	2	OCF (4)	OD (3)	IO (5)		
JR C, e JR NC, e JR Z, e JR NZ, e	2	OCF (4)	OD (3)	IO (5)* * If condition is met		
JP (HL)	1	OCF (4)				
JP (IX)	2	OCF (4)/OCF (4)				
DJNZ, e	2	OCF (5)	OD (3)	IO (5)* * If B$\neq$ 0		
CALL nn CALL cc, nn cc true	3	OCF (4)	ODL (3)	ODH (4) SP-1 →	SWH (3) SP-1 →	SWL (3)
CALL cc, nn cc false	3	OCF (4)	ODL (3)	ODH (3)		
RET	1	OCF (4)	SRL (3) SP+1 →	SRH (3)	SP+1 →	
RET cc	1	OCF (5)	SRL (3)* * If cc is true SP+1 →	SRH (3)*	SP+1 →	
RETI RETN	2	OCF (4)/OCF (4)	SRL (3) SP+1 →	SRH (3)	SP+1 →	
RST p	1	OCF (5) SP-1 →	SWH (3) SP-1 →	SWL (3)		

(continued on page 86)

Table 4-1. Z80 Instruction Breakdown by Machine Code (continued from page 85).

		MACHINE CYCLE				
INSTRUCTION TYPE	BYTES	M1	M2	M3	M4	M5
IN A, (n)	2	OCF (4)	OD (3)	PR (4)		
IN r, (c)	2	OCF (4)/OCF (4)	PR (4)			
INI IND	2	OCF (4)/OCF (5)	PR (4)	MW (3)		
INIR INDR	2	OCF (4)/OCF (5)	PR (4)	MW (3)	IO (5)	
OUT (n) , A	2	OCF (4)	OD (3)	PW (4)		
OUT (C), r	2	OCF (4)/OCF (4)	PW (4)			
OUTI OUTD	2	OCF (4)/OCF (5)	MR (3)	PW (4)		
OTIR OTDR	2	OCF (4)/OCF (5)	MR (3)	PW (4)	IO (5)	
INTERRUPTS						
NMI	—	OCF (5) * SP-1 →	SWH (3) SP-1 →	SWL (3)	*Op Code Ignored	
INT						
MODE 0	—	INTA (6) (CALL INSERTED)	ODL (3)	ODH (4) SP-1 →	SWH (3) SP-1 →	SWL (3) →
	—	INTA (6) (RST INSERTED) SP-1 →	SWH (3) SP-1 →	SWL (3)		
MODE 1		INTA (7) (RST 38H INTERNAL) SP-1 →	SWH (3) SP-1 →	SWL (3)		
MODE 2	—	INTA (7) (VECTOR SUPPLIED) SP-1 →	SWH (3) SP-1 →	SWL (3)	MRL (3)	MRH (3)

86

Table 4-2. Dc Characteristics.

$T_A = 0°C$ to $70°C$, $V_{CC} = 5V \pm 5\%$ unless otherwise specified

SYMBOL	PARAMETER	MIN.	TYP.	MAX.	UNIT	TEST CONDITION
V_{ILC}	Clock Input Low Voltage	-0.3		0.8	V	
V_{IHC}	Clock Input High Voltage	Vcc-.6		Vcc+.3	V	
V_{IL}	Input Low Voltage	-0.3		0.8	V	
V_{IH}	Input High Voltage	2.0		V_{CC}	V	
V_{OL}	Output Low Voltage			0.4	V	$I_{OL} = 1.8mA$
V_{OH}	Output High Voltage	2.4			V	$I_{OH} = -250 \mu A$
I_{CC}	Power Supply Current			150*	mA	
I_{LI}	Input Leakage Current			± 10	μA	$V_{IN} = 0$ to V_{CC}
I_{LOH}	Tri-State Output Leakage Current in Float			10	μA	$V_{OUT} = 2.4$ to V_{CC}
I_{LOL}	Tri-State Output Leakage Current in Float			-10	μA	$V_{OUT} = 0.4V$
I_{LD}	Data Bus Leakage Current in Input Mode			± 10	μA	$0 \leqslant V_{IN} \leqslant V_{CC}$

*200mA for -4, -10 or -20 devices

NOTE: All outputs are rated at one standard TTL load.

CAPACITANCE
$T_A = 25°C$, f = 1MHz unmeasured pins returned to ground

SYMBOL	PARAMETER	MAX.	UNIT
$C\Phi$	Clock Capacitance	35	pF
C_{IN}	Input Capacitance	5	pF
C_{OUT}	Output Capacitance	10	pF

*Comment

Stresses above those listed under "Absolute Maximum Ratings" may cause permanent damage to the device. This is a stress rating only and functional operation of the device at these or any other condition above those indicated in the operational sections of this specification is not implied. Exposure to absolute maximum rating conditions for extended periods may affect device reliability.

(continued on page 88)

Table 4-2. Dc Characteristics (continued from page 87).

SIGNAL	SYMBOL	PARAMETER	MIN.	MAX.	UNIT	TEST CONDITIONS
		T_A = 0°C to 70°C, Vcc = +5V ±5%, Unless Otherwise Noted				
Φ	t_c	Clock Period	.25	[12]	μsec	
	$t_{w(\Phi H)}$	Clock Pulse Width, Clock High	110	(D)	nsec	
	$t_{w(\Phi L)}$	Clock Pulse Width, Clock Low	110	2000	nsec	
	$t_{r, f}$	Clock Rise and Fall Time		30	nsec	
A_{0-15}	$t_{D(AD)}$	Address Output Delay		110	nsec	
	$t_{F(AD)}$	Delay to Float		90	nsec	
	t_{acm}	Address Stable Prior to $\overline{MREQ}$ (Memory Cycle)	[1]		nsec	C_L = 50pF
	t_{aci}	Address Stable Prior to $\overline{IORQ}$, $\overline{RD}$ or $\overline{WR}$ (I/O Cycle)	[2]		nsec	
	t_{ca}	Address Stable From $\overline{RD}$, $\overline{WR}$, $\overline{IORQ}$ or $\overline{MREQ}$	[3]		nsec	Except T3.M1
	t_{caf}	Address Stable From $\overline{RD}$ or $\overline{WR}$ During Float	[4]		nsec	
D_{0-7}	$t_{D(D)}$	Data Output Delay		150	nsec	
	$t_{F(D)}$	Delay to Float During Write Cycle		90	nsec	
	$t_{S\Phi(D)}$	Data Setup Time to Rising Edge of Clock During M1 Cycle	35		nsec	
	$t_{S\overline{\Phi}(D)}$	Data Setup Time to Falling Edge at Clock During M2 and M5	50		nsec	C_L = 50pF
	t_{dcm}	Data Stable Prior to $\overline{WR}$ (Memory Cycle)	[5]		nsec	
	t_{dci}	Data Stable Prior to $\overline{WR}$ (I/O Cycle)	[6]		nsec	
	t_{cdf}	Data Stable From $\overline{WR}$	[7]		nsec	
	t_H	Input Hold Time	0		nsec	
$\overline{MREQ}$	$t_{DL\overline{\Phi}(MR)}$	$\overline{MREQ}$ Delay From Falling Edge of Clock, $\overline{MREQ}$ Low	20	85	nsec	
	$t_{DH\Phi(MR)}$	$\overline{MREQ}$ Delay From Rising Edge of Clock, $\overline{MREQ}$ High		85	nsec	
	$t_{DH\overline{\Phi}(MR)}$	$\overline{MREQ}$ Delay From Falling Edge of Clock, $\overline{MREQ}$ High		85	nsec	C_L = 50pF
	$t_{w(\overline{MRL})}$	Pulse Width, $\overline{MREQ}$ Low	[8]		nsec	
	$t_{w(\overline{MRH})}$	Pulse Width, $\overline{MREQ}$ High	[9]		nsec	
$\overline{IORQ}$	$t_{DL\Phi(IR)}$	$\overline{IORQ}$ Delay From Rising Edge of Clock, $\overline{IORQ}$ Low		75	nsec	
	$t_{DL\overline{\Phi}(IR)}$	$\overline{IORQ}$ Delay From Falling Edge of Clock, $\overline{IORQ}$ Low		85	nsec	C_L = 50pF
	$t_{DH\Phi(IR)}$	$\overline{IORQ}$ Delay From Rising Edge of Clock, $\overline{IORQ}$ High		85	nsec	
	$t_{DH\overline{\Phi}(IR)}$	$\overline{IORQ}$ Delay From Falling Edge of Clock, $\overline{IORQ}$ High		85	nsec	
$\overline{RD}$	$t_{DL\Phi(RD)}$	$\overline{RD}$ Delay From Rising Edge of Clock, $\overline{RD}$ Low		85	nsec	
	$t_{DL\overline{\Phi}(RD)}$	$\overline{RD}$ Delay From Falling Edge of Clock, $\overline{RD}$ Low		95	nsec	C_L = 50pF
	$t_{DH\Phi(RD)}$	$\overline{RD}$ Delay From Rising Edge of Clock, $\overline{RD}$ High		85	nsec	
	$t_{DH\overline{\Phi}(RD)}$	$\overline{RD}$ Delay From Falling Edge of Clock, $\overline{RD}$ High		85	nsec	
$\overline{WR}$	$t_{DL\Phi(WR)}$	$\overline{WR}$ Delay From Rising Edge of Clock, $\overline{WR}$ Low		65	nsec	
	$t_{DL\overline{\Phi}(WR)}$	$\overline{WR}$ Delay From Falling Edge of Clock, $\overline{WR}$ Low		80	nsec	C_L = 50pF
	$t_{DH\Phi(WR)}$	$\overline{WR}$ Delay From Falling Edge of Clock, $\overline{WR}$ High		80	nsec	
	$t_{w(\overline{WR}L)}$	Pulse Width, $\overline{WR}$ Low	[10]		nsec	

NOTES:

A Data should be enabled onto the CPU data bus when $\overline{RD}$ is active. During interrupt acknowledge data should be enabled when M1 and IORQ are both active.

B The $\overline{RESET}$ signal must be active for a minimum of 3 clock cycles. .

SIGNAL	SYMBOL	PARAMETER	MIN.	MAX.	UNIT	TEST CONDITION
$\overline{M1}$	$t_{DL(M1)}$	$\overline{M1}$ Delay From Rising Edge of Clock $\overline{M1}$ Low		100	nsec	$C_L = 50pF$
	$t_{DH(M1)}$	$\overline{M1}$ Delay From Rising Edge of Clock, $\overline{M1}$ High		100	nsec	
$\overline{RFSH}$	$t_{DL(RF)}$	$\overline{RFSH}$ Delay From Rising Edge of Clock, $\overline{RFSH}$ Low		130	nsec	$C_L = 50pF$
	$t_{DH(RF)}$	$\overline{RFSH}$ Delay From Rising Edge of Clock $\overline{RFSH}$ High		120	nsec	
$\overline{WAIT}$	$t_{S(WT)}$	$\overline{WAIT}$ Setup Time to Falling Edge of Clock	70		nsec	
$\overline{HALT}$	$t_{D(HT)}$	$\overline{HALT}$ Delay Time From Falling Edge of Clock		300	nsec	$C_L = 50pF$
$\overline{INT}$	$t_{s(IT)}$	$\overline{INT}$ Setup Time to Rising Edge of Clock	80		nsec	
$\overline{NMI}$	$t_{w(NML)}$	Pulse Width, $\overline{NMI}$ Low	80		nsec	
$\overline{BUSRQ}$	$t_{s(BQ)}$	$\overline{BUSRQ}$ Setup Time to Rising Edge of Clock	50		nsec	
$\overline{BUSAK}$	$t_{DL(BA)}$	$\overline{BUSAK}$ Delay From Rising Edge of Clock, $\overline{BUSAK}$ Low		100	nsec	$C_L = 50pF$
	$t_{DH(BA)}$	$\overline{BUSAK}$ Delay From Falling Edge of Clock, $\overline{BUSAK}$ High		100	nsec	
$\overline{RESET}$	$t_{s(RS)}$	$\overline{RESET}$ Setup Time to Rising Edge of Clock	60		nsec	
	$t_{F(C)}$	Delay to/From Float ($\overline{MREQ}$, $\overline{IORQ}$, $\overline{RD}$ and $\overline{WR}$)		80	nsec	
	t_{mr}	$\overline{M1}$ Stable Prior to $\overline{IORQ}$ (Interrupt Ack.)	[11]		nsec	

LOAD CIRCUIT FOR OUTPUT

[1] $t_{acm} = t_w (\Phi H) + t_f - 65$

[2] $t_{aci} = t_c - 70$

[3] $t_{ca} = t_w (\Phi L) + t_r - 50$

[4] $t_{caf} = t_w (\Phi L) + t_r - 45$

[5] $t_{dcm} = t_c - 170$

[6] $t_{dci} = t_w (\Phi L) + t_r - 170$

[7] $t_{cdf} = t_w (\Phi L) + t_r - 70$

[8] $t_w (\overline{MRL}) = t_c - 30$

[9] $t_w (\overline{MRH}) = t_w (\Phi H) + t_f - 20$

[10] $t_w (\overline{WR}) = t_c - 30$

[11] $t_{mr} = 2t_c + t_w (\Phi H) + t_f - 65$

[12] $t_c = t_w (\Phi H) + t_w (\Phi L) + t_r + t_f$

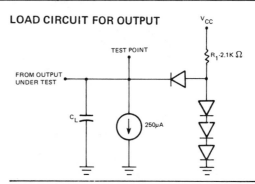

NOTES (Cont'd.)
C.   Output Delay vs. Load Capacitance
      $T_A = 70° C$ $V_{CC} = 5V \pm 5\%$
      Add 10 nsec delay for each 50pF increase in load up to a maximum of 200pF for the data bus and 100pF for address and control lines
D.   Although static by design, testing guarantees $t_w (\Phi H)$ of 200 μsec maximum.

Table 4-3. Ac Characteristics.

$T_A = 0°C$ to $70°C$, $V_{CC} = +5V \pm 5\%$, Unless Otherwise Noted

SIGNAL	SYMBOL	PARAMETER	MIN.	MAX.	UNIT	TEST CONDITION
Φ	t_c	Clock Period	.4	[12]	μsec	
	$t_w(\Phi H)$	Clock Pulse Width, Clock High	180	(D)	nsec	
	$t_w(\Phi L)$	Clock Pulse Width, Clock Low	180	2000	nsec	
	$t_{r,f}$	Clock Rise and Fall Time		30	nsec	
A_{0-15}	$t_{D(AD)}$	Address Output Delay		145	nsec	
	$t_{F(AD)}$	Delay to Float		110	nsec	$C_L = 50pF$
	t_{acm}	Address Stable Prior to $\overline{MREQ}$ (Memory Cycle)	[1]		nsec	
	t_{aci}	Address Stable Prior to $\overline{IORQ}$, $\overline{RD}$ or $\overline{WR}$ (I/O Cycle)	[2]		nsec	
	t_{ca}	Address Stable From $\overline{RD}$, $\overline{WR}$, $\overline{IORQ}$ or $\overline{MREQ}$	[3]		nsec	Except T3-M1
	t_{caf}	Address Stable From $\overline{RD}$ or $\overline{WR}$ During Float	[4]		nsec	
D_{0-7}	$t_{D(D)}$	Data Output Delay		230	nsec	
	$t_{F(D)}$	Delay to Float During Write Cycle		90	nsec	
	$t_{S\Phi(D)}$	Data Setup Time to Rising Edge of Clock During M1 Cycle	50		nsec	
	$t_{S\overline{\Phi}(D)}$	Data Setup Time to Falling Edge at Clock During M2 to M5	60		nsec	$C_L = 50pF$
	t_{dcm}	Data Stable Prior to $\overline{WR}$ (Memory Cycle)	[5]		nsec	
	t_{dci}	Data Stable Prior to $\overline{WR}$ (I/O Cycle)	[6]		nsec	
	t_{cdf}	Data Stable From $\overline{WR}$	[7]		nsec	
	t_H	Input Hold Time	0		nsec	
$\overline{MREQ}$	$t_{DL\Phi(MR)}$	$\overline{MREQ}$ Delay From Falling Edge of Clock, $\overline{MREQ}$ Low		100	nsec	
	$t_{DH\Phi(MR)}$	$\overline{MREQ}$ Delay From Rising Edge of Clock, $\overline{MREQ}$ High		100	nsec	
	$t_{DH\overline{\Phi}(MR)}$	$\overline{MREQ}$ Delay From Falling Edge of Clock, $\overline{MREQ}$ High		100	nsec	$C_L = 50 pF$
	$t_w(\overline{MRL})$	Pulse Width, $\overline{MREQ}$ Low	[8]		nsec	
	$t_w(\overline{MRH})$	Pulse Width, $\overline{MREQ}$ High	[9]		nsec	
$\overline{IORQ}$	$t_{DL\Phi(IR)}$	$\overline{IORQ}$ Delay From Rising Edge of Clock, $\overline{IORQ}$ Low		90	nsec	
	$t_{DL\overline{\Phi}(IR)}$	$\overline{IORQ}$ Delay From Falling Edge of Clock, $\overline{IORQ}$ Low		110	nsec	$C_L = 50 pF$
	$t_{DH\Phi(IR)}$	$\overline{IORQ}$ Delay From Rising Edge of Clock, $\overline{IORQ}$ High		100	nsec	
	$t_{DH\overline{\Phi}(IR)}$	$\overline{IORQ}$ Delay From Falling Edge of Clock, $\overline{IORQ}$ High		110	nsec	
$\overline{RD}$	$t_{DL\Phi(RD)}$	$\overline{RD}$ Delay From Rising Edge of Clock, $\overline{RD}$ Low		100	nsec	
	$t_{DL\overline{\Phi}(RD)}$	$\overline{RD}$ Delay From Falling Edge of Clock, $\overline{RD}$ Low		130	nsec	$C_L = 50pF$
	$t_{DH\Phi(RD)}$	$\overline{RD}$ Delay From Rising Edge of Clock, $\overline{RD}$ High		100	nsec	
	$t_{DH\overline{\Phi}(BD)}$	$\overline{RD}$ Delay From Falling Edge of Clock, $\overline{RD}$ High		110	nsec	
$\overline{WR}$	$t_{DL\Phi(WR)}$	$\overline{WR}$ Delay From Rising Edge of Clock, $\overline{WR}$ Low		80	nsec	
	$t_{DL\overline{\Phi}(WR)}$	$\overline{WR}$ Delay From Falling Edge of Clock $\overline{WR}$ Low		90	nsec	$C_L = 50pF$
	$t_{DH\Phi(WR)}$	$\overline{WR}$ Delay From Falling Edge of Clock, $\overline{WR}$ High		100	nsec	
	$t_w(\overline{WRL})$	Pulse Width, $\overline{WR}$ Low	[10]		nsec	

NOTES:

A   Data should be enabled onto the CPU data bus when RD is active. During interrupt acknowledge data should be enabled when $\overline{M1}$ and $\overline{IORQ}$ are both active.

B   The $\overline{RESET}$ signal must be active for a minimum of 3 clock cycles.

SIGNAL	SYMBOL	PARAMETER	MIN.	MAX.	UNIT	TEST CONDITIONS
$\overline{M1}$	$t_{DL(M1)}$	$\overline{M1}$ Delay From Rising Edge of Clock $\overline{M1}$ Low		130	nsec	C_L = 50pF
	$t_{DH(M1)}$	$\overline{M1}$ Delay From Rising Edge of Clock $\overline{M1}$ High		130	nsec	
$\overline{RFSH}$	$t_{DL(RF)}$	$\overline{RFSH}$ Delay From Rising Edge of Clock, $\overline{RFSH}$ Low		180	nsec	C_L = 30pF
	$t_{DH(RF)}$	$\overline{RFSH}$ Delay From Rising Edge of Clock, $\overline{RFSH}$ High		150	nsec	
$\overline{WAIT}$	$t_{S(WT)}$	$\overline{WAIT}$ Setup Time to Falling Edge of Clock	70		nsec	
$\overline{HALT}$	$t_{D(HT)}$	$\overline{HALT}$ Delay Time From Falling Edge of Clock		300	nsec	C_L = 50pF
$\overline{INT}$	$t_{s(IT)}$	$\overline{INT}$ Setup Time to Rising Edge of Clock	80		nsec	
$\overline{NMI}$	$t_w(\overline{NML})$	Pulse Width, $\overline{NMI}$ Low	80		nsec	
$\overline{BUSRQ}$	$t_{s(BQ)}$	$\overline{BUSRQ}$ Setup Time to Rising Edge of Clock	80		nsec	
$\overline{BUSAK}$	$t_{DL(BA)}$	$\overline{BUSAK}$ Delay From Rising Edge of Clock, $\overline{BUSAK}$ Low		120	nsec	C_L = 50 pF
	$t_{DH(BA)}$	$\overline{BUSAK}$ Delay From Falling Edge of Clock, $\overline{BUSAK}$ High		110	nsec	
$\overline{RESET}$	$t_{s(RS)}$	$\overline{RESET}$ Setup Time to Rising Edge of Clock	90		nsec	
	$t_{F(C)}$	Delay to/from Float ($\overline{MREQ}$, $\overline{IORQ}$, $\overline{RD}$ and $\overline{WR}$)		100	nsec	
	t_{mr}	$\overline{M1}$ Stable Prior to $\overline{IORQ}$ (Interrupt Ack.)	[11]		nsec	

[1] $t_{acm} = t_w(\Phi H) + t_f - 75$

[2] $t_{aci} = t_c - 80$

[3] $t_{ca} = t_w(\Phi L) + t_r - 40$

[4] $t_{caf} = t_w(\Phi L) + t_r - 60$

[5] $t_{dcm} = t_c - 210$

[6] $t_{dci} = t_w(\Phi L) + t_r - 210$

[7] $t_{cdf} = t_w(\Phi L) + t_r - 80$

[8] $t_w(\overline{MRL}) = t_c - 40$

[9] $t_w(\overline{MRH}) = t_w(\Phi H) + t_f - 30$

[10] $t_w(\overline{WR}) = t_c - 40$

[11] $t_{mr} = 2 t_c + t_w(\Phi H) + t_f - 80$

[12] $t_c = t_w(\Phi H) + t_w(\Phi L) + t_r + t_f$

LOAD CIRCUIT FOR OUTPUT

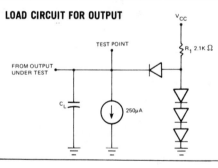

NOTES (Cont'd.)
C.   Output Delay vs. Load Capacitance
     T_A = 70°C V_{CC} = 5V±5%
     Add 10 nsec delay for each 50pF increase in load up
     to a maximum of 200pF for the data bus and 100pF for
     address and control lines.
D.   Although static by design, testing guarantees $t_w(\Phi H)$ of
     200 μ sec maximum.

Table 4-4. Ordering Information for Mostek Chips.

PART NO.	PACKAGE TYPE	MAX CLOCK FREQUENCY	TEMPERATURE RANGE
MK3880N Z80-CPU	Plastic	2.5 MHz	0° to +70°C
MK3880P Z80-CPU	Ceramic	2.5 MHz	
MK3880J Z80-CPU	Cerdip	2.5 MHz	
MK3880N-4 Z80-CPU	Plastic	4.0 MHz	
MK3880P-4 Z80-CPU	Ceramic	4.0 MHz	
MK3880J-4 Z80-CPU	Cerdip	4.0 MHz	
MK3880P-10 Z80-CPU	Ceramic	2.5 MHz	-40°C to +85°C

The INT Mode 0 is the 8080A mode and requires the user to place an instruction on the data bus for the CPU to execute. If a RST instruction is used, the CPU stacks the Program Counter and begins execution at the Restart Address. If a CALL instruction is used, the CALL Op Code is placed on the data bus during the INTA cycle (M1). M2 and M3 are normal Memory Read cycles not INTA cycles) of the CALL address (low byte first). Program Counter is stacked in M4 and M5.

Mode 2 is used by the Z80 System Peripherals and operates as follows: During the INTA cycle (M1) a Vector is sent in from the highest priority interrupting device. M2 and M3 are used to Stack the Program Counter. The Vector (low byte) and an internal Interrupt Register (I) from a pointer to a table containing the addresses of Interrupt Service Routines. During M4 and M5 the Service Routines address is read from this table into the CPU. The next M1 cycle will fetch an OP Code from the address received is M4 and M5.

Z80-CPU SPECIFICATIONS

Absolute maximum ratings are given below. Ac and dc electrical characteristics and ordering information may be found in Tables 4-2 through 4-4. For Z80 CPU ac timing characteristics see Fig. 4-12.

Temperature Under Bias ....Specified Operating Range
Storage Temperature ....$-65°$ to $+150°$ C
Voltage on Any Pin with Respect to Ground ....$-0.3V$ to $+7$ V
Power Dissipation 1.5W

Chapter 5

Z80-Parallel Input/Output

The Z80 Parallel I/O Circuit is a programmable, two port device which provides a TTL compatible interface between peripheral devices and the Z80-CPU. The CPU can configure the Z80-PIO to interface with a wide range of peripheral devices with no other external logic required. Typical peripheral devices that are fully compatible with the Z80-PIO include most keyboards, paper tape readers and punches, printers, PROM programmers, etc. The Z80-PIO utilizes N-channel silicon gate depletion load technology and is packaged in a 40 pin DIP. Major features of the Z80-PIO include:

- Two independent 8 bit bidirectional peripheral interface ports with 'handshake' data transfer control
- Interrupt driven 'handshake' for fast response
- Any one of four distinct modes of operation may be selected for a port including:
    Byte output
    Byte input
    Byte bidirectional bus (Available on Port A only)
    Bit control mode
    All with interrupt controlled handshake
- Daisy-chain priority interrupt logic included to provide for automatic interrupt vectoring without external logic
- Eight outputs are capable of driving Darlington transistors
- All inputs and outputs fully TTL compatible
- Single 5 volt supply and single phase clock required.

One of the unique features of the Z80-PIO that separates it from other interface controllers is that all data transfer between the peripheral device and the CPU is accomplished under total interrupt control. The interrupt logic of the PIO permits full usage of the efficient interrupt capabilities of the Z80-CPU during I/O transfers. All logic necessary to implement a fully nested interrupt structure is included in the PIO so that additional circuits are not required. Another unique feature of the PIO is that it can be programmed to interrupt required. Another unique feature of the PIO is that it can be programmed to interrupt the CPU on the occurrence of specified status conditions in the peripheral device. For example, the PIO can be programmed to interrupt if any specified peripheral alarm conditions should occur. This interrupt capability reduces the amount of time that the processor must spend in polling peripheral status.

ARCHITECTURE

A block diagram of the Z80-PIO is shown in Fig. 5-1. The internal structure of the Z80-PIO consists of a Z80-CPU bus interface, internal control logic, Port A I/O logic, Port B I/O logic, and interrupt control logic. The CPU bus interface logic allows the PIO to interface directly to the Z80-CPU with no other external logic. However, address decoders and/or line buffers may be required for large systems. The internal control logic synchronizes the CPU data bus to the peripheral device interfaces (Port A and Port B). The two I/O ports (A and B) are virtually identical and are used to interface directly to peripheral devices.

The Port I/O logic is composed of 6 registers with "handshake" control logic as shown in Fig. 5-2. The registers include: an 8 bit data input register, an 8 bit data output register, a 2 bit mode control register, an 8 bit mask register, an 8 bit input/output select register, and a 2 bit mask control register.

The 2-bit mode control register is loaded by the CPU to select the desired operating mode (byte output, byte input, byte bidirectional bus, or bit control mode). All data transfer between the peripheral device and

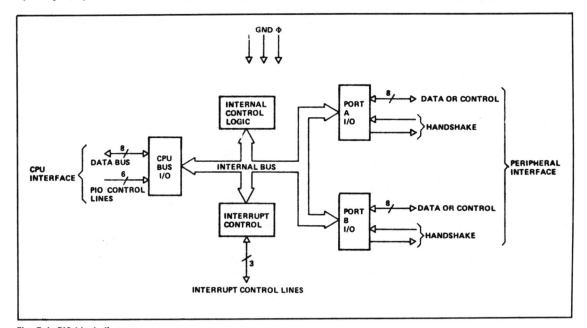

Fig. 5-1. PIO block diagram.

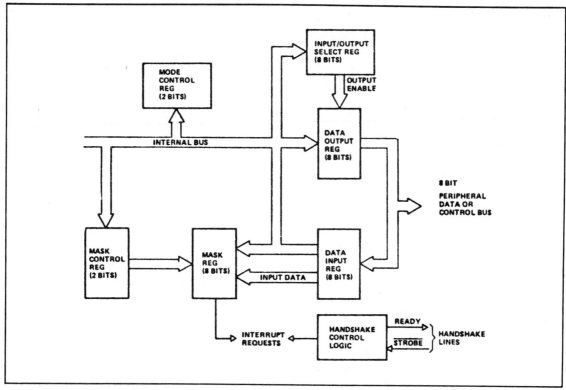

Fig. 5-2. Port I/0 block diagram.

the CPU is achieved through the data input and data output registers. Data may be written into the output register by the CPU or read back to the CPU from the input register at any time. The handshake lines associated with each port are used to control the data transfer between the PIO and the peripheral device.

The 8-bit mask register and the 8-bit input/output select register are used only in the bit control mode. In this mode any of the 8 peripheral data or control bus pins can be programmed to be an input or an output as specified by the select register. The mask register is used in this mode in conjunction with a special interrupt feature. This feature allows an interrupt to be generated when any or all of the unmasked pins reach a specified state (either high or low). The 2-bit mask control register specifies the active state desired (high or low) and if the interrupt should be generated when all unmasked pins are active (AND condition) or when any unmasked pin is active (OR condition). This feature reduces the requirement for CPU status checking of the peripheral by allowing an interrupt to be automatically generated on specific peripheral status conditions. For example, in a system with 3 alarm conditions, an interrupt may be generated if any one occurs or if all three occur.

The interrupt control logic section handles all CPU interrupt protocol for nested priority interrupt structures. The priority of any device is determined by its physical location in a daisy-chain configuration. Two lines are provided in each PIO to form this daisy chain. The device closest to the CPU has the highest priority. Within a PIO, Port A interrupts have higher priority than those of Port B. In the byte input, byte output or bidirectional modes, an interrupt can be generated whenever a new byte transfer is requested by

95

the peripheral. In the bit control mode an interrupt can be generated when the peripheral status matches a programmed value. The PIO provides for complete control of nested interrupts. That is, lower priority devices may not interrupt higher priority devices that have not had their interrupt service routine completed by the CPU. Higher priority devices may interrupt the servicing of lower priority devices.

When an interrupt is accepted by the CPU in mode 2, the interrupting device must provide an 8-bit interrupt vector for the CPU. This vector is used to form a pointer to a location in the computer memory where the address of the interrupt service routine is located. The 8-bit vector from the interrupting device forms the least significant 8 bits of the indirect pointer while the I Register in the CPU provides the most significant 8 bits of the pointer. Each port (A and B) has an independent interrupt vector. The least significant bit of the vector is automatically set to a 0 within the PIO since the pointer must point to two adjacent memory locations for a complete 16-bit address.

The PIO decodes the RETI (Return from interrupt) instruction directly from the CPU data bus so that each PIO in the system knows at all times whether it is being serviced by the CPU interrupt service routine without any other communication with the CPU.

PIN DESCRIPTION

A diagram of the Z80-PIO pin configuration is shown in Fig. 5-3. This section describes the function of each pin.

D_7-D_0. Z80-CPU Data Bus (bidirectional, tristate). This bus is used to transfer all data and commands between the Z80-CPU and the Z80-PIO. D_0 is the least significant bit of the bus.

B/$\overline{A}$ Sel. Port B or A Select (input, active high). This pin defines which port will be accessed during a data transfer between the Z80-CPU and the Z80-PIO. A low level of this pin selects Port A while a high level selects Port B. Often Address bit A_0 from the CPU will be used for this selection function.

C/$\overline{D}$ Sel. Control or Data Select (input, active high). This pin defines the type of data transfer to be performed between the CPU and the PIO. A high level on this pin during a CPU write to the PIO causes the Z80 data bus to be interpreted as a command for the port selected by the B/A Select line. A low level on this pin means that the Z80 data bus is being used to transfer data between the CPU and the PIO. Often Address bit A_1 from the CPU will be used for this function.

$\overline{CE}$. Chip Enable (input, active low). A low level on this pin enables the PIO to accept command or data inputs from the CPU during a write cycle or to transmit data to the CPU during a read cycle. This signal is generally a decode of four I/O port numbers that encompass port A and B, data and control.

Φ. System Clock (input). The Z80-PIO uses the standard Z80 system clock to synchronize certain signals internally. This is a single phase clock.

$\overline{M1}$. Machine Cycle One Signal from CPU (input, active low). This signal from the CPU is used as a sync pulse to control several internal PIO operations. When $\overline{M1}$ is active and the $\overline{RD}$ signal is active, the Z80-CPU is fetching an instruction from memory. Conversely, when $\overline{M1}$ is active and $\overline{IORQ}$ is active, the CPU is acknowledging an interrupt. In addition, the $\overline{M1}$ signal has two other functions within the Z80-PIO.

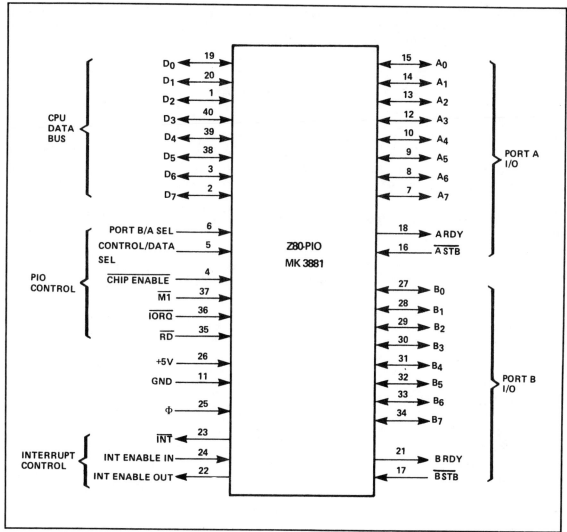

Fig. 5-3. PIO pin configuration.

1. $\overline{M1}$ synchronizes the PIO interrupt logic.
2. When $\overline{M1}$ occurs without an active $\overline{RD}$ or $\overline{IORQ}$ signal the PIO logic enters a reset state.

$\overline{\text{IORQ}}$. Input/Output Request from Z80-CPU (input, active low). The $\overline{IORQ}$ signal is used in conjunction with the B/A Select, C/D Select, $\overline{CE}$, and $\overline{RD}$ signals to transfer commands and data between the Z80-CPU and the Z80-PIO. When $\overline{CE}$, $\overline{RD}$ and $\overline{IORQ}$ are active, the port addressed by B/A will transfer data to the CPU (a read operation). Conversely, when $\overline{CE}$ and $\overline{IORQ}$ are active but $\overline{RD}$ is not active, then the port addressed by B/A will be written into from the CPU with either data or control information as specified by the C/D Select signal. Also, if $\overline{IORQ}$ and $\overline{M1}$ are active simultaneously, the CPU is acknowledging an interrupt and the interrupting port will automatically place its interrupt vector on the CPU data bus if it is the highest device requesting an interrupt.

$\overline{\text{RD}}$. Read Cycle Status from the Z80-CPU (input, active low). If $\overline{\text{RD}}$ is active a MEMORY READ or I/O READ operation is in progress. The $\overline{\text{RD}}$ signal is used with B/A Select, C/D Select, $\overline{\text{CE}}$ and $\overline{\text{IORQ}}$ signals to transfer data from the Z80-PIO to the Z80-CPU.

IEI. Interrupt Enable In (input, active high). This signal is used to form a priority interrupt daisy chain when more than one interrupt driven device is being used. A high level on this pin indicates that no other devices of higher priority are being serviced by a CPU interrupt service routine.

IEO. Interrupt Enable Out (output, active high). The IEO signal is the other signal required to form a daisy chain priority scheme. It is high only if IEI is high and the CPU is not servicing an interrupt from this PIO. Thus this signal blocks lower priority devices from interrupting while a higher priority device is being serviced by its CPU interrupt service routine.

$\overline{\text{INT}}$. Interrupt Request (output, open drain, active low). When INT is active the Z80-PIO is requesting an interrupt from the Z80-CPU.

A_0-A_7. Port A Bus (bidirectional, tri-state). This 8 bit bus is used to transfer data and/or status or control information between Port A of the Z80-PIO and a peripheral device. A_0 is the least significant bit of the Port A data bus.

A STB. Port A Strobe Pulse from Peripheral Device (input, active low). The meaning of this signal depends on the mode of operation selected for Port A as follows:

1. Output mode: The positive edge of this strobe is issued by the peripheral to acknowledge the receipt of the data made available by the PIO.
2. Input mode: The strobe is issued by the peripheral to load data from the peripheral into the Port A input register. Data is loaded into the PIO when the signal is active.
3. Bidirectional mode: When this signal is active, data from the Port A output register is gated onto Port A bidirectional data bus. The positive edge of the strobe acknowledges the receipt of the data.
4. Control mode: The strobe is inhibited internally.

A RDY. Register A Ready (output, active high). The meaning of this signal depends on the mode of operation selected for Port A as follows:

1. Output mode: This signal goes active to indicate that the Port A output register has been loaded and the peripheral data bus is stable and ready for transfer to the peripheral device.
2. Input mode: This signal is active when the Port A input register is empty and is ready to accept data from the peripheral device.
3. Bidirectional mode: This signal is active when data is available in Port A output register for transfer to the peripheral device.   In this mode data is not placed on the Port A data bus unless A STB is active.
4. Control mode: This signal is disabled and forced to a low state.

B_0-B_7. Port B Bus (bidirectional, tristate). This 8 bit bus is used to transfer data and/or status or control information between Port B of the PIO and a peripheral device. The Port B data bus is capable of supplying 1.5ma@1.5V to drive Darlington transistors. B_0 is the least significant bit of the bus.

B STB. Port B Strobe Pulse from Peripheral Device (input, active low). The meaning of this signal is similar to that of $\overline{\text{A STB}}$ with the following exception:

In the Port A bidirectional mode this signal strobes data from the peripheral device into the Port A input register.

B RDY. Register B Ready (output, active high). The meaning of this signal is similar to that of A Ready with the following exception:

In the Port A bidirectional mode this signal is high when the Port A input register is empty and ready to accept data from the peripheral device.

PROGRAMMING

Reset

The Z80-PIO automatically enters a reset state when power is applied. The reset state performs the following functions:

1. Both port mask registers are reset to inhibit all port data bits.
2. Port data bus lines are set to a high impedance state and the Ready "handshake" signals are inactive (low). Mode 1 is automatically selected.
3. The vector address registers are not reset.
4. Both port interrupt enable flip-flops are reset.
5. Both port output registers are reset.

In addition to the automatic power on reset, the PIO can be reset by applying an $\overline{\text{M1}}$ signal (see Fig. 5-4) without the presence of a $\overline{\text{RD}}$ or $\overline{\text{IORQ}}$ signal. If no $\overline{\text{RD}}$ or $\overline{\text{IORQ}}$ is detected during $\overline{\text{M1}}$ the PIO will enter the reset state immediately after the $\overline{\text{M1}}$ signal goes inactive. The purpose of this reset is to allow a single external gate to generate a reset without a power down sequence. This approach was required due to the 40 pin packaging limitation. It is recommended that in breadboard systems and final systems with a "Reset" push button that a $\overline{\text{M1}}$ reset be implemented for the PIO.

A software RESET is possible as described below, however, use of this method during early system debug may not be desirable because of non-functional system hardware (bus buffers or memory for example).

Once the PIO has entered the internal reset state it is held there until the PIO receives a control word from the CPU.

LOADING THE INTERRUPT VECTOR

The PIO has been designed to operate with the Z80-CPU using the mode 2 interrupt response. This mode requires that an interrupt vector be supplied by the interrupting device. This vector is used by the CPU to form the address for the interrupt service routine of that port. This vector is placed on the Z80 data bus during an interrupt acknowledge cycle by the highest priority device requesting service at that time. The

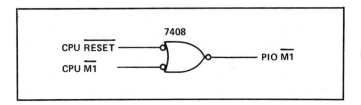

Fig. 5-4. PIO reset circuit.

desired interrupt vector is loaded into the PIO by writing a control word to the desired port of the PIO with the following format:

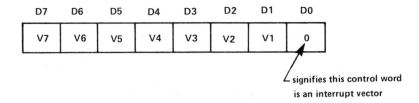

D0 is used in this case as a flag bit which when low causes V7 thru V1 to be loaded into the vector register. At interrupt acknowledge time, the vector of the interrupting port will appear on the Z80 data bus exactly as shown in the format above.

SELECTING AN OPERATING MODE

Port A of the PIO may be operated in any of four distinct modes: Mode 0 (output mode), Mode 1 (input mode), Mode 2 (bidirectional mode), and Mode 3 (control mode). Note that the mode numbers have been selected for mnemonic significance; i.e., 0=Out, 1=In, 2=Bidirectional. Port B can operate in any of these modes except Mode 2.

The mode of operation must be established by writing a control word to the PIO in the following format:

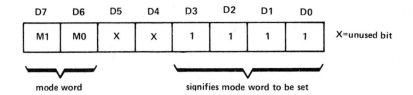

Bits D7 and D6 form the binary code for the desired mode according to the following table:

D7	D6	MODE
0	0	0 (output)
0	1	1 (input)
1	0	2 (bidirectional)
1	1	3 (control)

Bits D5 and D4 are ignored. Bits D3-D0 must be set to 1111 to indicate "Set Mode".

Selecting Mode 0 enables any data written to the port output register by the CPU to be enabled onto the port data bus. The contents of the output register may be changed at any time by the CPU simply by writing a new data word to the port. Also the current contents of the output register may be read back to the Z80-CPU at any time through the execution of an input instruction.

With Mode 0 active, a data write from the CPU causes the Ready handshake line of that port to go high to notify the peripheral that data is available. This signal remains high until a strobe is received from the peripheral. The rising edge of the strobe generates an interrupt (if it has been enabled) and causes the Ready line to go inactive. This very simple handshake is similar to that used in many peripheral devices.

Selecting Mode 1 puts the port into the input mode. To start handshake operation, the CPU merely performs an input read operation from the port. This activates the Ready line to the peripheral to signify that data should be loaded into the empty input register. The peripheral device then strobes data into the port input register using the strobe line. Again, the rising edge of the strobe causes an interrupt request (if it has been enabled) and deactivates the Ready signal. Data may be strobed into the input register regardless of the state of the Ready signal if care is taken to prevent a data overrun condition.

Mode 2 is a bidirectional data transfer mode which uses all four handshake lines. Therefore only Port A may be used for Mode 2 operation. Mode 2 operation uses the Port A handshake signals for output control and the Port B handshake signals for input control. Thus, both A RDY and B RDY may be active simultaneously. The only operational difference between Mode 0 and the output portion of Mode 2 is that data from the Port A output register is allowed on to the port data bus only when $\overline{\text{A STB}}$ is active in order to achieve a bidirectional capability.

Mode 3 operation is intended for status and control applications and does not utilize the handshake signals. When Mode 3 is selected, the next control word sent to the PIO must define which of the port data bus lines are to be inputs and which are outputs. The format of the control word is shown below:

D7	D6	D5	D4	D3	D2	D1	D0
I/O_7	I/O_6	IO/_5	I/O_4	I/O_3	I/O_2	I/O_1	I/O_0

If any bit is set to a one, then the corresponding data bus line will be used as an input. Conversely, if the bit is reset, the line will be used as an output.

During Mode 3 operation the strobe signal is ignored and the Ready line is held low. Data may be written to a port or read from a port by the Z80-CPU at any time during Mode 3 operation. (An exception to this is when Port A is in Mode 2 and Port B is in Mode 3). When reading a port, the data returned to the CPU will be composed of input data from port data bus lines assigned as inputs plus port output register data from those lines assigned as outputs.

SETTING THE INTERRUPT CONTROL WORD

The interrupt control word for each port has the following format:

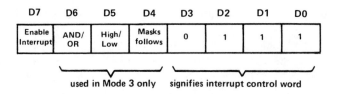

D7	D6	D5	D4	D3	D2	D1	D0
Enable Interrupt	AND/ OR	High/ Low	Masks follows	0	1	1	1

used in Mode 3 only   signifies interrupt control word

If bit D7=1 the interrupt enable flip-flop of the port is set and the port may generate an interrupt. If bit D7=0 the enable flag is reset and interrupts may not be generated. If an interrupt occurs while D7=0, it will be latched internally by the PIO and passed onto the CPU when PIO interrupts are Re-Enabled (D7=1). Bits D6, D5 and D4 are used mainly with Mode 3 operation, however, setting bit D4 of the interrupt control word during any mode of operation will cause a pending interrupt to be reset. These three bits are used to allow for interrupt operation in Mode 3 when any group of the I/O lines go to certain defined states. Bit D6 (AND/OR) defines the logical operation to be performed in port monitoring. If bit D6=1, and AND function is specified and if D6=0, an OR function is specified. For example, if the AND function is specified, all bits must go to a specified state before an interrupt will be generated while the OR function will generate an interrupt if any specified bit goes to the active state.

Bit D5 defines the active polarity of the port data bus line to be monitored. If bit D5=1 the port data lines are monitored for a high state while if D5=0 they will be monitored for a low state.

If bit D4=1 the next control word sent to the PIO must define a mask as follows:

D7	D6	D5	D4	D3	D2	D1	D0
MB_7	MB_6	MB_5	MB_4	MB_3	MB_2	MB_1	MB_0

Only those port lines whose mask bit is zero will be monitored for generating an interrupt.

The interrupt enable flip-flop of a port may be set or reset without modifying the rest of the interrupt control word by using the following command:

Int Enable	X	X	X	0	0	1	1

If an external Asynchronous interrupt could occur while the processor is writing the disable word to the PIO (03H) then a system problem may occur. If interrupts are enabled in the processor it is possible that the Asynchronous interrupt will occur while the processor is writing the disable word to the PIO. The PIO will generate an INT and the CPU will acknowledge it; however, by this time, the PIO will have received the disable word and deactivated its interrupt structure. The result is that the PIO will not send in its interrupt vector during the interrupt acknowledge cycle because it is disabled and the CPU will fetch an erroneous vector resulting in a program fault. The cure for this problem is to disable interrupts within the CPU with the DI instruction just before the PIO is disabled and then re-enable interrupts with the EI instruction. This action causes the CPU to ignore any faulty interrupts produced by the PIO while it is being disabled. The code sequence would be:

```
              :
    LD A,03H
    DI              ; DISABLE CPU.
    OUT (PIO),A     ; DISABLE PIO.
    EI              ; ENABLE CPU.
              .
              .
```

OUTPUT TIMING MODE (MODE 0)

Figure 5-5A illustrates the timing associated with Mode 0 operation. An output cycle is always started by the execution of an output instruction by the CPU. A $\overline{WR}$* pulse is generated by the PIO during a CPU I/O write operation and is used to latch the data from the CPU data bus into addressed port's (A or B) output register. The rising edge of the $\overline{WR}$* pulse then raises the READY line after the next falling edge of Φ to indicate that data is available for the peripheral device. In most systems, the rising edge of the READY signal can be used as a latching signal in the peripheral device. The READY signal will remain active until a positive edge is received from the $\overline{STROBE}$ line indicating that the peripheral has taken the data shown in Fig. 5-5A. If already active, READY will be forced low 1½ Φ cycles after the falling edge of $\overline{IORQ}$ if the port's output register is written into. READY will return high on the first falling edge of Φ after the rising edge of $\overline{IORQ}$ as shown in Fig. 5-5B. This action guarantees that READY is low while port data is changing and that a positive edge is generated on READY whenever an Output instruction is executed.

By connecting READY to $\overline{STROBE}$ a positive pulse with a duration of one clock period can be created as shown in Fig. 5-5C. The positive edge of READY/$\overline{STROBE}$ will not generate an interrupt because the positive portion of $\overline{STROBE}$ is less than the width of $\overline{M1}$ and as such will not generate an interrupt due to the internal logic configuration of the PIO.

If the PIO is not in a reset status (i.e., a control mode has been selected), the output register may be loaded before Mode 0 is selected. This allows port output lines to become active in a user defined state. For example, assume the outputs are desired to become active in a logic one state, the following would be the initialization sequence:

1. PIO RESET
2. Load Interrupt Vector
3. Select Mode 1 (input) (automatic due or RESET)
4. Write FF to Data Port
5. Select Mode 0 (Outputs go to "1's")
6. Enable Interrupt if desired

INPUT TIMING MODE (MODE 1)

Figure 5-6A illustrates the timing of an input cycle. The peripheral initiates this cycle using the $\overline{STROBE}$ line after the CPU has performed a data read. A low level on this line loads data into the port input register and the rising edge of the $\overline{STROBE}$ line activates the interrupt request line $\overline{(INT)}$ if the interrupt enable is set and this is the highest priority requesting device. The next falling edge of the clock line (Φ) will then

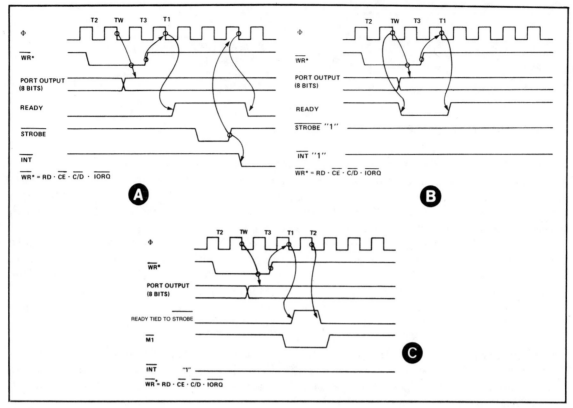

Fig. 5-5. Mode 0 (output) timing.

reset the Ready line to an inactive state signifying that the input register is full and further loading must be inhibited until the CPU reads the data. The CPU will in the course of its interrupt service routine, read the data from the interrupting port. When this occurs, the positive edge from the CPU $\overline{RD}$ signal will raise the READY line with the next low going transition of Φ, indicating that new data can be loaded into the PIO.

Since RESET causes READY to go low a dummy Input instruction may be needed in some systems to cause READY to go high the first time in order to start "handshaking".

If already active, READY will be forced low one and one-half Φ periods following the falling edge of $\overline{IORQ}$ during a read of a PIO port as shown in Fig. 5-6B. If the user strobes data into the PIO only when READY is high, the forced state of READY will prevent input register data from changing while the CPU is reading the PIO. Ready will go high again after the rising edge of the $\overline{IORQ}$ as previously described.

BIDIRECTIONAL TIMING MODE (MODE 2)

This mode is merely a combination of Mode 0 and Mode 1 using all four handshake lines. Since it requires all four lines, it is available only on Port A. When this mode is used on Port A, Port B must be set to the Bit Control Mode. The same interrupt vector will be returned for a Mode 3 interrupt on Port B and an input

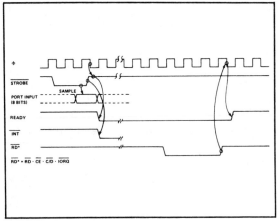

Fig. 5-6a. Mode 1 (input) timing.

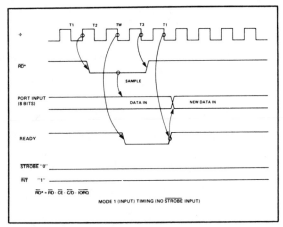

Fig. 5-6b. Mode 1 (input) timing (no strobe input).

transfer interrupt during Mode 2 operation of Port A. Ambiguity is avoided if Port B is operated in a polled mode and the Port B mask register is set to inhibit all bits. Furthermore, interrupts from Port B (Mode 3) will not be generated when Port A is programmed for Mode 2, as $\overline{BSTB}$ would have to be active (low) in order to generate interrupts. ($\overline{BSTB}$ is normally high).

Figure 5-7 illustrates the timing for this mode. It is almost identical to that previously described for Mode 0 and Mode 1 with the Port A handshake lines used for output control and the Port B lines used for input control. The difference between the two modes is that, in Mode 2, data is allowed out onto the bus only when the A $\overline{STROBE}$ is low. The rising edge of this strobe can be used to latch the data into the peripheral since the data will remain stable until after this edge. The input portion of Mode 2 operates identically to

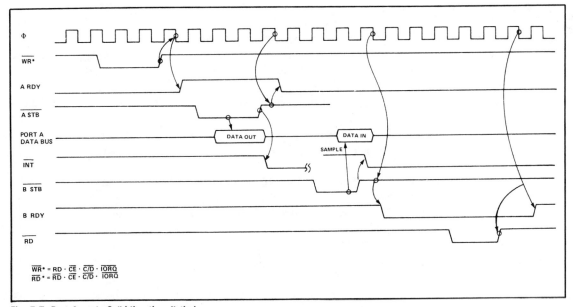

Fig. 5-7. Port A mode 2 (bidirectional) timing.

Mode 1. Note that both Port A and Port B must have their interrupts enabled to achieve an interrupt driven bidirectional transfer.

The peripheral must not gate data onto a port data bus while $\overline{\text{A STB}}$ is active. Bus contention is avoided if the peripheral uses $\overline{\text{B STB}}$ to gate input data onto the bus. The PIO uses the $\overline{\text{B STB}}$ low level to sample this data. The PIO has been designed with a zero hold time requirement for the data when latching in this mode so that this simple gating structure can be used by the peripheral. That is, the data can be disabled from the bus immediately after the strobe rising edge. Note that if $\overline{\text{A STB}}$ is low during a read operation of Port A (in response to a B STB interrupt) the data in the output register will be read by the CPU instead of the correct data in the data input register. The correct data is latched in the input register it just cannot be read by the CPU while $\overline{\text{A STB}}$ is low. If the A STB signal could go low during a CPU Read, it should be blocked from reaching the $\overline{\text{A STB}}$ input of the PIO while B RDY is low (the CPU read will occur while B RDY is low as the $\overline{\text{RD}}$ signal returns B RDY high).

CONTROL TIMING MODE (MODE 3)

The control mode does not utilize the handshake signals and a normal port write or port read can be executed at any time. When writing, the data will be latched into output registers with the same timing as Mode 0. A RDY will be forced low whenever Port A is operated in Mode 3. B RDY will be held low whenever Port B is operated in Mode 3 unless Port A is in Mode 2. In the latter case, the state of B RDY will not be affected.

When reading the PIO, the data returned to the CPU will be composed of output register data from those port data lines assigned as outputs and input register data from those port data lines assigned as inputs. The input register will contain data which was present immediately prior to the falling edge of $\overline{\text{RD}}$ (Fig. 5-8A.).

An interrupt will be generated if interrupts from the port are enabled and the data on the port data lines satisfies the logical equation defined by the 8-bit mask control registers. Another interrupt will not be generated until a change occurs in the status of the logical equation. A Mode 3 interrupt will be generated only if the result of a Mode 3 logical operation changes from false to true. For example, assume that the Mode 3 logical equation is an "OR" function. An unmasked port data line becomes active and an interrupt is requested. If a second unmasked port data line becomes active concurrently with the first, a new interrupt will not be requested since a change in the result of the Mode 3 logical operation has not occurred. Note that port pins defined as outputs can contribute to the logical equation if their positions are unmasked.

If the result of a logical operation becomes true immediately prior to or during $\overline{\text{M1}}$, an interrupt will be requested after the trailing edge of $\overline{\text{M1}}$, provided the logical equation remains true after $\overline{\text{M1}}$ returns high. Figure 5-8B is an example of Mode 3 interrupts. The port has been placed in Mode 3 and OR logic selected and signals are defined to be high. All but bits A0 and A1 are masked out and are not monitored thereby creating a two input positive logic OR gate. In the timing diagram A0 is shown going high and creating an interrupt ($\overline{\text{INT}}$ goes low) and the CPU responds with an Interrupt Acknowledge cycle ($\overline{\text{INTA}}$). The PIO port with its interrupt pending sends in its Vector and the CPU goes off into the Interrupt Service Routine. A0 is shown going inactive either by itself or perhaps as a result of action taken in the Interrupt Service Routine (making the logical equation false). An arrow is shown at the point in time where the Service

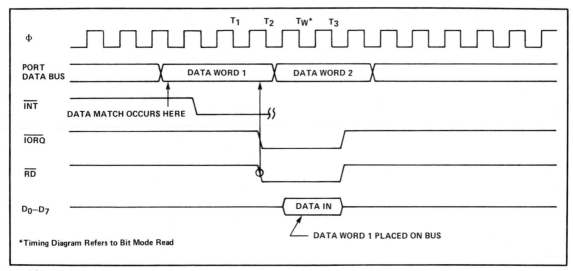

Fig. 5-8a. Mode 3 timing.

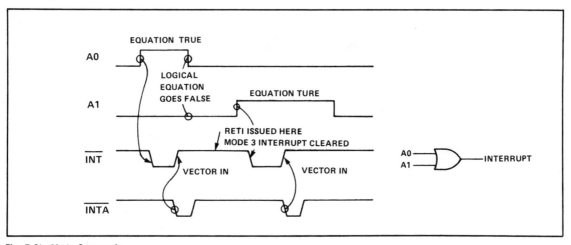

Fig. 5-8b. Mode 3 example.

Routine issues the RETI instruction which clears the PIO interrupt structure. A 1 is next shown going high making the logical equation-true and generating another interrupt. Two important points need to be made from this example:

1. A1 must not go high before A0 goes low or else the logical equation will not go false—a requirement for A1 to be able to generate an interrupt.

2. In order for A1 to generate an interrupt it must be high after the RETI issued by A0's Service Routine clears the PIO's Interrupt structure. In other words, if A1 were a positive pulse that occurred after A0 went low (to make the equation false) and went low before the RETI had cleared the Interrupt Structure it would have been missed. The logic equation must become false after the INTA for A0's service and then must be true or go true after RETI clears the previous interrupt for another interrupt to occur.

INTERRUPT SERVICING

Some time after an interrupt is requested by the PIO, the CPU will send out an interrupt acknowledge ($\overline{M1}$ and $\overline{IORQ}$). During this time the interrupt logic of the PIO will determine the highest priority port which is requesting an interrupt. (This is simply the device with its Interrupt Enable Input high and its Interrupt Enable Output low). To insure that the daisy-chain enable lines stabilize, devices are inhibited from changing their interrupt request status when $\overline{M1}$ is active. The highest priority device places the contents of its interrupt vector register onto the Z80 data bus during interrupt acknowledge.

Figure 5-9 illustrates the timing associated with interrupt requests. During $\overline{M1}$ time, no new interrupt requests can be generated. This gives time for the Int Enable signals to ripple through up to four PIO circuits. The PIO with IEI high and IEO low during $\overline{INTA}$ will place the 8-bit interrupt vector of the appropriate port on the data bus at this time.

If an interrupt requested by the PIO is acknowledged, the requesting port is 'under service'. IEO of this port will remain low until a return from interrupt instruction (RETI) is executed while IEI of the port is high. If an interrupt request is not acknowledged, IEO will be forced high for one $\overline{M1}$ cycle after the PIO decodes the opcode 'ED'. This action guarantees that the two byte RETI instruction is decoded by the proper PIO port (Fig. 5-10).

Figure 5-11 illustrates a typical nested interrupt sequence that could occur with four ports connected in the

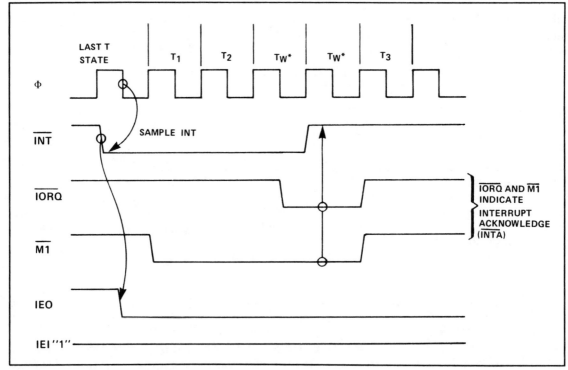

Fig. 5-9. Interrupt acknowledge timing.

108

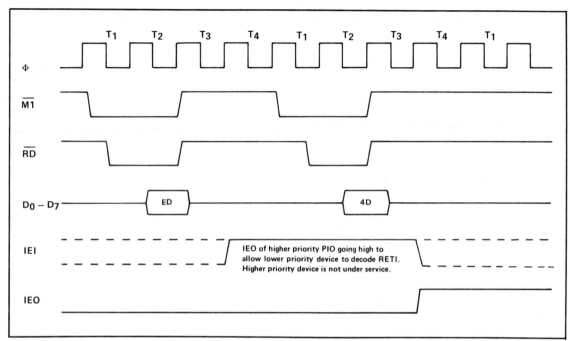

Fig. 5-10. Return from interrupt cycle.

daisy chain. In this sequence Port 2A requests and is granted an interrupt. While this port is being serviced, a higher priority port (1B) requests and is granted an interrupt. The service routine for the higher priority port is completed and a RETI instruction is executed to indicate to the port that its routine is complete. At this time the service routine of the lower priority port is completed.

EXTENDING THE INTERRUPT DAISY CHAIN

Without any external logic, a maximum of four Z80-PIO devices may be daisy-chained into a priority interrupt structure. This limitation is required so that the interrupt enable status (IEO) ripples through the entire chain between the beginning of $\overline{M1}$, and the beginning of $\overline{IORQ}$ during an interrupt acknowledge cycle. Since the interrupt enable status cannot change during $\overline{M1}$, the vector address returned to the CPU is assured to be from the highest priority device which requested an interrupt.

If more than four PIO devices must be accommodated, a "look-ahead" structure may be used as shown in Fig. 5-12. With this technique more than thirty PIO's may be chained together using standard TTL logic.

I/O DEVICE INTERFACE

In this example, the Z80-PIO is connected to an I/O terminal device which communicates over an 8-bit parallel bidirectional data bus as illustrated in Fig. 5-13A. Mode 2 operation (bidirectional) is selected by sending the following control word to Port A:

Next, the proper interrupt vector is loaded (refer to CPU Manual for details on the operation of the interrupt).

V7	V6	V5	V4	V3	V2	V1	0

Interrupts are then enabled by the rising edge of the first $\overline{M1}$ after the interrupt mode word is set unless that $\overline{M1}$ defines an interrupt acknowledge cycle. If a mask follows the interrupt mode word, interrupts are enabled by the rising edge of the first $\overline{M1}$ following the setting of the mask.

Data can now be transferred between the peripheral and the CPU. The timing for this transfer is as described in earlier sections of this chapter.

CONTROL INTERFACE

A typical control mode application is illustrated in Fig. 5-14. Suppose an industrial process is to be monitored. The occurrence of any abnormal operating condition is to be reported to a Z80-CPU based control system. The process control and status word has the following format:

D7	D6	D5	D4	D3	D2	D1	D0
Special Test	Turn On Power	Power Failure Alarm	Halt Process-ing	Temp. Alarm	Temp Heaters On	Pressur-ize System	Pressure Alarm

The PIO may be used as follows. First Port A is set for Mode 3 operation by writing the following control word to Port A.

D7	D6	D5	D4	D3	D2	D1	D0
1	1	X	X	1	1	1	1

Whenever Mode 3 is selected, the next control word sent to the port must be an I/O select word. In this example we wish to select port data lines A5, A3, and A0 as inputs and so the following control word is written:

D7	D6	D5	D4	D3	D2	D1	D0
0	0	1	0	1	0	0	1

Next the desired interrupt vector must be loaded (refer to the CPU manual for details);

D7	D6	D5	D4	D3	D2	D1	D0
V7	V6	V5	V4	V3	V2	V1	V0

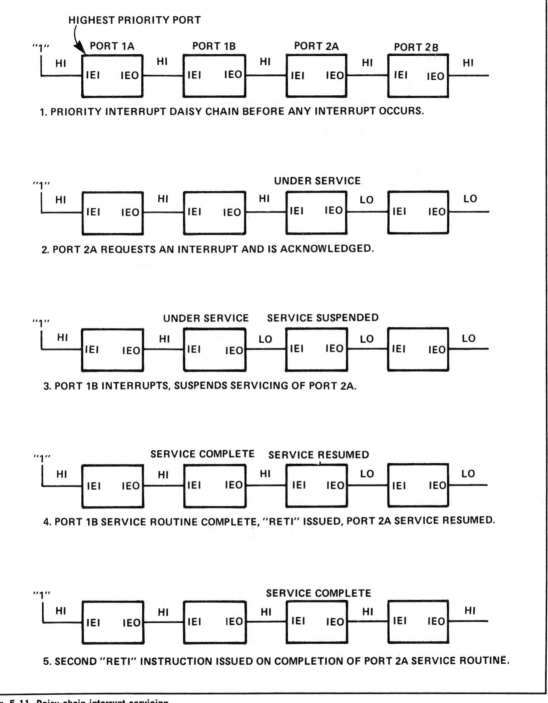

Fig. 5-11. Daisy-chain interrupt servicing.

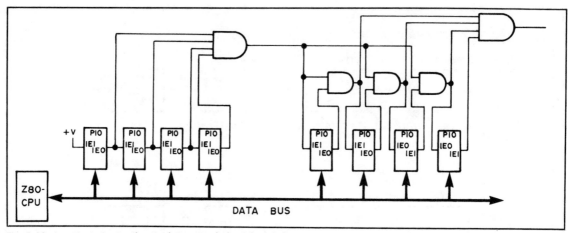

Fig. 5-12. A method of extending the interrupt priority daisy chain.

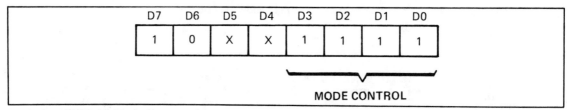

D7	D6	D5	D4	D3	D2	D1	D0
1	0	X	X	1	1	1	1

MODE CONTROL

Fig. 5-13a. Example I/O interface.

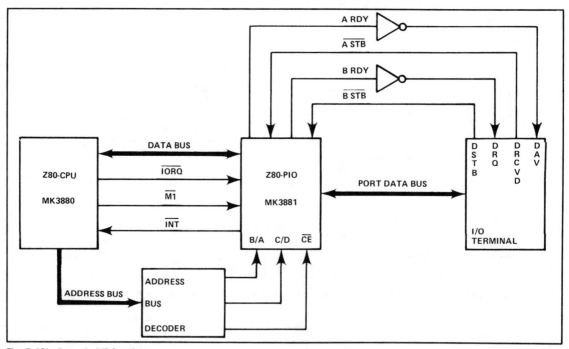

Fig. 5-13b. Example I/O interface.

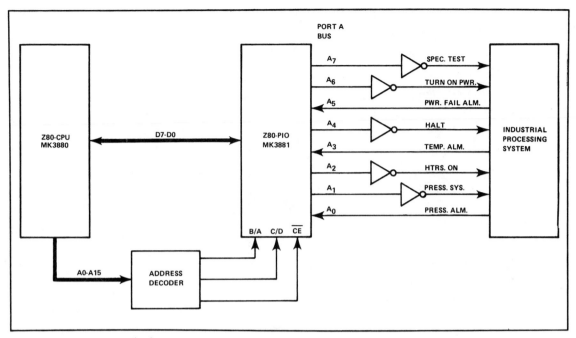

Fig. 5-14. Control mode application.

An interrupt control word is next sent to the port:

D7	D6	D5	D4	D3	D2	D1	D0
1	0	1	1	0	1	1	1

Enable Interrupts — OR Logic — Active High — Mask Follows — Interrupt Control

The mask word following the interrupt mode word is:

D7	D6	D5	D4	D3	D2	D1	D0
1	1	0	1	0	1	1	0

Selects A5, A3 and A0 to be monitored

Now, if a sensor puts a high level on line A5, A3, or A0, an interrupt request will be generated. The mask word may select any combination of inputs or outputs to cause an interrupt. For example, if the mask word above had been:

D7	D6	D5	D4	D3	D2	D1	D0
0	1	0	1	0	1	1	0

then an interrupt request would also occur if bit A7 (special Test) of the output register was set.

113

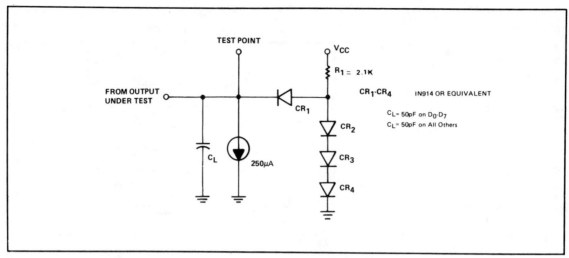

Fig. 5-15. Output load circuit.

Assume that the following port assignments are to be used:

$$E0_H = \text{Port A Data}$$
$$E1_H = \text{Port B Data}$$
$$E2_H = \text{Port A Control}$$
$$E3_H = \text{Port B Control}$$

Table 5-1. Dc Characteristics.

Symbol	Parameter	Min	Max	Unit	Test Condition
V_{ILC}	Clock Input Low Voltage	-0.3	0.80	V	
V_{IHC}	Clock Input High Voltage	V_{CC}-.6	V_{CC}+.3	V	
V_{IL}	Input Low Voltage	-0.3	0.8	V	
V_{IH}	Input High Voltage	2.0	V_{CC}	V	
V_{OL}	Output Low Voltage		0.4	V	I_{OL} = 2.0mA
V_{OH}	Output High Voltage	2.4		V	I_{OH} = -250μA
I_{CC}	Power Supply Current		70*	mA	
I_{LI}	Input Leakage Current		±10	μA	V_{IN} = 0 to V_{CC}
I_{LOH}	Tri-State Output Leakage Current in Float		10	μA	V_{OUT}=2.4 to V_{CC}
I_{LOL}	Tri-State Output Leakage Current in Float		-10	μA	V_{OUT} = 0.4 V
I_{LD}	Data Bus Leakage Current in Input Mode		±10	μA	0$\leqslant V_{IN} \leqslant V_{CC}$
I_{OHD}	Darlington Drive Current	-1.5		mA	V_{OH}=1.5V Port B Only

* 150mA for -4, -10, and -20 devices.

All port numbers are in hexadecimal notation. This particular assignment of port numbers is convenient since A_0 of the address bus can be used as the Port B/A Select and A_1 of the address bus can be used as the Control/Data Select. The Chip Enable would be the decode of CPU address bits A_7 through A_2 (111000). Note that if only a few peripheral devices are being used, a Chip Enable decode may not be required since a higher order address bit could be used directly.

Figures 5-15 and 5-16 show the load circuit and timing characteristics of the CPU. For ordering information on MOSTEK chips see Fig. 5-17.

PROGRAMMING SUMMARY

Load Interrupt Vector

V7	V6	V5	V4	V3	V2	V1	0

Set Mode

M1	M0	X	X	1	1	1	1

Mode Number	M_1	M_0	Mode
0	0	0	Output
1	0	1	Input
2	1	0	Bidirectional
3	1	1	Bit Control

Table 5-2. Capacitance.

$T_A = 25°C$, $f = 1$ MHz

Symbol	Parameter	Max	Unit	Test Condition
C_ϕ	Clock Capacitance	10	pF	Unmeasured Pins
C_{IN}	Input Capacitance	5	pF	Returned to Ground
C_{OUT}	Output Capacitance	10	pF	

*Comment

Stresses above those listed under "Absolute Maximum Rating" may cause permanent damage to the device. This is a stress rating only and functional operation of the device at these or any other condition above those indicated in the operational sections of this specification is not implied. Exposure to absolute maximum rating conditions for extended periods may affect device reliability.

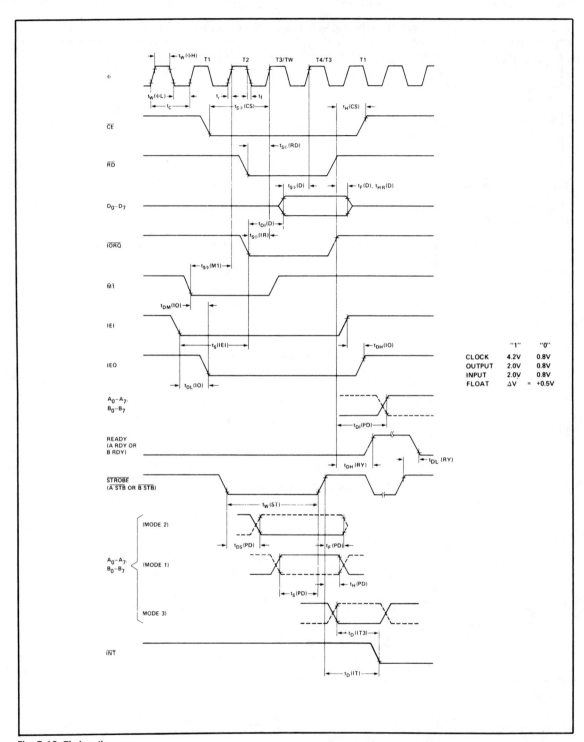

Fig. 5-16. Timing diagram.

Fig. 5-17. Ordering information for Mostek chips.

PART NO.	DESIGNATOR	PACKAGE TYPE	MAX CLOCK FREQUENCY	TEMPERATURE RANGE
MK3881N	Z80-PIO	Plastic	2.5 MHz	
MK3881P	Z80-PIO	Ceramic	2.5 MHz	
MK3881J	Z80-PIO	Cerdip	2.5 MHz	
MK3881N-4	Z80A-PIO	Plastic	4.0 MHz	0° to 70°C
MK3881P-4	Z80A-PIO	Ceramic	4.0 MHz	
MK3881J-4	Z80A-PIO	Cerdip	4.0 MHz	
MK3881P-10	Z80-PIO	Ceramic	4.0 MHz	-40° to +85°C

When selecting Mode 3, the next word to the PIO must set the I/O Register:

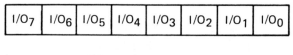

I/O = 1 Sets bit to Input
I/O = 0 bits to Output

Set Interrupt Control

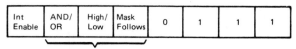

Used in I Mode 3 Only

If the "mask follows" bit is high, the next control word written to the PIO must be the mask:

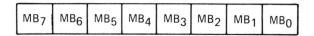

MB = 0, Monitor bit
MB = 1, Mask bit from being monitored

Also, the interrupt enable flip-flop of a port may be set or reset without modifying the rest of the interrupt control word by using the following command:

Int Enable	X	X	X	0	0	1	1

117

Table 5-3. Ac Characteristics MK3881, MK3881, MK3881-10, MK3881-20, Z80-PIO.

$T_A = 0°C$ to $70°C$, $V_{CC} = +5V \pm 5\%$, unless otherwise noted

SIGNAL	SYMBOL	PARAMETER	MIN	MAX	UNIT	COMMENTS
Φ	t_c	Clock Period	400	[1]	nsec	
	$t_W (ΦH)$	Clock Pulse Width, Clock High	170	2000	nsec	
	$t_W (ΦL)$	Clock Pulse Width, Clock Low	170	2000	nsec	
	t_r, t_f	Clock Rise and Fall Times		30	nsec	
	t_h	Any Hold Time for Specified Set-Up Time	0		nsec	
C/D SEL $\overline{CE}$ ETC.	$t_S Φ(CS)$	Control Signal Set-up Time to Rising Edge of Φ During Read or Write Cycle	280		nsec	
$D_0 \cdot D_7$	$t_{DR(D)}$	Data Output Delay from Falling Edge of RD		430	nsec	[2]
	$t_S Φ(D)$	Data Set-Up Time to Rising Edge of Φ During Write or $\overline{M1}$ Cycle	50		nsec	$C_L = 50pF$
	$t_{DI(D)}$	Data Output Delay from Falling Edge of IORQ During $\overline{INTA}$ Cycle		340	nsec	[3]
	$t_{F(D)}$	Delay to Floating Bus (Output Buffer Disable Time)		160	nsec	
IEI	$t_S (IEI)$	IEI Set-Up Time to Falling Edge of $\overline{IORQ}$ During $\overline{INTA}$ Cycle	140		nsec	
IEO	$t_{DH (IO)}$	IEO Delay Time from Rising Edge of IEI		210	nsec	[5]
	$t_{DL (IO)}$	IEO Delay Time from Falling Edge of IEI		190	nsec	[5] $C_L = 50pF$
	$t_{DM (IO)}$	IEO Delay from Falling Edge of M1 (Interrupt Occurring Just Prior to M1) See Note A.		300	nsec	[5]
$\overline{IORQ}$	$t_S Φ(IR)$	$\overline{IORQ}$ Set-Up Time to Rising Edge of Φ During Read or Write Cycle	250		nsec	
$\overline{M1}$	$t_S Φ (M1)$	$\overline{M1}$ Set-Up Time to Rising Edge of Φ During $\overline{INTA}$ or M1 Cycle. See Note B.	210		nsec	
$\overline{RD}$	$t_S Φ (RD)$	$\overline{RD}$ Set-Up Time to Rising Edge of Φ During Read or $\overline{M1}$ Cycle	240		nsec	
$A_0 \cdot A_7$ $B_0 \cdot B_7$	$t_S (PD)$	Port Data Set-Up Time to Rising Edge of $\overline{STROBE}$ (Mode 1)	260		nsec	
	$t_{DS (PD)}$	Port Data Output Delay from Falling Edge of $\overline{STROBE}$ (Mode 2)		230	nsec	[5]
	$t_F (PD)$	Delay to Floating Port Data Bus from Rising Edge of $\overline{STROBE}$ (Mode 2)		200	nsec	$C_L = 50pF$
	$t_{DI (PD)}$	Port Data Stable from Rising Edge of $\overline{IORQ}$ During $\overline{WR}$ Cycle (Mode 0)		200	nsec	[5]
$\overline{ASTB}$ $\overline{BSTB}$	$t_W (ST)$	Pulse Width, $\overline{STROBE}$	150 [4]		nsec nsec	
$\overline{INT}$	$t_D (IT)$	$\overline{INT}$ Delay Time from Rising Edge of $\overline{STROBE}$		490	nsec	
	$t_D (IT3)$	$\overline{INT}$ Delay Time from Data Match During Mode 3 Operation		420	nsec	
ARDY BRDY	$t_{DH (RY)}$	Ready Response Time from Rising Edge of $\overline{IORQ}$		$t_c + 460$	nsec	[5] $C_L = 50pF$
	$t_{DL (RY)}$	Ready Response Time from Rising Edge of $\overline{STROBE}$		$t_c + 400$	nsec	[5]

A. $2.5 t_c > (N-2) t_{DL(IO)} + t_{DM (IO)} + t_{S(IEI)} +$ TTL Buffer Delay, if any

B. $\overline{M1}$ must be active for a minimum of 2 clock periods to reset the PIO.

[1] $t_c = t_W (ΦH) + t_W (ΦL) + t_r + t_f$
[2] Increase $t_{DR(D)}$ by 10 nsec for each 50pF increase in loading up to 200pF max.
[3] Increase $t_{DI (D)}$ by 10 nsec for each 50pF increase in loading up to 200pF max.
[4] For Mode 2: $t_W (ST) > t_S(PD)$
[5] Increase these values by 2 nsec for each 10pF increase in loading up to 100pF max.

Table 5-4. Ac Characteristics MK3881-4, Z80A-PIO.

T_A=0°C to 70°C, V_{CC} = +5V ± 5%, unless otherwise noted

SIGNAL	SYMBOL	PARAMETER	MIN	MAX	UNIT	COMMENTS
Φ	t_c	Clock Period	250	[1]	nsec	
	$t_W (\Phi H)$	Clock Pulse Width, Clock High	105	2000	nsec	
	$t_W (\Phi L)$	Clock Pulse Width, Clock Low	105	2000	nsec	
	t_r, t_f	Clock Rise and Fall Times		30	nsec	
	t_h	Any Hold Time for Specified Set-Up Time	0		nsec	
C/D SEL CE ETC.	$t_S \Phi(CS)$	Control Signal Set-Up Time to Rising Edge of Φ During Read or Write Cycle	145		nsec	
D_0-D_7	$t_{DR(D)}$	Data Output Delay From Falling Edge of $\overline{RD}$		380	nsec	[2]
	$t_S \Phi(D)$	Data Set-Up Time to Rising Edge of Φ During Write or $\overline{M1}$ Cycle	50		nsec	C_L = 50pF
	$t_{DI (D)}$	Data Output Delay from Falling edge of $\overline{IORQ}$ During $\overline{INTA}$ Cycle		250	nsec	[3]
	$t_F (D)$	Delay to Floating Bus (Output Buffer Disable Time)		110	nsec	
IEI	$t_S (IEI)$	IEI Set-Up Time to Falling edge of $\overline{IORQ}$ during $\overline{INTA}$ Cycle	140		nsec·	
IEO	$t_{DH (IO)}$	IEO Delay Time from Rising Edge of IEI		160	nsec	[5]
	$t_{DL (IO)}$	IEO Delay Time from Falling Edge of IEI		130	nsec	[5] C_L = 50pF
	$t_{DM (IO)}$	IEO Delay from Falling Edge of $\overline{M1}$ (Interrupt Occurring Just Prior to $\overline{M1}$) See Note A.		190	nsec	[5]
$\overline{IORQ}$	$t_S \Phi(IR)$	$\overline{IORQ}$ Set-Up Time to Rising Edge of Φ During Read or Write Cycle	115		nsec	
$\overline{M1}$	$t_S \Phi(M1)$	$\overline{M1}$ Set-Up Time to Rising Edge of Φ During $\overline{INTA}$ or $\overline{M1}$ Cycle. See Note B.	90		nsec	
$\overline{RD}$	$t_S \Phi(RD)$	$\overline{RD}$ Set-Up Time to Rising Edge of Φ During Read or $\overline{M1}$ Cycle	115		nsec	
A_0-A_7, B_0-B_7	$t_S (PD)$	Port Data Set-Up Time to Rising Edge of $\overline{STROBE}$ (MODE 1)	230		nsec	
	$t_{DS (PD)}$	Port Data Output Delay from Falling Edge of STROBE (Mode 2)		210	nsec	[5]
	$t_F (PD)$	Delay to Floating Port Data Bus from Rising Edge of STROBE (Mode 2)		180	nsec	C_L = 50pF
	$t_{DI (PD)}$	Port Data Stable from Rising Edge of $\overline{IORQ}$ During $\overline{WR}$ Cycle (Mode 0)		180	nsec	[5]
$\overline{ASTB}$ $\overline{BTSB}$	$t_W (ST)$	Pulse Width, $\overline{STROBE}$	150 [4]		nsec nsec	
$\overline{INT}$	$t_D (IT)$	$\overline{INT}$ Delay Time from Rising Edge of STROBE		440	nsec	
	$t_D (IT3)$	$\overline{INT}$ Delay Time from Data Match During Mode 3 Operation		380	nsec	
ARBY, BRDY	$t_{DH (RY)}$	Ready Response Time from Rising Edge of $\overline{IORQ}$		t_c + 410	nsec	[5] C_L = 50pF
	$t_{DL (RY)}$	Ready Response Time from Rising Edge of $\overline{STROBE}$		t_c+ 360	nsec	[5]

A. $2.5 t_c >$ (N-2)$t_{DL(IO)}$ + $t_{DM (IO)}$ + $t_{S(IEI)}$ + TTL Buffer Delay, if any

B. M1 must be active for a minimum of 2 clock periods to reset the PIO.

[1] $t_c = t_W (\Phi H) + t_W (\Phi L) + t_r + t_f$

[2] Increase $t_{DR(D)}$ by 10 nsec for each 50pF increase in loading up to 200pF max.

[3] Increase $t_{DI (D)}$ by 10 nsec for each 50pF increase in loading up to 200pF max.

[4] For Mode 2: $t_W (ST) > t_S(PD)$

[5] Increase these values by 2 nsec for each 10pF increase in loading up to 100pF max.

PIO SPECIFICATIONS

Absolute maximum ratings are given below. Other specifications are given on Tables 5-1 through 5-4.

Temperature Under Bias	Specified operating range
Storage Temperature	$-65°C$ to $+150°C$
Voltage On Any Pin With	$-0.3V$ to $+7V$
Respect To Ground	
Power Dissipation	.6W

Chapter 6

Z80-Clock Timer Circuit

The Z80-Counter Timer Circuit (CTC) is a programmable component with four independent channels that provide counting and timing functions for microcomputer systems based on the Z80-CPU. The CPU can configure the CTC channels to operate under various modes and conditions as required to interface with a wide range of devices. In most applications, little or no external logic is required. The Z80-CTC utilizes N-channel silicon gate depletion load technology and is packed in a 28-pin DIP. The Z80-CTC requires only a single 5-volt supply and a one-phase 5 volt clock. Major features of the Z80-CTC include:

- All inputs and outputs fully TTL compatible.
- Each channel may be selected to operate in either Counter Mode or Timer Mode.
- Used in either mode, a CPU-readable Down Counter indicates number of counts-to-go until zero.
- A Time Constant Register can automatically reload the Down Counter at Count Zero in Counter and Timer Mode.
- Selectable positive or negative trigger initiates time operation in Timer Mode. The same input is monitored for event counts in Counter Mode.
- Three channels have Zero Count/Timeout outputs capable of driving Darlington transistors.
- Interrupts may be programmed to occur on the zero count condition in any channel.
- Daisy-chain priority interrupt logic included to provide for automatic interrupt vectoring without external logic.

Electrical specifications and ac timing characteristics for the clock are given in Tables 6-1 through 6-4 and Fig 6-1. Figure 6-2 gives ordering specifications for the MOSTEK Chips.

Table 6-1. CTC Specifications.

ABSOLUTE MAXIMUM RATINGS.

Temperature Under Bias..Specified Operating Range
Storage Temperature..−65° to +150° C
Voltage on Any Pin with Respect to Ground...−0.3V to +7 V
Power Dissipation...0.8 V

D.C. CHARACTERISTICS.

TA = 0°C to 70°C, Vcc = 5V ± 5% unless otherwise specified

SYMBOL	PARAMETER	MIN	MAX	UNIT	TEST CONDITION
V_{ILC}	Clock Input Low Voltage	−0.3	0.80	V	
V_{IHC}	Clock Input High Voltage (1)	V_{CC}−.6	V_{CC} +.3	V	
V_{IL}	Input Low Voltage	−0.3	0.8	V	
V_{IH}	Input High Voltage	2.0	V_{CC}	V	
V_{OL}	Output Low Voltage		0.4	V	I_{OL} = 2 mA
V_{OH}	Output High Voltage	2.4		V	I_{OH} = −250 μA
I_{CC}	Power Supply Current		120	mA	T_C = 400 nsec**
I_{LI}	Input Leakage Current		±10	μA	V_{IN} = 0 to V_{CC}
I_{LOH}	Tri-State Output Leakage Current In Float		10	μA	V_{OUT} = 2.4 to V_{CC}
I_{LOL}	Tri-State Output Leakage Current In Float		−10	μA	V_{OUT} = 0.4V
I_{OHD}	Darlington Drive Current	−1.5		mA	V_{OH} = 1.5V

**T_C = 250 nsec for MK 3882-4

ARCHITECTURE

A block diagram of the Z80-CTC is shown in Fig. 6-3. The internal structure of the Z80-CTC consists of a Z80-CPU bus interface, Internal Control Logic, four sets of Counter/Timer Channel Logic, and Interrupt Control Logic. The four independent counter/timer channels are identified by sequential numbers from 0 to 3. The CTC has the capability of generating a unique interrupt vector for each separate channel (for automatic vectoring to an interrupt service routine). The 4 channels can be connected into four contiguous slots in the standard Z80 priority chain with channel number 0 having the highest priority. The CPU bus interface logic allows the CTC device to interface directly to the CPU with no other external logic. However, port address decoders and/or line buffers may be required for large systems.

Table 6-2. Capacitance.

TA = 25°C, f = 1 MHz

SYMBOL	PARAMETER	MAX	UNIT	TEST CONDITION
C_ϕ	Clock Capacitance	20	pF	Unmeasured Pins
C_{IN}	Input Capacitance	5	pF	Returned to Ground
C_{OUT}	Output Capacitance	10	pF	

*COMMENT
Stresses above those listed under "Absolute Maximum Rating" may cause permanent damage to the device. This is a stress rating only and functional operation of the device at these or any other condition above those indicated in the operational sections of this specification is not implied. Exposure to absolute maximum rating conditions for extended periods may affect device reliability.

Table 6-3. Ac Characteristics MK3882, MK3882-10, Z80-CTC.

TA = 0° C to 70° C, Vcc = +5 V ± 5%, unless otherwise noted

Signal	Symbol	Parameter	Min	Max	Unit	Comments
Φ	t_C	Clock Period	400	(1)	ns	
	$t_W(\Phi H)$	Clock Pulse Width, Clock High	170	2000	ns	
	$t_W(\Phi L)$	Clock Pulse Width, Clock Low	170	2000	ns	
	t_r, t_f	Clock Rise and Fall Times		30	ns	
	t_H	Any Hold Time for Specified Setup Time	0		ns	
CS, CE, etc.	$t_S\Phi(CS)$	Control Signal Setup Time to Rising Edge of Φ During Read or Write Cycle	160		ns	
D$_0$-D$_7$	$t_{DR}(D)$	Data Output Delay from Rising Edge of RD During Read Cycle		480	ns	(2)
	$t_S\Phi(D)$	Data Setup Time to Rising Edge of Φ During Write or M1 Cycle	60		ns	
	$t_{DI}(D)$	Data Output Delay from Falling Edge of IORQ During INTA Cycle		340	ns	(2)
	$t_F(D)$	Delay to Floating Bus (Output Buffer Disable Time)		230	ns	
IEI	$t_S(IEI)$	IEI Setup Time to Falling Edge of $\overline{IORQ}$ During INTA Cycle	200		ns	
IEO	$t_{DH}(IO)$	IEO Delay Time from Rising Edge of IEI		220	ns	(3)
	$t_{DL}(IO)$	IEO Delay Time from Falling Edge of IEI		190	ns	(3)
	$t_{DM}(IO)$	IEO Delay from Falling Edge of $\overline{M1}$ (Interrupt Occurring just Prior to $\overline{M1}$)		300	ns	(3)
$\overline{IORQ}$	$t_S\Phi(IR)$	IORQ Setup Time to Rising Edge of Φ During Read or Write Cycle	250		ns	
$\overline{M1}$	$t_S\Phi(M1)$	M1 Setup Time to Rising Edge of Φ During INTA or M1 Cycle	210		ns	
$\overline{RD}$	$t_S\Phi(RD)$	RD Setup Time to Rising Edge of Φ During Read or M1 Cycle	240		ns	
$\overline{INT}$	$t_{DCK}(IT)$	INT Delay Time from Rising Edge of CLK/TRG		$2t_C(\Phi) + 200$		Counter Mode
	$t_D\Phi(IT)$	INT Delay Time from Rising Edge of Φ		$t_C(\Phi) + 200$		Timer Mode
CLK/TRG$_{0-3}$	$t_C(CK)$	Clock Period	$2t_C(\Phi)$			Counter Mode
	t_r, t_f	Clock and Trigger Rise and Fall Times		50	ns	
	$t_S(CK)$	Clock Setup Time to Rising Edge of Φ for Immediate Count	210		ns	Counter Mode
	$t_S(TR)$	Trigger Setup Time to Rising Edge of Φ for Enabling of Prescaler on Following Rising Edge of Φ	210		ns	Timer Mode
	$t_W(CTH)$	Clock and Trigger High Pulse Width	200		ns	Counter and Timer Modes
	$t_W(CTL)$	Clock and Trigger Low Pulse Width	200		ns	Counter and Timer Modes
ZC/TO$_{0-2}$	$t_{DH}(ZC)$	ZC/TO Delay Time from Rising Edge of Φ, ZC/TO High		190	ns	Counter and Timer Modes
	$t_{DL}(ZC)$	ZC/TO Delay Time from Falling Edge of Φ, ZC/TO Low		190	ns	Counter and Timer Modes

NOTES:
(1) $t_C = t_W(\Phi H) + t_W(\Phi L) + t_r + t_f$.
(2) Increase delay by 10 nsec for each 50 pF increase in loading 200pF maximum for data lines and 100pF for control lines.
(3) Increase delay by 2nsec for each 10pF increase in loading, 100pF maximum.
(4) RESET must be active for a minimum of 3 clock cycles.

OUTPUT LOAD CIRCUIT

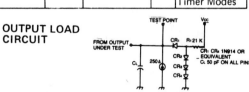

Table 6-4. Ac Characteristics MK3882-4, Z80A-CTC.

TA = 0° C to 70° C, Vcc = +5 V ± 5%, unless otherwise noted

Signal	Symbol	Parameter	Min	Max	Unit	Comments
Φ	t_C	Clock Period	250	(1)	ns	
	$t_W(\Phi H)$	Clock Pulse Width, Clock High	105	2000	ns	
	$t_W(\Phi L)$	Clock Pulse Width, Clock Low	105	2000	ns	
	t_r, t_f	Clock Rise and Fall Times		30	ns	
	t_H	Any Hold Time for Specified Setup Time	0		ns	
CS, CE, etc	$t_S\Phi(CS)$	Control Signal Setup Time to Rising Edge of Φ During Read or Write Cycle	145		ns	
D0-D7	$t_{DR}(D)$	Data Output Delay from Falling Edge of $\overline{RD}$ During Read Cycle		380	ns	(2)
	$t_S\Phi(D)$	Data Setup Time to Rising Edge of Φ During Write or M1 Cycle	50		ns	
	$t_{DI}(D)$	Data Output Delay form Falling Edge of IORQ During INTA Cycle		160	ns	(2)
	$t_F(D)$	Delay to Floating Bus (Output Buffer Disable Time)		110	ns	
IEI	$t_S(IEI)$	IEI Setup Time to Falling Edge of $\overline{IORQ}$ During INTA Cycle	140		ns	
IEO	$t_{DH}(IO)$	IEO Delay Time from Rising Edge of IEI		160	ns	(3)
	$t_{DL}(10)$	IEO Delay Time from Falling Edge of IEI		130	ns	(3)
	$t_{DM}(10)$	IEO Delay from Falling Edge of $\overline{M1}$ (Interrupt Occurring just Prior to $\overline{M1}$)		190	ns	(3)
$\overline{IORQ}$	$t_S\Phi(IR)$	IORQ Setup Time to Rising Edge of Φ During Read or Write Cycle	115		ns	
$\overline{M1}$	$t_S\Phi(M1)$	M1 Setup Time to Rising Edge of Φ During INTA or M1 Cycle	90		ns	
$\overline{RD}$	$t_S\Phi(RD)$	RD Setup Time to Rising Edge of Φ During Read or M1 Cycle	115		ns	
$\overline{INT}$	$t_{DCK}(IT)$	INT Delay Time from Rising Edge of CLK/TRG		$2t_C(\Phi) + 140$		Counter Mode
	$t_D\Phi(IT)$	$\overline{INT}$ Delay Time from Rising Edge of Φ		$t_C(\Phi) + 140$		Timer Mode
CLK/TRG0-3	$t_C(CK)$	Clock Period	$2t_C(\Phi)$		ns	Counter Mode
	t_r, t_f	Clock and Trigger Rise and Fall Times		30		
	$t_S(CK)$	Clock Setup Time to Rising Edge of Φ for Immediate Count	130		ns	Counter Mode
	$t_S(TR)$	Trigger Setup Time to Rising Edge of Φ for enabling of Prescaler on Following Rising Edge of Φ	130		ns	Timer Mode
	$t_W(CTH)$	Clock and Trigger High Pulse Width	120		ns	Counter and Timer Modes
	$t_W(CTL)$	Clock and Trigger Low Pulse Width	120		ns	Counter and Timer Modes
ZC/TO0-2	$t_{DH}(ZC)$	ZC/TO Delay Time from Rising Edge of Φ, ZC/TO High		120	ns	Counter and Timer Modes
ZC/TO0-2	$t_{DL}(ZC)$	ZC/TO Delay Time from Falling Edge of Φ, ZC/TO Low		120	ns	Counter and Timer Modes

NOTES:
(1.) $t_C = t_W(\Phi H) + t_W(\Phi L) + t_r + t_f$.
(2.) Increase delay by 10 nsec for each 50 pF increase in loading, 200pF maximum for data lines and 100pF for control lines.
(3.) Increase delay by 2nsec for each 10pF increase in loading, 100pF maximum.
(4.) $\overline{RESET}$ must be active for a minimum of 3 clock cycles.

OUTPUT LOAD CIRCUIT

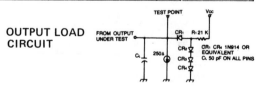

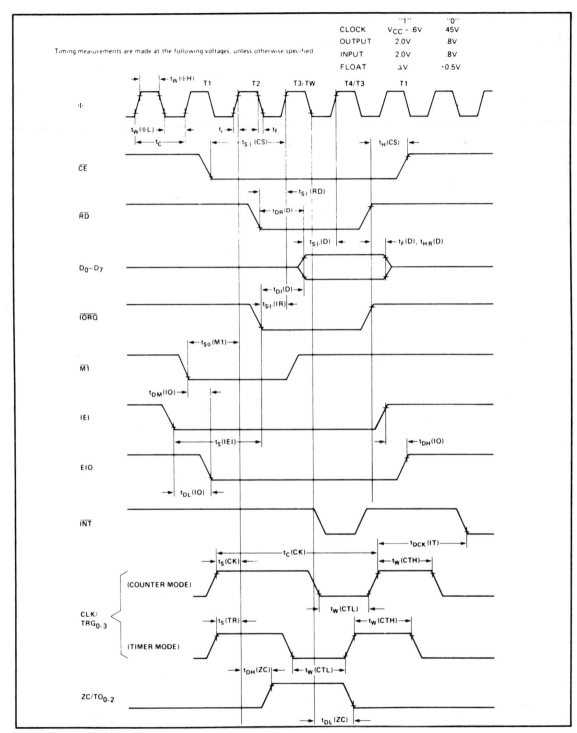

Fig. 6-1. Ac timing diagram.

PART NO.	DESIGNATOR	PACKAGE TYPE	MAX. CLOCK FREQUENCY	TEMPERATURE RANGE
MK3882N	Z80-PIO	Plastic	2.5 MHz	0° to 70°C
MK3882P	Z80-PIO	Ceramic	2.5 MHz	
MK3882-J	Z80-PIO	Cerdip	2.5 MHz	
MK3882N-4	Z80A-PIO	Plastic	4.0 MHz	
MK3882P-4	Z80A-PIO	Ceramic	4.0 MHz	
MK3882J-4	Z80A-PIO	Cerdip	4.0 MHz	
MK3882P-10	Z80-PIO	Ceramic	2.5 MHz	-40° to +85°C

Fig. 6-2. Ordering information for Mostek chips.

STRUCTURE OF CHANNEL LOGIC

The structure of one of the four sets of Counter/Timer Channel Logic is shown in Fig. 6-4. This logic is composed of 2 registers, 2 counters and control logic. The registers are an 8-bit Time Constant Register and an 8-bit Channel Control Register. The counters are an 8-bit CPU-readable Down Counter and an 8-bit Prescaler.

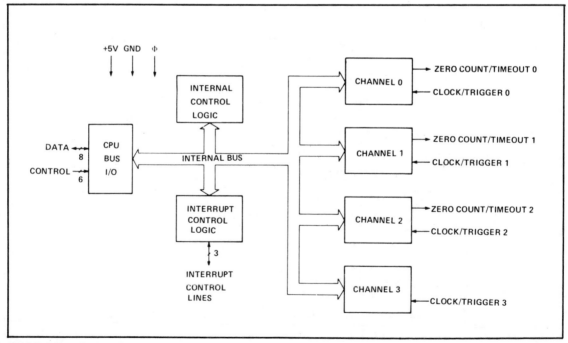

Fig. 6-3. Z80-CTC block diagram.

126

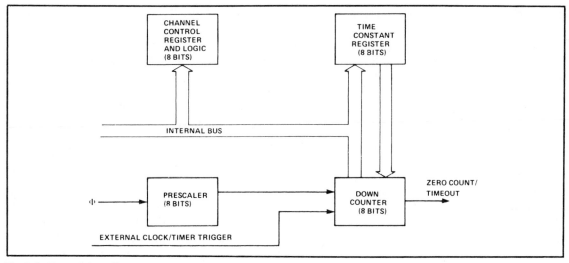

Fig. 6-4. Channel block diagram.

The Channel Control Register and Logic

The Channel Control Register (8-bit) and Logic is written to by the CPU to select the modes and parameters of the channel. Within the entire CTC device there are four such registers, corresponding to the four Counter/Timer Channels. Which of the four is being written to depends on the encoding of two channel select input pins: CS0 and CS1 (usually attached to A0 and A1 of the CPU address bus). This is illustrated in the truth table below:

	CS1	CS0
Ch0	0	0
Ch1	0	1
Ch2	1	0
Ch3	1	1

In the control word written to program each Channel Control Register, bit 0 is always set, and the other 7 bits are programmed to select alternatives on the channel's operating modes and parameters, as shown in the diagram below. (For a more complete discussion see the section "CTC Operating Modes" and "CTC Programming" later in this chapter.)

Channel Control Register

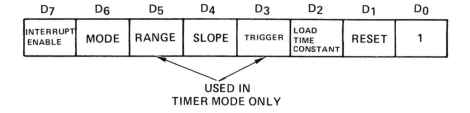

127

The Prescaler

Used in the Timer Mode only, the Prescaler is an 8-bit device which can be programmed by the CPU via the Channel Control Register to divide its input, the System Clock (Φ), by 16 or 256. The output of the Prescaler is then fed as an input to clock the Down Counter, which initially, and every time it clocks down to zero, is reloaded automatically with the contents of the Time Constant Register. In effect this again divides the System Clock by an additional factor of the time constant. Every time the Down Counter counts down to zero, its output, Zero Count/Timeout (ZC/TO), is pulsed high.

The Time Constant Register

The Time Constant Register is an 8-bit register, used in both Counter Mode and Timer Mode, programmed by the CPU just after the Channel Control Word with an integer time constant value of 1 through 256. This register loads the programmed value into the Down Counter when the CTC is first initialized and reloads the same value into the Down Counter automatically whenever it counts down thereafter to zero. If a new time constant is loaded into the Time Constant Register while a channel is counting or timing, the present down count will be completed before the new time constant is loaded into the Down Counter. (For details of how a time constant is written to a CTC channel, see the section "CTC Programming.")

The Down Counter

The Down Counter is an 8-bit register used in both Counter Mode and Timer Mode loaded initially, and later when it counts down to zero, by the Time Constant Register. The Down Counter is decremented by each external clock edge in the Counter Mode, or in the Timer Mode, by the clock output of the Prescaler. At any time, by performing a simple I/O Read at the port address assigned to the selected CTC channel, the CPU can access the contents of this register and obtain the number of counts-to-zero. Any CTC channel may be programmed to generate an interrupt request sequence each time the zero count is reached.

In channels 0, 1, and 2, when the zero count condition is reached, a signal pulse appears at the corresponding ZC/TO pin. Due to package pin limitations, however, channel 3 does not have this pin and so may be used only in applications where this output pulse is not required.

INTERRUPT CONTROL LOGIC

The Interrupt Control Logic insures that the CTC acts in accordance with Z80 system interrupt protocol for nested priority interrupting and return from interrupt. The priority of any system is determined by its physical location in a daisy-chain configuration. Two signal lines (IEI and IEO) are provided in CTC devices to form this system daisy chain. The device closest to the CPU has the highest priority; within the CTC, interrupt priority is predetermined by channel number, with channel 0 having highest priority down to channel 3 which has the lowest priority. The purpose of a CTC-generated interrupt, as with any other peripheral device, is to force the CPU to execute an interrupt service routine. According to Z80 system interrupt protocol, lower priority devices or channels may not interrupt higher priority devices or channels that have already interrupted and have not had their interrupt service routines completed. However, high priority devices or channels may interrupt the servicing of lower priority devices or channels.

A CTC channel may be programmed to request an interrupt every time its Down Counter reaches a count of zero. (To utilize this feature requires that the CPU be programmed for interrupt Mode 2.) Some time after the interrupt request, the CPU will send out an interrupt acknowledge, and the CTC's Interrupt Control Logic will determine the highest-priority channel which is requesting an interrupt within the CTC device. Then if the CTC's IEI input is active, indicating that it has priority within the system daisy chain, it will place an 8-bit Interrupt Vector on the system data bus. The high-order 5 bits of this vector will have been written to the CTC earlier as part of the CTC initial programming process; the next two bits will be provided by the CTC's Interrupt Control Logic as a binary code corresponding to the highest-priority channel requesting an interrupt; finally the low-order bit of the vector will always be zero according to a convention described below.

Interrupt Vector

D_7	D_6	D_5	D_4	D_3	D_2	D_1	D_0
V_7	V_6	V_5	V_4	V_3	X	X	0

0	0	CHANNEL 0
0	1	CHANNEL 1
1	0	CHANNEL 2
1	1	CHANNEL 3

This interrupt vector is used to form a pointer to a location in memory where the address of the interrupt service routine is stored in a table. The vector represents the least significant 8 bits, while the CPU reads the contents of the I register to provide the most significant 8-bits of the 16-bit pointer. The address in memory pointed to will contain the low-order byte, and the next highest address will contain the high-order byte of an address which in turn contains the first opcode of the interrupt service routine. Thus in mode 2, a single 8-bit vector stored in an interrupting CTC can result in an indirect call to any memory location.

Z80 16-Bit Pointer (Interrupt Starting Address)

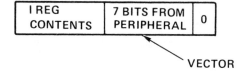

| I REG CONTENTS | 7 BITS FROM PERIPHERAL | 0 |

VECTOR

There is a Z80 system convention that all addresses in the interrupt service routine table should have their low-order byte in an even location in memory, and their high-order byte in the next highest location in memory, which will always be odd so that the least significant bit of any interrupt vector will always be even. Hence the least significant bit of any interrupt vector will always be zero.

The RETI instruction is used at the end of any interrupt service routine to initialize the daisy chain enable line IEO for proper control of nested priority interrupt handing. The CTC monitors the system data bus and decodes this instruction when it occurs. Thus the CTC channel control logic will know when the CPU has completed servicing an interrupt, without any further communication with the CPU being necessary.

PIN DESCRIPTION

A diagram of the Z80-CTC pin configuration is shown in Fig. 6-5. This section describes the function of each pin. The channel Counter and Timer Modes and a channel block diagram may be seen in Figs. 6-6 through 6-8.

D7-D0. Z80-CPU Data Bus (bi-directional, tri-state). This bus is used to transfer all data and command words between the Z80-CPU and the Z80-CTC. There are 8-bits on this bus, of which D0 is the least significant.

CS1 - CS0. Channel Select (input, active high). These pins form a 2-bit binary address code for selecting one of the four independent CTC channels for an I/O Write or Read (See truth table below.)

	CS1	CS0
Ch0	0	0
Ch1	0	1
Ch2	1	0
Ch3	1	1

$\overline{\text{CE}}$. Chip Enable (input, active low). A low level on this pin enables the CTC to accept control words. Interrupt Vectors, or time constant data words from the Z80 Data Bus during an I/O Write cycle, or to transmit the contents of the Down Counter to the CPU during an I/O Read cycle. In most applications this signal is decoded from the 8 least significant bits of the address bus for any of the four I/O port addresses that are mapped to the four Counter/Timer Channels.

Clock (Φ). System Clock (input). This single-phase clock is used by the CTC to synchronize certain signals internally.

$\overline{\text{M1}}$. Machine Cycle One Signal from CPU (input, active low). When $\overline{\text{M1}}$ is active and the $\overline{\text{RD}}$ signal is active, the CPU is fetching an instruction from memory. When $\overline{\text{M1}}$ is active and the $\overline{\text{IORQ}}$ signal is active, the CPU is acknowledging an interrupt, alerting the CTC to place an Interrupt Vector on the Z80 Data Bus if it has daisy chain priority and one of its channels has requested an interrupt.

$\overline{\text{IORQ}}$. Input/Output Request from CPU (input, active low). The $\overline{\text{IORQ}}$ signal is used in conjunction with the $\overline{\text{CE}}$ and $\overline{\text{RD}}$ signals to transfer data and Channel Control Words between the Z80-CPU and the CTC. During a CTC Write Cycle, $\overline{\text{IORQ}}$ and $\overline{\text{CE}}$ must be true and $\overline{\text{RD}}$ false. The CTC does not receive a specific write signal, instead generating its own internally from the inverse of a valid $\overline{\text{RD}}$ signal. In a CTC Read Cycle, $\overline{\text{IORQ}}$, $\overline{\text{CE}}$ and $\overline{\text{RD}}$ must be active to place the contents of the Down Counter on the Z80 Data Bus. If

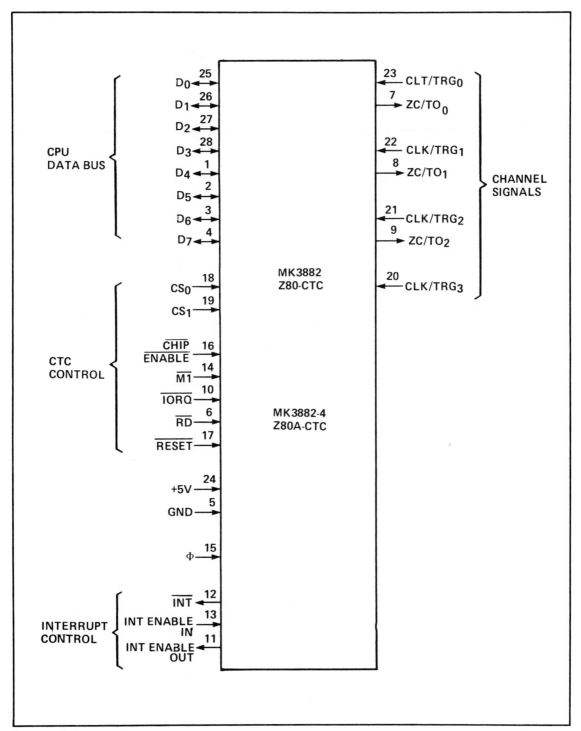

Fig. 6-5. Z80-CTC pin configuration.

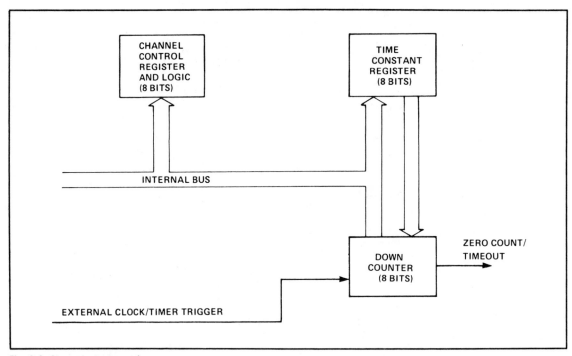

Fig. 6-6. Channel-counter mode.

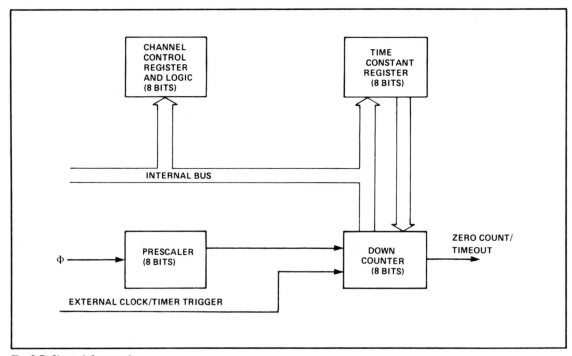

Fig. 6-7. Channel-timer mode.

132

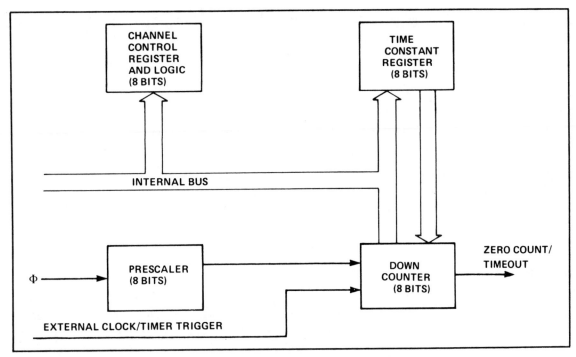

Fig. 6-8. Channel block diagram.

IORQ and M1 are both true, the CPU is acknowledging an interrupt request, and the highest-priority interrupting channel will place its Interrupt Vector on the Z80 Data Bus.

RD. Read Cycle Status from the CPU (input, active low). The RD signal is used in conjunction with the IORQ and CE signals to transfer data and Channel Control Words between the Z80-CPU and the CTC. During a CTC Write Cycle, IORQ and CE must be true and RD false. The CTC does not receive a specific write signal, instead generating its own internally from the inverse of a valid RD signal. In a CTC Read Cycle, IORQ, CE and RD must be active to place the contents of the Down Counter on the Z80 Data Bus.

IEI. Interrupt Enable In (input, active high). This signal is used to help form a system-wide interrupt daisy chain which establishes priorities when more than one peripheral device in the system has interrupting capability. A high level on this pin indicates that no other interrupting devices of higher priority in the daisy chain are being serviced by the Z80-CPU.

IEO. Interrupt Enable Out (output, active high). The IEO signal, in conjunction with IEI, is used to form a system-wide interrupt priority daisy chain. IEO is high only if IEI is high and the CPU is not servicing an interrupt from any CTC channel. Thus this signal blocks lower priority devices from interrupting while a higher priority interrupting device is being serviced by the CPU.

INT. Interrupt Request (output, open drain, active low). This signal goes true when any CTC channel which has been programmed to enable interrupts has a zero-count condition in its Down Counter.

RESET. Reset (input, active low). This signal stops all channels from counting and resets channel interrupt enable bits in all control registers, thereby disabling CTC-generated interrupts. The ZC/TO and INT outputs go to their inactive states, IEO reflects IEI, and the CTC's data bus output drivers go to the high impedance state.

CLK/TRG3—CLK/TRG0. External Clock/Timer Trigger (input, user-selectable active high or low). There are four CLK/TRG pins, corresponding to the four independent CTC channels. In the Counter Mode, every active edge on this pin decrements the Down Counter. In the Timer Mode, an active edge on this pin initiates the timing function. The user may select the active edge to be either rising or falling.

ZC/TO2—ZC/TO0. Zero Count/Timer (output, active high). There are three ZC/TO pins, corresponding to CTC channels 2 through 0. (Due to package pin limitations channel 3 has no ZC/TO pin.) In either Counter Mode or Timer Mode, when the Down Counter decrements to zero an active high-going pulse appears at this pin.

OPERATING MODES

At power-on, the Z80-CTC state is undefined. Asserting RESET puts the CTC in a known state. Before any channel can begin counting or timing, a Channel Control Word and a time constant data word must be written to the appropriate registers of that channel. Further, if any channel has been programmed to enable interrupts, an Interrupt Vector word must be written to the CTC's Interrupt Control Logic. (For further details, refer to the section "CTC Programming." When the CPU has written all of these words to the CTC, all active channels will be programmed for immediate operation in either the Counter Mode or the Timer Mode.

COUNTER MODES

In this mode the CTC counts edges of the CLK/TRG input. The Counter Mode is programmed for a channel when its Channel Control Word is written with bit 6 set. The Channel's External Clock (CLK/TRG) input is monitored for a series of triggering edges; after each, in synchronization with the next rising edge of Φ (the System Clock), the Down Counter (which was initialized with the time constant data word at the start of any sequence of down-counting) is decremented. Although there is no set-up time requirement between the triggering edge of the External Clock and the rising edge of Φ, (Clock), the Down Counter will not be decremented until the following Φ pulse. (See the parameter ts(CK) "Ac Characteristics.") A channel's External Clock input is pre-programmed by bit 4 of the Channel Control Word to trigger the decrementing sequence with either a high or a low edge. See Fig. 6-9 for a timing diagram of CTC counting and timing modes.

In any of Channels 0, 1, or 2, when the Down Counter is successively decremented from the original time constant until finally it reaches zero, the Zero Count (ZC/TO) output pin for that channel will be pulsed active (high). (However, due to package pin limitations, channel 3 does not have this pin and so may only be used in applications where this output pulse is not required.) Further, if the channel has been so pre-programmed by bit 7 of the Channel Control Word, an interrupt request sequence will be generated. (For more details, see the section "CTC Interrupt Servicing.")

134

As the above sequence is proceeding, the zero count condition also results in the automatic reload of the Down Count with the original time constant data word in the Time Constant Register. There is no interruption in the sequence of continued down-counting. If the Time-Constant Register is written to with a new time constant data word while the Down Counter is decrementing, the present count will be completed before the new time constant will be loaded into the Down Counter.

TIMER MODE

In this mode the CTC generates timing intervals that are an integer value of the system clock period. The Timer Mode is programmed for a channel when its Channel Control Word is written with bit 6 reset. The channel then may be used to measure intervals of time based on the System Clock period. The System Clock is fed through two successive counters, the Prescaler and the Down Counter. Depending on the preprogrammed bit 5 in the Channel Control Word, the Prescaler divides the System Clock by a factor of either 16 or 256. The output of the Prescaler is then used as a clock to decrement the Down Counter, which may be pre-programmed with any time constant integer between 1 and 256. As in the Counter Mode, the time constant is automatically reloaded into the Down Counter at each zero-count condition, and counting

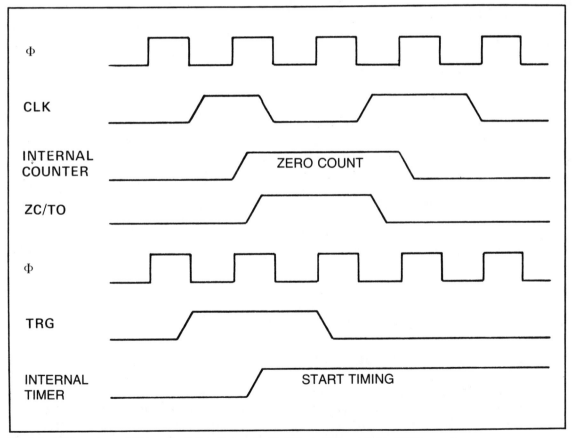

Fig. 6-9. CTC counting and timing. The timing diagram for the CTC counting and timing Modes.

continues. Also at zero-count, the channel's Time Out (ZC/TO) output (which is the output of the Down Counter) is pulsed, resulting in a uniform pulse train of precise period given by the product.

$$t_c * P * TC$$

where t_c is the System Clock period, P is the Prescaler factor of 16 or 256 and TC is the pre-programmed time constant.

Bit 3 of the Channel Control Word is pre-programmed to select whether timing will be automatically initiated, or whether it will be initiated, with a triggering edge at the channel's Timer Trigger (CLK/TRG) input. If bit 3 is reset the timer automatically begins operation at the start of the CPU cycle following the I/O Write machine cycle that loads the time constant data word to the channel. If bit 3 is set the timer begins operation on the second succeeding rising edge of Φ after the Timer Trigger edge following the loading of the time constant data word. If no time constant data word is to follow then the timer begins operation on the second succeeding rising edge of Φ after the Timer Trigger edge following the control word write cycle. Bit 4 of the Channel Control Word is pre-programmed to select whether the Timer Trigger will be sensitive to a rising or falling edge. Although there is no set-up requirement between the active edge of the Timer Trigger and the next rising edge of Φ. If the Timer Trigger edge occurs closer than a specified minimum set-up time to the rising edge of Φ, the Down Counter will not begin decrementing until the following rising edge of Φ. (See parameter ts(TR) "Ac Characteristics".)

If bit 7 in the Channel Control Word is set, the zero-count condition in the Down Counter, besides causing a pulse at the channel's Time Out pin, will be used to initiate an interrupt request sequence. (For more details, see the section: "CTC Interrupt Servicing.")

PROGRAMMING

Before a Z80-CTC channel can begin counting or timing operations, a Channel Control Word and a Time Constant data word must be written to it by the CPU. These words will be stored in the Channel Control Register and the Time Constant Register of that channel. In addition, if any of the four channels have been programmed with bit 7 of their Channel Control Words to enable interrupts, an Interrupt Vector must be written to the appropriate register in the CTC. Due to automatic features in the Interrupt Control Logic, one pre-programmed Interrupt Vector suffices for all four channels.

LOADING THE CHANNEL CONTROL REGISTER

To load a Channel Control Word, the CPU performs a normal I/O Write sequence to the port address corresponding to the desired CTC channel. Two CTC input pins, namely CS0 and CS1, are used to form a 2-bit binary address to select one of four channels within the device. In many system architectures, these two input pins are connected to Address Bus lines A0 and A1, respectively, so that the four channels in a CTC device will occupy contiguous I/O port addresses. A word written to a CTC channel will be interpreted as a Channel Control Word, and loaded into the Channel Control Register, its bit 0 is a logic 1.

The other seven bits of this word select operating modes and conditions as indicated in the diagram below. Following the diagram the meaning of each bit will be discussed in detail.

Channel Control Register

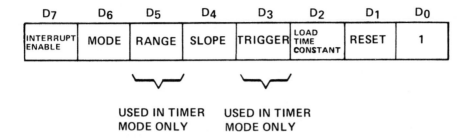

Bit 7 = 1. The channel is enabled to generate an interrupt request sequence every time the Down Counter reaches a zero-count condition. To set this bit to 1 in any of the four Channel Control Registers necessitates that an Interrupt Vector also be written to the CTC before operation begins. Channel interrupts may be programmed in either Counter Mode or Timer Mode. If an updated Channel Control Word is written to a channel already in operation, with bit 7 set, the interrupt enable selection will not be retroactive to a preceding zero-count condition.

Bit 7 = 0. Channel interrupts disabled. Any pending interrupt by the channel will be cleared.

Bit 6 = 1. Counter Mode selected. The Down Counter is decremented by each triggering edge of the External Clock (CLK/TRG) input. The Prescaler is not used.

Bit 6 = 0. Timer Mode selected. The Prescaler is clocked by the System Clock Φ, and the output of the Prescaler in turn clocks the Down Counter. The output of the Down Counter (the channel's ZC/TO output) is a uniform pulse train of period given by the product:

$$tc * P * TC$$

where t_c is the period of System Clock Φ, P is the Prescaler factor of 16 or 256, and TC is the time constant data word.

Bit 5 = 1. (Defined for Timer Mode only.) Prescaler factor is 256.

Bit 5 = 0. (Defined for Timer Mode only.) Prescaler factor is 16.

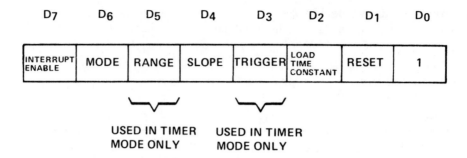

D7	D6	D5	D4	D3	D2	D1	D0
INTERRUPT ENABLE	MODE	RANGE	SLOPE	TRIGGER	LOAD TIME CONSTANT	RESET	1

USED IN TIMER MODE ONLY   USED IN TIMER MODE ONLY

Bit 4 = 1. Timer Mode—positive edge trigger starts timer operation. Counter Mode—positive edge decrements the down counter.

Bit 4 = 0. Timer Mode—negative edge trigger starts timer operation. Counter Mode—negative edge decrements the down counter.

Bit 3 = 1. Timer Mode Only - external trigger is valid for starting timer operation after rising edge of T_2 of the machine cycle following the one that loads the time constant. The Prescaler is decremented 2 clock cycles later if the setup time is met, otherwise 3 clock cycles. Once timer has been started it will free run at the rate determined by the Time Constant register.

Bit 3 = 0. Timer mode Only - timer begins operation on the rising edge of T_2 of the machine cycle following the one that loads the time constant.

Bit 2 = 1. The time constant data word for the Time Constant Register will be the next word written to this channel. If an updated Channel Control Word and time constant data word are written to a channel while it is already in operation, the Down Counter will continue decrementing to zero before the new constant is loaded into it.

Bit 2 = 0. No time constant data word for the Time Constant Register should be expected to follow. To program bit 2 to this state implies that this Channel Control Word is intended to update the status of a channel already in operation, since a channel will not operate without a correctly programmed data word in the Time Constant Register, and a set bit 2 in this Channel Control Word provides the only way of writing to the Time Constant Register.

Bit 1 = 1. Reset channel. Channel stops counting or timing. This is not a stored condition. Upon writing into this bit a reset pulse discontinues current channel operation, however, none of the bits in the channel control register are changed. If both bit 2 = 1 and bit 1 = 1 the channel will resume operation upon loading a time constant.

Bit 1 = 0. Channel continues current operation.

DISABLING THE CTC'S INTERRUPT STRUCTURE

If an external Asynchronous interrupt could occur while the processor is writing the disable word to the CTC (01H); a system problem may occur. If interrupts are enabled in the processor it is possible that the Asynchronous interrupt will occur while the processor is writing the disable word to the CTC. The CTC will generate an INT and the CPU will acknowledge it, however, by this time, the CTC will have received the disable word and de-activated its interrupt structure. The result is that the CTC will not send in its interrupt vector during the interrupt acknowledge cycle because it is disabled and the CPU will fetch an erroneous vector resulting in a program fault. The cure for this problem is to disable interrupts within the CPU with the DI instruction just before the CTC is disabled and then re-enable interrupts with the EI instruction. This action causes the CPU to ignore any interrupts produced by the CTC while it is being disabled. The code sequence would be:

```
LD A, 01H
DI               ;DISABLE CPU.
OUT (CTC), A     :DISABLE CTC.
EI               ;ENABLE CPU.
—
—
```

The high order 5 bits of this Interrupt Vector must be written to the CTC in advance as part of the initial programming sequence. To do so, the CPU must write to the I/O port address corresponding to the CTC channel 0, just as it would if a Channel Control Word were being written to that channel, except that bit 0 of the word being written must contain a 0. (As explained above in the section, "Loading the Channel Control

Register," if bit 0 of a word written to a channel were set to 1, the word would be interpreted as a Channel Control Word, so a 0 in bit 0 signals the CTC to load the incoming word into the Interrupt Vector Register.) Bits 1 and 2, however are not used when loading this vector. At the time when the interrupting channel must place the Interrupt Vector on the Z80 Data Bus, the Interrupt Control Logic of the CTC automatically supplies a binary code in bits 1 and 2 identifying which of the four CTC channels is to be serviced.

Interrupt Vector Register

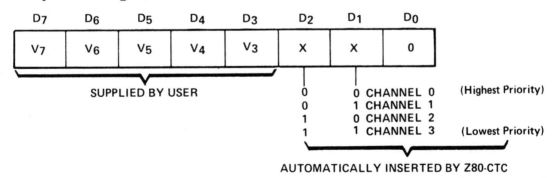

LOADING THE TIME CONSTANT REGISTER

A channel may not begin operation in either Timer Mode or Counter Mode unless a time constant data word is written into the Time Constant Register by the CPU. This data word will be expected on the next I/O Write to this channel following the I/O Write of the Channel Control Word, provided that bit 2 of the Channel Control Word is set. The time constant data word may be an integer value in the range 1-256. If all eight bits in this word are zero, it is interpreted as 256. If a time constant data word is loaded to a channel already in operation, the Down Counter will continue decrementing to zero before the new time constant is loaded from the Time Constant Register to the Down Counter.

Time Constant Register

D_7	D_6	D_5	D_4	D_3	D_2	D_1	D_0
TC_7	TC_6	TC_5	TC_4	TC_3	TC_2	TC_1	TC_0

MSB   LSB

LOADING THE INTERRUPT VECTOR REGISTER

The Z80-CTC has been designed to operate with the Z80-CPU programmed for mode 2 interrupt response. Under the requirements of this mode, when a CTC channel requests an interrupt and is acknowledged, a 16-bit pointer must be formed to obtain a corresponding interrupt service routine starting address from a table in memory. The upper 8 bits of this pointer are provided by the CPU's I register, and the lower 8 bits of the pointer are provided by the CTC in the form of an Interrupt Vector unique to the particular channel that requested the interrupt. (For further details, see the section:"CTC Interrupt Servicing".)

Mode 2 Interrupt Operation

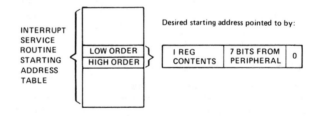

TIMING

This section illustrates the timing relationships of the relevant CTC pins for the following types of operation: writing a word to the CTC, reading a word from the CTC, counting, and timing. For timing diagrams relating to interrupt servicing and an ac Timing Diagram (see Fig. 6-15) which quantitatively specifies the timing relationships, see the section latter in this chapter.

WRITE CYCLE

Figure 6-10 illustrates the timing associated with the CTC Write Cycle. This sequence is applicable to loading either a Channel Control Word, an Interrupt Vector, or a time constant data word.

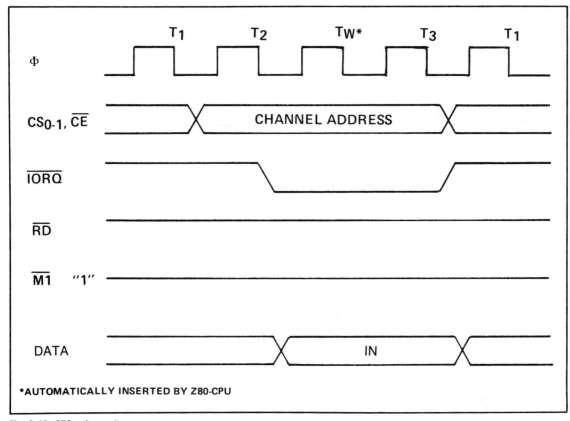

Fig. 6-10. CTC write cycle.

In the sequence shown, during clock cycle T_1, the Z80-CPU prepares for the Write Cycle with a false (high) signal at CTC input pin $\overline{RD}$ (Read). Since the CTC has no separate Write signal input, it generates its own internally from the false $\overline{RD}$ input. Later, during clock cycle T_2, the Z80-CPU initiates the Write Cycle with true (low) signals at CTC input pins $\overline{IORQ}$ (I/O Request) and $\overline{CE}$ (Chip Enable). (Note: $\overline{M1}$ must be false to distinguish the cycle form an interrupt acknowledge.) Also at this time a 2-bit binary code appears at CTC inputs CS1 inputs CS0 (Channel Select 1 and 0), specifying which of the four CTC channels is being written to, and the word being written appears on the Z80 Data Bus. Now everything is ready for the word to be latched into the appropriate CTC internal register in synchronization with the rising edge beginning clock cycle T_3. No additional wait states are allowed.

READ CYCLE

Figure 6-11 illustrates the timing associated with the CTC Read Cycle. This sequence is used any time the CPU reads the current contents of the Down Counter. During clock cycle T_2, the Z80-CPU initiates the Read Cycle with true signals at input pins $\overline{RD}$ (Read), $\overline{IORQ}$ (I/O Request), and $\overline{CE}$ (Chip Enable). Also at this time a 2-bit binary code appears at CTC inputs CS1 and CS0 (Channel Select 1 and 0), specifying which

141

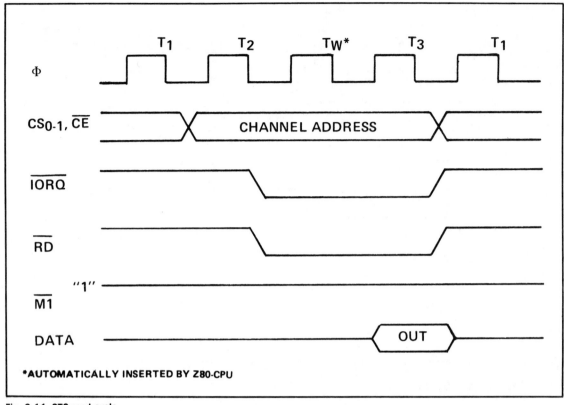

Fig. 6-11. CTC read cycle.

of the four CTC channels is being read from. (Note: $\overline{\text{M1}}$ must be false to distinguish the cycle from an interrupt acknowledge.) On the rising edge of the cycle T_3 the valid contents of the Down Counter as of the rising edge of cycle T_2 will be available on the Z80 Data Bus. No additional wait states are allowed.

In the Counter Mode, the edge (rising edge is active in this example) from the external hardware connected to pin CKL/TRG decrements the Down Counter in synchronization with the System Clock Φ. As specified in the ac Characteristics this CLK/TRG pulse must have a minimum width and the minimum period must not be less than twice the system clock period. Although there is no set-up requirement between the active edge of the CLK/TRG and the rising edge of Φ if the CLK/TRG edge occurs closer than a specified minimum time, the decrement of the Down Counter will be delayed one cycle of Φ. Immediately after the decrement of the Down Counter, 1 to 0, the ZC/TO output is pulsed true.

In the Time Mode, a pulse trigger (user-selectable as either active high or active low) at the CLK/TRG pin enables timing function on the second succeeding rising edge of Φ. As in the Counter Mode, the triggering pulse is detected asynchronously and must have a minimum width. The timing function is initiated in synchronization with Φ, and a minimum set-up time is required between the active edge of the CLK/TRG and the next rising edge of Φ. If the CLK/TRG edge occurs closer than this, the initiation of the timer function will be delayed one cycle of Φ.

INTERRUPT SERVICING

Each CTC channel may be individually programmed to request an interrupt every time its Down Counter reaches a count of zero. The purpose of a CTC-generated interrupt, as for any other peripheral device, is to force the CPU to execute an interrupt service routine. To utilize this feature the Z80-CPU must be programmed for mode 2 interrupt response. Under the requirements of this mode, when a CTC channel requests an interrupt and is acknowledged, a 16-bit pointer must be formed to obtain a corresponding interrupt service routine starting address from a table in memory. The lower 8 bits of the pointer are provided by the CTC in the form of an Interrupt Vector unique to the particular channel that requested the interrupt.

The CTC's Interrupt Control Logic insures that it acts in accordance with Z80 system interrupt protocol for nested priority interrupt and proper return from interrupt. The priority of any system device is determined by its physical location in a daisy-chain configuration. Two signal lines (IEI and IEO) are provided in the CTC and all Z80 peripheral devices to form the system daisy chain. The device closest to the CPU has the highest priority; with in the CTC, interrupt priority is predetermined by channel number, with channel 0 having highest priority. According to Z80 system interrupt protocol, low priority devices or channels may not interrupt higher priority devices or channels that have already interrupted and not had their interrupt service routines completed. However, high priority devices or channels may interrupt the servicing of lower priority devices or channels. (For further details, see section "Interrupt Control Logic".)

The next two sections describe the nominal timing relationships of the relevant CTC pins for the Interrupt Acknowledge Cycle and the Return from Interrupt Cycle. The last section discusses a typical example of daisy chain interrupt servicing.

INTERRUPT ACKNOWLEDGE CYCLE

Figure 6-12 illustrates the timing associated with the Interrupt Acknowledge Cycle. Some time after an interrupt is requested by the CTC, the CPU will send out an interrupt acknowledge ($\overline{M1}$ and $\overline{IORQ}$). To insure that the daisy chain enable lines stabilize, channels are inhibited from changing their interrupt request status when $\overline{M1}$ is active. $\overline{M1}$ is active about two clock cycles earlier than $\overline{IORQ}$, and $\overline{RD}$ is false to distinguish the cycle from an instruction fetch. During this time the interrupt logic of the CTC will determine the highest priority interrupting channel within the CTC places its Interrupt Vector onto the Data Bus when $\overline{IORQ}$ goes active. Two wait states (T_W*) are automatically inserted at this time to allow the daisy chain to stabilize. Additional wait states may be added.

RETURN FROM INTERRUPT CYCLE

Figure 6-13 illustrates the timing associated with the RETI Instruction. This instruction is used at the end of an interrupt service routine to initialize the daisy chain enable lines for proper control of nested priority interrupt handling. The CTC decodes the two-byte RETI code internally and determines whether it is inter led for a channel being serviced.

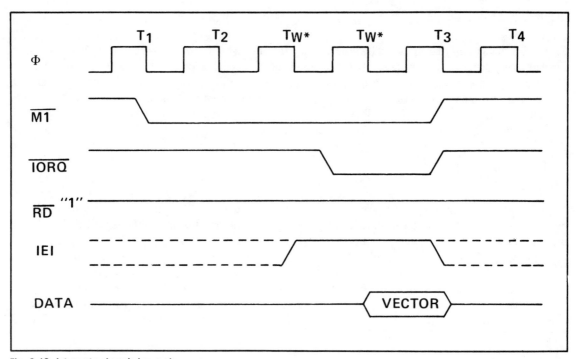

Fig. 6-12. Interrupt acknowledge cycle.

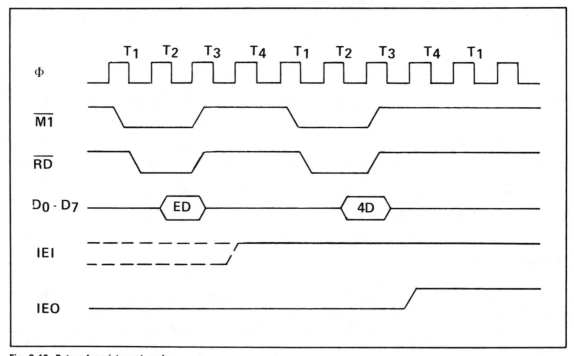

Fig. 6-13. Return from interrupt cycle.

When several Z80 peripheral chips are in the daisy chain IEI will become active on the chip currently under service when an EDH opcode is decoded. If the following opcode is 4DH, the peripheral being serviced will be re-initialized and its IEO will become active. Additional wait states are allowed.

DAISY CHAIN INTERRUPT SERVICING

Figure 6-14 illustrates a typical nested interrupt sequence which may occur in the CTC. In this example, channel 2 interrupts and is granted service. While this channel is being serviced, higher priority channel 1 interrupts and is granted service. The service routine for the higher priority channel is completed, and a RETI instruction (see the previous section for further details) is executed to signal the channel that its routine is complete. At this time, the service routine of the lower priority channel 2 is resumed and completed.

AS AN INTERRUPT CONTROLLER

All of the Z80 family parts contain circuitry 'for prioritizing interrupts and supplying the vector to the CPU. However, in many Z80 based systems interrupts must be processed from devices which do not contain this interrupt circuitry. To handle this requirement the MK3882 CTC can be used, providing prioritized, independently vectored, maskable, edge selectable, count programmable external interrupt inputs. The MK3882 parts may be cascaded, expanding the system to as many as 256 interrupt inputs. See Fig. 6-15 for Pin-Out documentation.

Each MK3882 contains 4 channels with counter inputs able to interrupt upon one or more (up to 256) edge transitions. The active transition may be programmed to be positive or negative. Each of the 4 channels

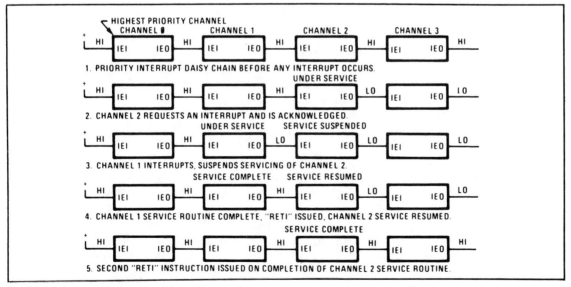

Fig. 6-14. Daisy-chain interrupt servicing.

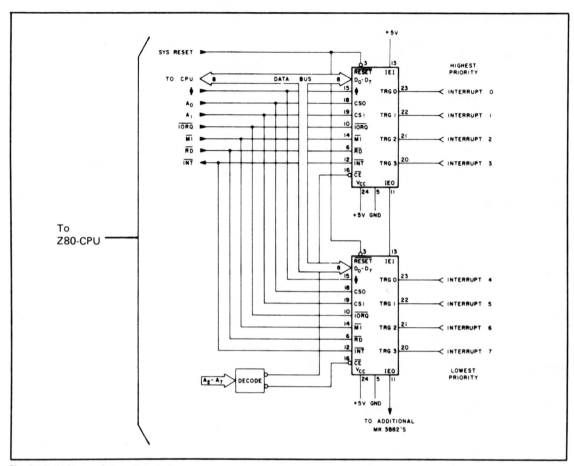

Fig. 6-15. CTC as an interrupt controller.

has a programmable vector which is used in powerful Z80 mode 2 interrupt processing. When an interrupt is processed the vector is combined with the CPU I register to determine where the interrupt service routine start address is located. Additionally, priority resolution is handled within the MK3882 when more than one interrupt request is made simultaneously. When more than one MK3882 is used, the prioritizing is done, with the IEI/IEO chain resolving inter-chip priorities. Each channel can be independently "masked" by disabling that channel's local interrupt.

When programming the MK3882 to handle an input as a general purpose interrupt line, the channel is put in the counter mode, with the count set to 1, the active edge specified and the vector is loaded. When the programmed edge occurs a mode 2 interrupt will be generated by the CTC and the Z80-CPU can vector directly to the service routine for the non-Z80 peripheral device. Note that after the interrupt, the CTC down counter is automatically reloaded with a count of one and the CTC channel begins looking for another active edge after the RETI of the interrupt routine. Therefore, once a particular channel is under service, no active edges will be recognized by that channel until execution of the RETI instruction of the corresponding interrupt routine. Of course, other channels of the CTC can generate interrupts and/or pending interrupts asynchronously, depending on their priority.

146

Chapter 7

Z80 Serial Input/Output Circuit

The Mostek Z80-SIO (Serial Input/Output) is a dual-channel, multi-function peripheral component designed to satisfy a wide variety of serial data communications requirements in microcomputer systems. Its basic function is a serial-to-parallel, parallel-to-serial converter/controller, but, within that role, it is configurable by systems software so its "personality" can be optimized for a given serial data communications application. See Fig. 7-1 for a block diagram of the SIO.

The Z80-SIO is capable of handling asynchronous and synchronous byte-oriented protocols, such as IBM Bisync, and synchronous bit-oriented protocols, such as HDLC and IBM SDLC. This versatile device can also be used to support virtually any other serial protocol for applications other than data communications (cassette or floppy disk interface, for example).

The Z80-DIO can generate and check CRC codes in any synchronous mode and can be programmed to check data integrity in various modes. The device also has facilities for modem controls in both channels. In applications where these controls are not needed, the modem controls can be used for general-purpose I/O.

STRUCTURE

- N-channel silicon-gate depletion-load technology
- 40-pin DIP
- Single 5V power supply

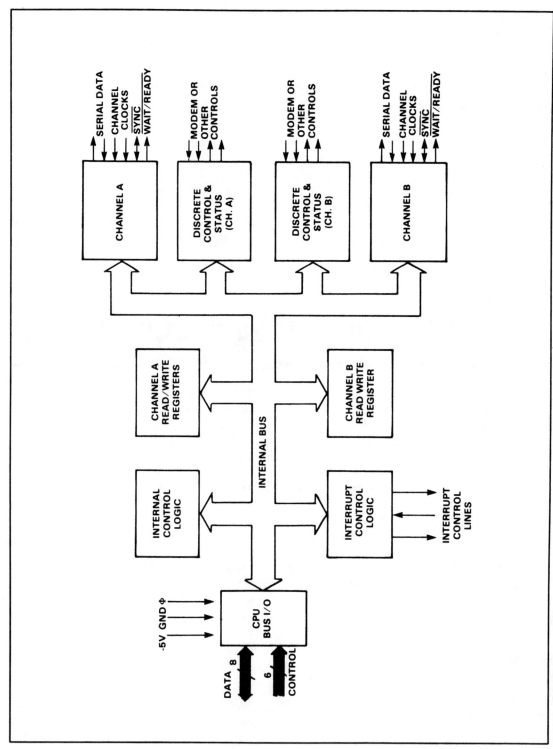

Fig. 7-1. Z80-SIO block diagram.

- Single-phase 5V clock
- All inputs and outputs TTL compatible

FEATURES

- Two independent full-duplex channels
- Data rates in synchronous or isosynchronous modes:
  - ☐ 0-550K bits/second with 2.5 MHz system clock rate
  - ☐ 0-800K bits/second with 4.0 MHz system clock rate
- Receiver data registers quadruply buffered; transmitter doubly buffered.
- Asynchronous features:
  - —5, 6, 7 or 8 bits/character
  - —1, 1½ or 2 stop bits
  - —Even, odd or no parity
  - —×1, ×16, ×32 and ×64 clock modes
  - —Break generation and detection
  - —Parity, overrun and framing error detection
  - —Binary synchronous features:
    - Internal or external character synchronization
    - One or two sync characters in separate registers
    - Automatic sync character insertion
    - CRC generation and checking

  - —HDLC and IBM SDLC-features:
    - Abort sequence generation and detection
    - Automatic zero insertion and deletion
    - Automatic flag insertion between messages
    - Address field recognition
    - 1-field residue handling
    - Valid receive message protected from overrun
    - CRC generation and checking
  - —Separate modem control inputs and outputs for both channels
  - —CRC-16 or CRC-CCITT block check
  - —Daisy-Chain Priority interrupt logic provides automatic interrupt vectoring without external logic
  - —Modem status can be monitored

PIN DESCRIPTION

D_0-D_7. System Data Bus (bidirectional, 3-state). The system data bus transfers data and commands between the CPU and the Z80-SIO. D_0 is the least significant bit.

B/A. Channel A Or B Select (input, High selects Channel B). This input defines which channel is accessed during a data transfer between the CPU and the Z80-SIO. Address bit A_0 from the CPU is often used for the selection function.

149

C/D̄. Control Or Data Select (input, High selects Control). This input defines the type of information transfer performed between the CPU and the Z80-SIO. A High at this input, during a CPU write to the Z80-SIO, causes the information on the data bus to be interpreted as a command for the channels elected by B/Ā. A Low at C/D̄ means that the information on the data bus is data. Address bit A_1 is often used for this function.

CĒ. Chip Enable (input, active Low). A low level at this input enables the Z80-SIO to accept command or data inputs from the CPU during a write cycle, or to transmit data to the CPU during a read cycle.

Φ. System Clock (input). The Z80-SIO uses the standard Z80A System Clock to synchronize internal signals. This is a single-phase clock.

M̄1. Machine Cycle One (input from Z80-CPU, active Low). When M̄1 is active, and R̄D̄ is also active. the Z80-CPU is fetching an instruction from memory. When M̄1 is active, while ĪŌRQ̄ is active, the Z80-SIO accepts M̄1 and ĪŌRQ̄ as an interrupt acknowledge if the Z80-SIO is the highest priority device that has interrupted the Z80-CPU.

ĪŌRQ̄. Input/Output (input from CPU, active Low). ĪŌRQ̄ is used in conjunction with B/Ā, C/D̄, CĒ and R̄D̄ to transfer commands and data between the CPU and the Z80-SIO. When CĒ, R̄D̄ and ĪŌRQ̄ are all active, the channel selected by B/Ā transfers data to the CPU (a read operation). When CĒ and ĪŌRQ̄ are active, but R̄D̄ is inactive, the channel selected by B/Ā is written to by the CPU with either data or control information, as specified by C/D̄. As mentioned previously, if ĪŌRQ̄ and M̄1 are active simultaneously, the CPU is acknowledging an interrupt and the Z80-SIO automatically places its interrupt vector on the CPU data bus, if it is the highest priority device requesting an interrupt.

R̄D̄. Read Cycle Status (input from CPU, active Low). If R̄D̄ is active, a memory or I/O read operation is in progress. R̄D̄ is used with B/Ā, CĒ and ĪŌRQ̄ to transfer data from the Z80-SIO to the CPU.

RESET. Reset (input, active Low). A Low RESET disables both receivers and transmitters, forces TxDA and TxDB marking, forces the modem controls High and disables all interrupts. The control registers must be rewritten after the Z80-SIO is reset and before data is transmitted or received.

IEI. Interrupt Enable In (input, active High). This signal is used with IEO to form a priority daisy chain when there is more than one interrupt-driven device. A High on this line indicates that no other device of higher priority is being serviced by a CPU interrupt service routine.

IEO. Interrupt Enable Out (output, active High). IEO is High only if IEI is High and the CPU is not servicing an interrupt from this Z80-SIO. Thus, this signal blocks lower priority devices from interrupting while a higher priority device is being serviced by its CPU interrupt service routine.

ĪNT̄. Interrupt Request (output, open drain, active Low). When the Z80-SIO is requesting an interrupt, it pulls ĪNT̄ low.

W/RDYA, W/RDYB. Wait/Ready A, Wait/Ready B (outputs, open drain when programmed for Wait function, driven High and Low when programmed for Ready function). These dual-purpose outputs may be programmed as Ready lines for a DMA controller or as Wait lines that synchronize the CPU to the Z80-SIO data rate. The reset state is open drain.

CTSA, CTSB. Clear To Send (inputs, active Low). When programmed as Auto Enables, a Low on these inputs enables the respective transmitter. If not programmed as Auto Enables, these inputs may be programmed as general-purpose inputs. Both inputs are Schmitt-trigger buffered to accommodate slow-risetime inputs. The Z80-SIO detects pulses on these inputs and interrupts the CPU on both logic level transitions. The Schmitt-trigger inputs do not guarantee a specified noise-level margin.

DCDA, DCDB. Data Carrier Detect (inputs, active Low). These signals are similar to the CTS inputs, except they can be used as receiver enables.

RxDA, RxDB. Receive Data (inputs, active High).

TxDA, TxDB. Transmit Data (outputs, active High).

RxCA, RxCB*. Receiver Clocks (inputs). See the following section on bonding options. The Receive Clocks may be 1, 16, 32 or 64 times the data rate in asynchronous modes. Receive data is sampled on the rising edge of $\overline{\text{RxC}}$.

TxCA, TxCB*. Transmitter Clocks (inputs). See section on bonding options. In asynchronous modes, the Transmitter clocks may be 1, 16, 32 or 64 times the data rate. The multiplier for the transmitter and the receiver must be the same. Both the $\overline{\text{TxC}}$ and $\overline{\text{RxC}}$ inputs are Schmitt-trigger buffered for relaxed rise-and fall-time requirements (no noise margin is specified). $\overline{\text{TxD}}$ changes on the falling edge of $\overline{\text{TxC}}$.

RTSA, RTSB. Request To Send (outputs, active Low). When the RTS bit is set, the RTS output goes low. When the RTS bit is reset in the Asynchronous mode, the output goes High after the transmitter is empty. In Synchronous modes, the $\overline{\text{RTS}}$ pin strictly follows the state of the RTS bit. Both pins can be used as general purpose outputs.

DTRA, DTRB. Data Terminal Ready (outputs, active Low). See note on bonding options. These outputs follow the state programmed into the DTR bit. They can also be programmed as general-purpose outputs.

SYNC A, SYNC B. Synchronization (inputs/outputs, active Low). These pins can act either as inputs or outputs. In the Asynchronous Receive mode, they are inputs similar to $\overline{\text{CTS}}$ and $\overline{\text{DCD}}$. In this mode, the transitions on these lines affect the state of the Sync/Hunt status bits in RR0. In the External Sync mode, these lines also act as inputs. When external synchronization is achieved, $\overline{\text{SYNC}}$ must be driven Low on the second rising edge of $\overline{\text{RxC}}$ after that rising edge of $\overline{\text{RxC}}$, on which the last bit of the sync character was received. In other words, after the sync pattern is detected, the external logic must wait for two full Receive Clock cycles to activate the $\overline{\text{SYNC}}$ input. Once $\overline{\text{SYNC}}$ is forced Low, it is wise to keep it Low until the CPU informs the external sync logic that synchronization has been lost or a new message is about to start. Character assembly begins on the rising edge of $\overline{\text{RxC}}$ that immediately precedes the falling edge of $\overline{\text{SYNC}}$ in the External Sync mode.

In the Internal Synchronization mode (Monosync and Bisync), these pins act as outputs that are active during the part of the receive clock ($\overline{\text{RxC}}$) cycle in which sync characters are recognized. The sync condition is not latched, so these outputs are active each time a sync pattern is recognized, regardless of character boundaries.

---

*These clocks may be directly driven by the Z80-CTC (Counter Timer Circuit) for fully programmable baud rate generation.

Bonding Options

The constraints of a 40-pin package make it impossible to bring out the Receive Clock, Transmit Clock, Data Terminal Ready and Sync signals for both channels. Therefore, Channel B must sacrifice a signal or have two signals bonded together. Since user requirements vary, three bondings options are offered:

MK3884 Z80-SIO has all four signals, but TxCB and RxCB are bonded together (Fig. 7-2).

MK3885 Z80-SIO sacrifices DTRB and keeps TxCB, RxCB and SYNCB (Fig. 7-3).

MK3887 Z80-SIO sacrifices SYNCB and keeps TxCB, RxCB and DTRB (Fig. 7-4).

ARCHITECTURE

The device internal structure includes a Z80-CPU interface, internal control and interrupt logic and two full-duplex channels. Associated with each channel are read and write registers and discrete control and status logic that provide the interface to modems or other external devices.

The read and write register group includes five 8-bit control registers, two sync-character registers and two status registers. The interrupt vector is written into an additional 8-bit register (Write Register 2) in

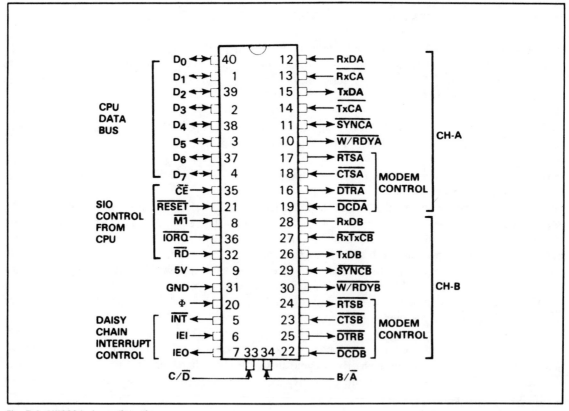

Fig. 7-2. MK3884 pin configuration.

152

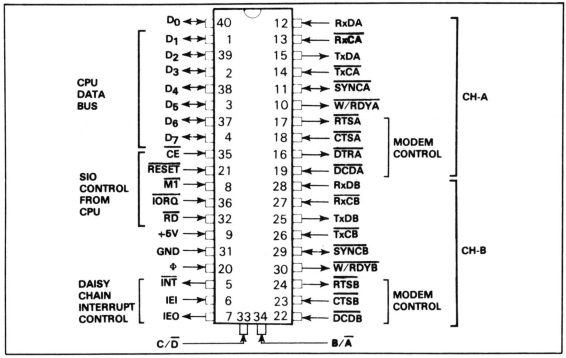

Fig. 7-3. MK3885 pin configuration.

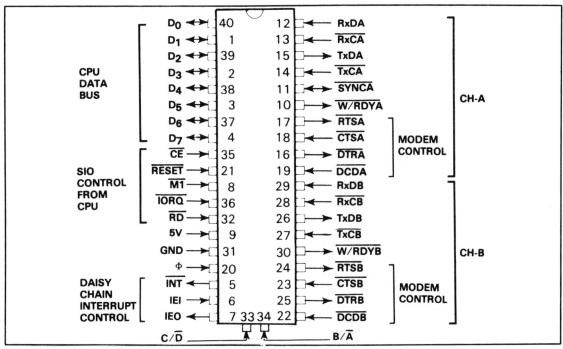

Fig. 7-4. MK3887 pin configuration.

153

Channel B that may be read through Read Register 2 in Channel B. The registers for both channels are designated in the text as follows:

WR0-WR7—Write Registers 0 through 7
RR0-RR2—Read Registers 0 through 2

The bit assignment and functional grouping of each register is configured to simplify and organize the programming process. Table 7-1 illustrates the functions assigned to each read or write register.

The logic for both channels provides formats, synchronization and validation for data transferred to and from the channel interface. The modem control inputs, Clear to Send (CTS) and Data Carrier Detect (DCD), are monitored by the discrete control logic under program control. All the modem control signals are general purpose in nature and can be used for functions other than modem control.

For automatic interrupt vectoring, the interrupt control logic determines which channel and which device within the channel has the highest priority. Priority is fixed with Channel A assigned a higher priority than Channel B; Receive, Transmit and External/Status interrupts are prioritized in that order within each channel.

Data Path

The transmit and receive data paths for each channel are shown in Fig. 7-5. The receiver has three 8-bit buffer registers in a FIFO arrangement (to provide a 3-byte delay) in addition to the 8-bit receive shift register. This arrangement creates additional time for the CPU to service an interrupt at the beginning of a block of high-speed data. The receive error FIFO stores parity and framing errors and other types of status information for each of the three bytes in the receive data FIFO.

Incoming data is routed through one of several paths depending on the mode and character length. In the

Table 7-1. Functional Assignments of Read and Write Registers.

WR0	Register pointers, CRC initialization commands for the various modes, etc.
WR1	Transmit/Receive interrupt and data transfer mode definition
WR2	Interrupt vector (Channel B only)
WR3	Receive parameters and controls
WR4	Transmit/Receive miscellaneous parameters and modes
WR5	Transmit parameters and controls
WR6	Sync character of SDLC address field
WR7	Sync character of SDLC flag
	(a) Write Register Functions
RR0	Transmit/Receive buffer status, interrupt status and external status
RR1	Special Receive Condition status
RR2	Modified interrupt vector (Channel B only)
	(b) Read Register Functions

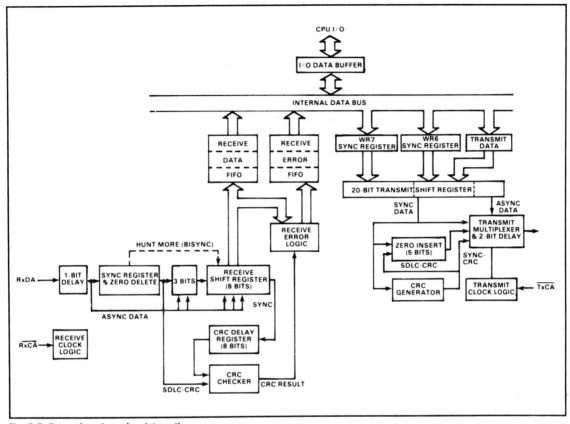

Fig. 7-5. Transmit and receive data path.

Asynchronous mode, serial data is entered into the 3-bit buffer if it has a character length of seven or eight bits, or is entered into the 8-bit receive shift register if it has a length of five or six bits.

In the Synchronous mode, however, the data path is determined by the phase of the receive process currently in operation. A Synchronous Receive operation begins with the receiver in the Hunt phase, during which the receiver searches the incoming data stream for a bit pattern that matches the preprogrammed sync characters (or flags in the SDLC mode). If the device is programmed for Monosync Hunt, a match is made with a single sync character stored in WR7. In Bisync Hunt, a match is made with dual sync characters stored in WR6 and WR7.

In either case, the incoming data passes through the receive sync registers and is compared against the programmed sync character in WR6 or WR7. In the Monosync mode, a match between the sync character programmed into WR7 and the character assembled in the receive sync register establishes synchronization.

In the Bisync mode, however, incoming data is shifted to the receive shift register while the next eight bits of the message are assembled in the receive sync register. The match between the assembled character in the receive sync registers with the programmed sync character in WR6 and WR7 establishes synchroniza-

155

tion. Once synchronization is established, incoming data bypasses the receive sync register and directly enters the 3-bit buffer.

In the SDLC mode, incoming data first passes through the receive sync register, which continuously monitors the receive data stream and performs zero deletion when indicated. Upon receiving five contiguous I's, the sixth bit is inspected. If the sixth bit is a 0, it is deleted from the data stream. If the sixth bit is a 1, the seventh bit is inspected. If that bit is a 0, a Flag sequence has been received; if it is a 1, an Abort sequence has been received.

The reformatted data enters the 3-bit buffer and is transferred to the receive shift register. Note that the SDLC receive operation also begins in the Hunt phase, during which the Z80-SIO tries to match the assembled character in the receive shift register with the flag pattern in WR7. Once the first flag character is recognized, all subsequent data is routed through the same path, regardless of character length.

Although the same CRC checker is used for both SDLC and synchronous data, the data path taken for each mode is different. In Bisync protocol, a byte-oriented operation requires that the CPU decide to include the data character in CRC. To allow the CPU ample time to make this decision, the Z80-SIO provides an 8-bit delay for synchronous data. In the SDLC mode, no delay is provided since the Z80-SIO contains logic that determines the bytes on which CRC is calculated.

The transmitter has an 8-bit transmit data register that is loaded from the internal data bus and a 20-bit transmit shift register that can be loaded from WR6, WR7 and the transmit data register. WR6 and WR7 contain sync characters in the Monosync or Bisync modes or address field (one character long) and flag, respectively, in the SDLC mode. During Synchronous modes, information contained in WR6 and WR7 is loaded into the transmit shift register at the beginning of the message and as a time filler, in the middle of the message if a Transmit Underrun condition occurs. In the SDLC mode, the flags are loaded into the transmit shift register at the beginning and end of message.

Asynchronous data in the transmit shift register is formatted with start and stop bits and is shifted out to the transmit multiplexer at the selected clock rate.

Synchronous (Monosync or Bisync) data is shifted out to the transmit multiplexer and also to the CRC generator at the x 1 clock rate.

SDLC/HDLC data is shifted out through the zero insertion logic, which is disabled while the flags are being sent. For all other fields (address, control and frame check) a 0 is inserted following five contiguous 1's in the data stream. The CRC generator result for SDLC data is also routed through the zero insertion logic.

FUNCTIONAL DESCRIPTION

The functional capabilities of the Z80-SIO can be described from two different points of view: as a data communications device, it transmits and receives serial data, and meets the requirements of various data communications protocols; as a Z80 family peripheral, it interacts with the Z80-CPU and other Z80 peripheral circuits, and shares their data, address and control busses, as well as being a part of the Z80 interrupt structure. As a peripheral to other microprocessors, the Z80-SIO offers valuable features such as non-vectored interrupts, polling, and simple handshake capabilities.

The first part of the following functional description describes the interaction between the CPU and Z80-SIO; the second part introduces its data communications capabilities.

I/O CAPABILITIES

The Z80-SIO offers the choice of Polling, Interrupt (vectored or non-vectored) and Block Transfer modes to transfer data, status, and control information to and from the CPU. The Block Transfer mode can be implemented under CPU or DMA control.

Polling. The Polled mode avoids interrupts. Status registers RR0 and RR1 are updated at appropriate times for each function being performed (for example, CRC Error status valid at the end of the message). All the interrupt modes of the Z80-SIO must be disabled to operate the device in a polled environment.

While in its Polling sequence, the CPU examines the status contained in RR0 for each channel; the RR0 status bits serve as an acknowledge to the Poll inquiry. The two RR0 status bits D_0 and D_2 indicate that a receive or transmit data transfer is needed. The status also indicates Error or other special status conditions (see "Z80-SIO Programming"). The Special Receive Condition status continued in RR1 does not have to be read in a Polling sequence because the status bits in RR1 are accompanied by a Receive Character Available status in RRO.

Interrupts. The Z80-SIO offers an elaborate interrupt scheme to provide fast interrupt response in real-time applications. As mentioned earlier, Channel B registers WR2 and RR2 contain the interrupt vector that points to an interupt service routine in the memory. To service operations in both channels and to eliminate the necessity of writing a status analysis routine, the Z80-SIO cna modify the interrupt vector in RR2 so it points directly to one of eight interrupt service routines. This is done under program control by setting a program bit (WR1, D_2) in Channel B called "Status Affects Vector." When this bit is set, the interrupt vector in WR2 is modified according to the assigned priority of the various interrupting conditions. The table in the Write Register 1 description (Z80-SIO Programming section) shows the modification details.

Transmit interrupts. Receive interrupts and External/Status interrupts are the main souces of interrupts. Each interrupt source is enabled under program control with Channel A having a higher priority than Channel B, and with Receiver, Transmit and External/Status interrupts prioritized in that order within each channel. When the Transmit interrupt is enabled, the CPU is interrupted by the transmit buffer becoming empty. (This implies that the transmitter must have had a data character written into it so it can become empty.) When enabled, the receiver can interrupt the CPU in one of three ways:

Interrupt on first receive character
Interrupt on all receive characters
Interrupt on a Special Receive condition

Interrupt On First Character is typically used with the Block Transfer mode.

Interrupt On All Receive Characters has the option of modifying the interrupt vector in the event of a parity error. The Special Receive Condition interrupt can occur on a character or message basis (End Of Frame interrupt in SDLC, for example). The Special Receive condition can cause an interrupt only if the Interrupt On First Receive Character or Interrupt On All Receive Characters mode is selected. In Interrupt On First Receive Character, an interrupt can occur from Special Receive conditions (except parity Error) after the first receive character interrupt (example: Receive Overrun interrupt).

The main function of the External/Status interrupt is to monitor the signal transitions of the $\overline{\text{CTS}}$, $\overline{\text{DCD}}$ and $\overline{\text{SYNC}}$ pins; however, an External/Status interrupt is also caused by a Transmit Underrun condition or by the detection of a Break (Asynchronous mode) or Abort (SDLC mode) sequence in the data stream. The interrupt caused by the Break/Abort sequence has a special feature that allows the Z80-SIO to interrupt when the Break/Abort sequence is detected or terminated. The feature facilitates the proper termination of the current message, correct initialization of the next message, and the accurate timing of the Break/Abort condition in external logic.

CPU/DMA Block Transfer. The Z80-SIO provides a Block Transfer mode to accommodate block transfer functions and DMA controllers (Z80-DMA or other designs). The Block Transfer mode uses the $\overline{\text{WAIT/READY}}$ output in conjunction with the Wait/Ready bits of Write Register 1. The $\overline{\text{WAIT/READY}}$ output can be defined under software control as a WAIT line in the CPU Block Transfer mode or as a READY line in the DMA Block Transfer mode.

To a DMA controller, the Z80-SIO READY output indicates that the Z80-SIO is ready to transfer data to or from memory. To the CPU, the WAIT output indicates that the Z80-SIO is not ready to transfer data, thereby requesting the CPU to extend the I/O cycle. The programming of bits 5, 6 and 7 of Write Register 1 and the logic states of the $\overline{\text{WAIT/READY}}$ line are defined in the Write Register 1 description (Z80-SIO Programming section.)

Data Communications Capabilities

In addition to the I/O capabilities previously discussed, the Z80-SIO provides two independent full-duplex channels as well as Asynchronous, Synchronous and SDLC (HDLC) operational modes. These modes facilitate the implementation of commonly used data communications protocols.

The specific features of these modes are described in the following sections. To preserve the independence and completeness of each section, some information common to all modes is repeated.

ASYNCHRONOUS OPERATION

To receive or transmit data in the Asynchronous mode, the Z80-SIO must be initialized with the following parameters: character length, clock rate, number of stop bits, even or odd parity, interrupt mode, and receiver or transmitter enable. The parameters are loaded into the appropriate write registers by the system program. WR4 parameters must be issued before WR1, WR3, and WR5 parameters or commands. Figure 7-6 illustrates.

158

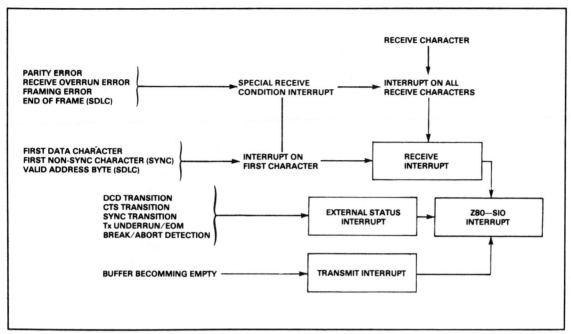

PARITY ERROR
RECEIVE OVERRUN ERROR
FRAMING ERROR
END OF FRAME (SDLC)

RECEIVE CHARACTER

SPECIAL RECEIVE CONDITION INTERRUPT

INTERRUPT ON ALL RECEIVE CHARACTERS

FIRST DATA CHARACTER
FIRST NON-SYNC CHARACTER (SYNC)
VALID ADDRESS BYTE (SDLC)

INTERRUPT ON FIRST CHARACTER

RECEIVE INTERRUPT

DCD TRANSITION
CTS TRANSITION
SYNC TRANSITION
Tx UNDERRUN/EOM
BREAK/ABORT DETECTION

EXTERNAL STATUS INTERRUPT

Z80—SIO INTERRUPT

BUFFER BECOMMING EMPTY

TRANSMIT INTERRUPT

Fig. 7-6. Interrupt structure.

If the data is transmitted over a modem or RS232C interface, the $\overline{\text{REQUEST TO SEND}}$ $(\overline{\text{RTS}})$ and $\overline{\text{DATA TERMINAL READY}}$ $(\overline{\text{DTR}})$ outputs must be set along with the Transmit Enable bit. Transmission cannot begin until the Transmit Enable bit is set.

The Auto Enables feature allows the programmer to send the first data character of the message to the Z80-SIO without waiting for $\overline{\text{CTS}}$. If the Auto Enables bit is set, the Z80-SIO will wait for the $\overline{\text{CTS}}$ pin to go Low before it begins data transmission. $\overline{\text{CTS}}$, $\overline{\text{DCD}}$, and $\overline{\text{SYNC}}$ are general-purpose I/O lines that may be used for functions other than their labeled purposes. If $\overline{\text{CTS}}$ is used for another purpose, the Auto Enables Bit must be programmed to 0.

Figure 7-7 illustrates asynchronous message formats. Table 7-2 shows WR3, WR4, and WR5 with bits set to indicate the applicable modes, parameters, and commands in asynchronous modes. WR2 (Channel B only) stores the interrupt vector and WR1 defines the interrupt modes and data transfer modes. WR6 and WR7 are not used in asynchronous modes. Table 7-3 shows the typical program steps that implement a full-duplex receive/transmit operation in either channel.

ASYNCHRONOUS TRANSMIT

The Transmit Data output (TxD) is held marking (High) when the transmitter has no data to send. Under program control, the Send Break (WR5, D_4) command can be issued to hold TxD spacing (Low) until the command is cleared.

159

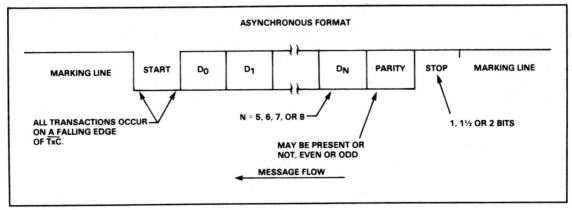

Fig. 7-7. Asynchronous message format.

The Z80-SIO automatically adds the start bit, the programmed parity bit (odd, even or no parity) and the programmed number of stop bits to the data character to be transmitted. When the character length is six or seven bits, the unused bits are automatically ignored by the Z80-SIO. If the character length is five bits or less, refer to the table in the Write Register 5 description (Z80-SIO Programming section) for the data format.

Serial data is shifted from TxD at a rate equal to 1, 1/16th, 1/32nd, or 1/64th of the clock rate supplied to the Transmit Clock input ($\overline{\text{TxC}}$). Serial data is shifted out on the falling edge of ($\overline{\text{TxC}}$).

If set, the External/Status Interrupt mode monitors the status of $\overline{\text{DCD}}$, $\overline{\text{CTS}}$ and $\overline{\text{SYNC}}$ throughout the transmission of the message. If these inputs change for a period of time greater than the minimum specified pulse width, the interrupt is generated. In a transmit operation, this feature is used to monitor the modem control signal $\overline{\text{CTS}}$.

ASYNCHRONOUS RECEIVE

Asynchronous Receive operation begins when the Receive Enable bit is set. If the Auto Enables option is selected, $\overline{\text{DCD}}$ must be Low as well. A Low (spacing) condition on the Receive Data input (RxD) indicates a start bit. If this Low persists for at least one-half of a bit time, the start bit is assumed to be valid and the data input is then sampled at mid-bit time until the entire character is assembled. This method of detecting a start bit improves error rejection when noise spikes exist on an otherwise marking line.

If the x1 clock mode is selected, bit synchronization must be accomplished externally. Receive data is sampled on the rising edge of RxC. The receiver inserts 1's when a character length of other than eight bits is used. If parity is enabled, the parity bit is not stripped from the assembled character for character lengths other than eight bits. For lengths other than eight bits, the receiver assembles a character length of the required number of data bits, plus a parity bit and 1's for any unused bits. For example, the receiver assembles a 5-bit character with the following format: $11\ P\ D_4\ D_3\ D_2\ D_1\ D_0$.

Since the receiver is buffered by three 8-bit registers in addition to the receive shift register, the CPU has enough time to service an interrupt and to accept the data character assembled by the Z80-SIO. The receiver also has three buffers that store error flags for each data character in the receive buffer. These error flags are loaded at the same time as the data characters.

After a character is received, it is checked for the following error conditions:

When parity is enabled, the Parity Error bit (RR1, D_4) is set whenever the parity bit of the character does not match with the programmed parity. Once this bit is set, it remains set until the Error Reset Command (WR0) is given.

The Framing Error bit (RR1, D_6) is set if the character is assembled without any stop bits (that is a Low level detected for a stop bit). Unlike the Parity Error bit, this bit is set (and not latched) only for the character on which it occurred. Detection of framing error adds an additional one-half of a bit time to the character time so the framing error is not interpreted as a new start bit.

If the CPU fails to read a data character while more than three characters have been received, the Receive Overrun bit (RR1, D_5) is set. When this occurs, the fourth character assembled replaces the third character in the receive buffers. With this arrangement, only the character that has been written over is flagged with the Receive Overrun Error bit. Like Parity Error, this bit can only be reset by the Error Reset command from the CPU. Both the Framing Error and Receive Overrun Error cause an interrupt with the interrupt vector indicating a Special Receive condition (if Status Affects Vector is selected).

Since the Parity Error and Receive Overrun Error flags are latched, the error status that is read reflects an error in the current word in the receive buffer plus any Parity or Overrun Errors received since the last Error Reset command. To keep correspondence between the state of the error buffers and the contents of the receive data buffers, the error status register must be read before the data. This is easily accomplished if vectored interrupts are used, because a special interrupt vector is generated for these conditions.

Table 7-2. Contents of Write Registers 3, 4 and 5 in Asynchronous Modes.

	BIT 7	BIT 6	BIT 5	BIT 4	BIT 3	BIT 2	BIT 1	BIT 0
WR3	00 = Rx 5 BITS/CHAR 10 = Rx 6 BITS/CHAR 01 = Rx 7 BITS/CHAR 11 = Rx 8 BITS/CHAR		AUTO ENABLES	0	0	0	0	Rx ENABLE
WR 4	00 = x1 CLOCK MODE 01 = X16 CLOCK MODE 10 = x32 CLOCK MODE 11 = x64 CLOCK MODE		0	0	00 = NOT USED 01 = 1 STOP BIT/CHAR 10 = 1½ STOP BITS/CHAR 11 = 2 STOP BITS/CHAR		EVEN-ODD PARITY	PARITY ENABLE
WR5	DTR	00 = Tx 5 BITS (OR LESS) CHAR 10 = Tx 6 BITS/CHAR 01 = Tx 7 BITS/CHAR 11 = Tx 8 BITS/CHAR		SEND BREAK	Tx ENABLE	0	RTS	0

Table 7-3. Asynchronous Mode.

FUNCTION	TYPICAL PROGRAM STEPS	COMMENTS
	REGISTER: INFORMATION LOADED:	
	WR0 CHANNEL RESET	Reset SIO
	WR0 POINTER 2	
	WR2 INTERRUPT VECTOR	Channel B only
	WR0 POINTER 4, RESET EXTERNAL/STATUS INTERRUPT	
	WR4 ASYNCHRONOUS MODE, PARITY INFORMATION, STOP BITS INFORMATION, CLOCK RATE INFORMATION	Issue Parameters
INITIALIZE	WR0 POINTER 3	
	WR3 RECEIVE ENABLE, AUTO ENABLES, RECEIVE CHARACTER LENGTH	
	WR0 POINTER 5	
	WR5 REQUEST TO SEND, TRANSMIT ENABLE, TRANSMIT CHARACTER LENGTH, DATA TERMINAL READY	Receive and Transmit both fully initialized. Auto Enables will enable Transmitter if $\overline{CTS}$ is active and Receiver if $\overline{DCD}$ is active.
	WR0 POINTER 1, RESET EXTERNAL/STATUS INTERRUPT	
	WR1 TRANSMIT INTERRUPT ENABLE, STATUS AFFECTS VECTOR, INTERRUPT ON ALL RECEIVE CHARACTERS, DISABLE WAIT/READY FUNCTION, EXTERNAL INTERRUPT ENABLE	Transmit/Receive interrupt mode selected. External Interrupt monitors the status $\overline{CTS}$. $\overline{DCD}$ and $\overline{SYNC}$ inputs and detects the Break sequence. Status Affects Vector in Channel B only.
	TRANSFER FIRST DATA BYTE TO SIO	This data byte must be transferred or no transmit interrupts will occur.
IDLE MODE	EXECUTE HALT INSTRUCTION OR SOME OTHER PROGRAM	Program is waiting for an interrupt from the SIO.
	Z80 INTERRUPT ACKNOWLEDGE CYCLE TRANSFERS RR2 TO CPU	When the interrupt occurs, the interrupt vector is modified by: 1. Receive Character Available; 2. Transmit Buffer Empty; 3. External/Status change; and 4. Special Receive condition.
	IF A CHARACTER IS RECEIVED: TRANSFER DATA CHARACTER TO CPU UPDATE POINTERS AND PARAMETERS RETURN FROM INTERRUPT	
DATA TRANSFER AND ERROR MONITORING	IF TRANSMITTER BUFFER IS EMPTY: TRANSFER DATA CHARACTER TO SIO UPDATE POINTERS AND PARAMETERS RETURN FROM INTERRUPT	Program control is transferred to one of the eight interrupt service routines.
	IF EXTERNAL STATUS CHANGES: TRANSFER RR0 TO CPU	If used with processors other than the Z80, the modified interrupt vector (RR2)

FUNCTION	TYPICAL PROGRAM STEPS	COMMENTS
	REGISTER: INFORMATION LOADED:	
	PERFORM ERROR ROUTINES (INCLUDE BREAK DETECTION) RETURN FROM INTERRUPT	should be returned to the CPU in the Interrupt Acknowledge sequence.
	IF SPECIAL RECEIVE CONDITION OCCURS: TRANSFER RR1 to CPU DO SPECIAL ERROR (E.G. FRAMING ERROR) RETURN FROM INTERRUPT	
	REDEFINE RECEIVE/TRANSMIT INTERRUPT MODES	When transmit or receive data transfer is complete.
TERMINATION	DISABLE TRANSMIT/RECEIVE MODES	
	UPDATE MODEM CONTROL OUTPUTS (E.G. RTS OFF)	In transmit the All Sent Status bit indicates transmission is complete.

While the External/Status interrupt is enabled, break detection causes an interrupt and the Break Detected status bit (RR0, D_7), is set. The Break Detected interrupt should be handled by issuing the Reset External/status Interrupt command to the Z80-SIO in response to the first Break Detected interrupt that has a Break status of 1 (RR0, D_7). The Z80-SIO monitors the Receive Data input and waits for the Break sequence to terminate, at which point the Z80-SIO interrupts the CPU with the Break status set to 0. The CPU must again issue the Reset External/Status Interrupt command in its interrupt service routine to reinitialize the break detection logic.

The External/Status interrupt also monitors the status of DCD. If the DCD pin becomes inactive for a period greater than the minimum specified pulse width, an interrupt is generated with the DCD status bit (RR0, D_3) set to 1. Note that the DCD input is inverted in the RR0 status register.

If the status is read after the data, the error data for the next word is also included if it has been stacked in the buffer. If operations are performed rapidly enough so the next character is not yet received, the status register remains valid. An exception occurs when the Interrupt On First Character Only mode is selected. A special interrupt in this Mode holds the error data and the character itself (even if read from the buffer) until the Error Reset command is issued. This prevents further data from becoming available in the receiver until the Reset command is issued, and allows CPU intervention on the character with the error even if DMA or block transfer techniques are being used.

If Interrupt On Every Character is selected, the interrupt vector is different if there is an error status in RR1. If a Receiver Overrun occurs, the most recent character received is loaded into the buffer; the character preceding it is lost. When the character that has been written over is read, the Receive Overrun bit is set and the Special Receive Condition vector is returned if Status Affects Vector is enabled.

163

In a polled environment, the Receive Character Available bit (RR0, D_0) must be monitored so the Z80-CPU can know when to read a character. This bit is automatically reset when the receive buffers are read. To prevent overwriting data in polled operations, the transmit buffer status must be checked before writing into the transmitter. The Transmit Buffer Empty bit is set to 1 whenever the transmit buffer becomes empty.

SYNCHRONOUS OPERATION

Before describing synchronous transmission and reception, the three types of character synchronization-Monosync, Bisync, and External Sync-require some explanation. These modes use the x1 clock for both Transmit and Receive operations. Data is sampled on the rising edge of the Receive Clock input ($\overline{\text{RxC}}$). Transmitter data transitions occur on the falling edge of the Transmit Clock input (TxC).

The differences between Monosync, Bisync, and External Sync are in the manner in which initial character synchronization is achieved. The mode of operation must be selected before sync characters are loaded because the registers are used differently in the various modes. Figure 7-8 shows the formats for all three of these synchronous modes.

Monosync. In a Receive operation, matching a single sync character (8-bit sync model) with the programmed sync character stored in WR7 implies character synchronization and enables data transfer.

Bisync. Matching two contiguous sync characters (16-bit sync mode) with the programmed sync characters stored in WR6 and WR7 implies character synchronization. In both the Monosync and Bisync

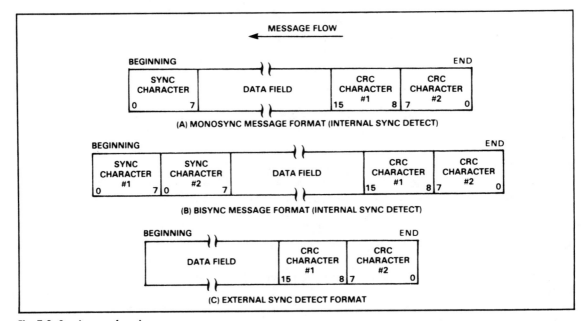

Fig. 7-8. Synchronous formats.

modes, $\overline{\text{SYNC}}$ is used as an output and is active for the part of the receive clock that detects the sync character.

External Sync. In this mode, character synchronization is established externally; $\overline{\text{SYNC}}$ is an input that indicates external character synchronization has been achieved. After the sync pattern is detected, the external logic must wait for two full Receive Clock Cycles to activate the $\overline{\text{SYNC}}$ input. The $\overline{\text{SYNC}}$ input must be held low until character synchronization is lost. Character assembly begins on the rising edge of $\overline{\text{RxC}}$ that precedes the falling edge of $\overline{\text{SYNC}}$.

In all cases after a reset, the receiver is in the Hunt phase, during which the Z80-SIO looks for character synchronization. The hunt can begin only when the receiver is enabled, and data transfer can begin only when character synchronization has been achieved. If character synchronization is lost, the Hunt phase can be re-entered by writing a control word with the Enter Hunt Phase bit set (WR3, D_4). In the Transmit mode, the transmitter always sends the programmed number of sync bits (8 or 16). In the Monosync mode, the transmitter transmits for WR6; the receiver compares against WR7.

In the Monosync, Bisync, and External Sync modes, assembly of received data continues until the Z80-SIO is reset, or until the receiver is disabled (by command or DCD in the Auto Enables mode), or until the CPU sets the Enter Hunt Phase bit.

After initial synchronization has been achieved, the operation of the Monosync, Bisync, and External Sync modes is quite similar. Any differences are specified in the following text.

Table 7-4 shows how WR3, WR4, and WR5 are used in synchronous receive and transmit operations. WR0 points to other registers and issues various commands, WR1 defines the interrupt modes, WR2 stores the interrupt vector and WR6 and WR7 store sync characters. Table 7-5 illustrates the typical program steps that implement a half-duplex Bisync transmit operation.

Table 7-4. Contents of Write Registers 3, 4, and 5 in Synchronous Modes.

	BIT 7	BIT 6	BIT 5	BIT 4	BIT 3	BIT 2	BIT 1	BIT 0
WR3	00=Rx 5 BITS/CHAR 10=Rx 6 BITS/CHAR 01=Rx 7 BITS/CHAR 11=Rx 8 BITS/CHAR		AUTO ENABLES	ENTER HUNT MODE	Rx CRC ENABLE	0	SYNC CHAR LOAD INHIBIT	RX ENABLE
WR4	0	0	00=8-BIT SYNC CHAR 01=16-BIT SYNC CHAR 10=SDLC MODE 11=EXT SYNC MODE		0 SELECTS SYNC MODES	0	EVEN/$\overline{\text{ODD}}$ PARITY	PARITY ENABLE
WR5	DTR	00=Tx 5 BITS (OR LESS)/CHAR 10=Tx 6 BITS/CHAR 01=Tx 7 BITS/CHAR 11=Tx 8 BITS/CHAR		SEND BREAK	Tx ENABLE	1 SELECTS CRC-16	RTS	Tx CRC ENABLE

Table 7-5. Bisync Transmit Code.

FUNCTION		TYPICAL PROGRAM STEPS	COMMENTS
	REGISTER:	INFORMATION LOADED:	
	WR0	CHANNEL RESET, RESET TRANSMIT CRC GENERATOR	Reset SIO, initialize CRC generator
	WR0	POINTER 2	
	WR2	INTERRUPT VECTOR	Channel B only
	WR0	POINTER 3	
	WR3	AUTO ENABLES	Transmission begins only after CTS is detected.
	WR0	POINTER 4	
	WR4	PARITY INFORMATION, SYNC MODES INFORMATION, x1 CLOCK MODE	Issue transmit parameters.
	WR0	POINTER 6	
	WR6	SYNC CHARACTER 1	
	WR0	POINTER 7, RESET EXTERNAL/STATUS INTERRUPTS	
INITIALIZE	WR7	SYNC CHARACTER 2	
	WR0	POINTER 1, RESET EXTERNAL/STATUS INTERRUPTS	
	WR1	STATUS AFFECTS VECTOR, EXTERNAL INTERRUPT ENABLE, TRANSMIT INTERRUPT ENABLE OR WAIT/READY ENABLE	External Interrupt mode Monitors the status of $\overline{CTS}$ and $\overline{DCD}$ input pins as well as the status of Tx Underrun/EOM latch. Transmit Interrupt Enable interrupts when the Transmit buffer becomes empty; the Wait/Ready mode can be used to transfer data using DMA or CPU Block Transfer.
	WR0	POINTER 5	Status Affects Vector (Channel B only)
	WR5	REQUEST TO SEND, TRANSMIT ENABLE, BISYNC CRC, TRANSMIT CHARACTER LENGTH	Transmit CRC Enable should be set when first non-sync data is sent to Z80-SIO.
		FIRST SYNC BYTE TO SIO	Need several sync characters in the beginning of message. Transmitter is fully initialized.
IDLE MODE		EXECUTE HALT INSTRUCTION OR SOME OTHER PROGRAM	Waiting for interrupt or Wait/Ready output to transfer data.
DATA TRANSFER AND STATUS MONITORING		**WHEN INTERRUPT (WAIT/READY) OCCURS:** INCLUDE/EXCLUDE DATA BYTE FROM CRC ACCUMULATION (IN SIO). TRANSFER DATA BYTE FROM CPU (OR MEMORY) TO SIO. DETECT AND SET APPROPRIATE FLAGS FOR CONTROL CHARACTERS (IN CPU).	Interrupt occurs (Wait/Ready becomes active) when first data byte is being sent. Wait mode allows CPU block tranfer from memory to SIO; Ready mode allows DMA block transfer from memory to SIO. The DMA chip can be programmed to capture special control characters (by examining only the bits that specify ASCII or EBCDIC control characters) and interrupt CPU.

166

FUNCTION	TYPICAL PROGRAM STEPS	COMMENTS
	RESET Tx UNDERRUN/EOM LATCH (WR0) IF LAST CHARACTER OF MESSAGE IS DETECTED. UPDATE POINTERS AND PARAMETERS (CPU). RETURN FROM INTERRUPT.	
	IF ERROR CONDITION OR STATUS CHANGE OCCURS: TRANSFER RR0 TO CPU EXECUTE ERROR ROUTINE RETURN FROM INTERRUPT	Tx Underrun/EOM indicates either transmit underrun (sync character being) sent to end of message (CRC-16 being sent)
TERMINATION	REDEFINE INTERRUPT MODES. UPDATE MODEM CONTROL OUTPUTS (E.G., TURN OFF RTS). DISABLE TRANSMIT MODE	Program should gracefully terminate message.

SYNCHRONOUS TRANSMIT

The system program must intialize the transmitter with the following parameters: odd or even parity, x1 clock mode, 8- or 16-bit sync character(s), CRC polynomial, Transmitter Enables, Request To Send, Data Terminal Ready, interrupt modes, and transmit character length. WR4 parameters must be issued before WR1, WR3, WR5, WR6, and WR7 parameters or commands.

One of two polynomials CRC-16($x^{16} + X^{15} + X^2 + 1$) or SDLC ($X^{16} + X^{12} + X^5 + 1$) may be used with synchronous modes. In either case (SDLC mode not selected), the CRC generator and checker are reset to all 0's. In the transmit initialization process, the CRC generator is initialized by setting the Reset Transmit CRC Generator command bits (WR0). Both the transmitter and the receiver use the same polynomial.

Transmit Interrupt Enable or Wait/Ready Enable can be selected to transfer the data. The External/ Status interrupt mode is used to monitor the status of the CLEAR TO SEND input as well as the Transmit Underrun/EOM latch. Optionally, the Auto Enables feature can be used to enable the transmitter when CTS is active monitored so the Z80-CPU can know when to read a character. This bit is automatically reset when the receive buffers are read. To prevent overwriting data in polled operations, the transmit buffer status must be checked before writing into the transmitter. The Transmit Buffer Empty bit is set to 1 whenever the transmit buffer becomes empty.

The first data transfer to the Z80-SIO can begin when the External/Status interrupt occurs (CTS status bit set) or immediately following the Transmit Enable command (if the Auto Enables modes are set).

Transmit data is held marking after reset or if the transmitter is not enabled. Break may be programmed to generate a spacing line that begins as soon as the Send Break bit is set. With the transmitter fully initialized and enabled, the default condition is continuous transmission of the 8- or 16-bit sync character.

Data Transfer and Status Monitoring

In this phase, there are several combinations of interrupts and Wait/Ready. Table 7-5 shows typical program steps that implement a bi-sync transmit mode.

Data Transfer Using Interrupts. If the Transmit Interrupt Enable bit (WR1, D_1) is set, an interrupt is generated each time the transmit buffer becomes empty. The interrupt can be satisfied either by writing another character into the transmitter or by resetting the Transmitter Interrupt Pending latch with a Reset Transmitter Pending command (WR0, CMD_5). If the interrupt is satisfied with this command and nothing more is written into the Transmitter, there can be no further Transmit Buffer Empty interrupts, because it is the process of the buffer becoming empty that causes the interrupts. This situation does cause a Transmit Underrun condition, which is expalined in the "Bisync Transmit Underrun" section.

Data Transfer Using WAIT/READY. To the CPU, the activation of $\overline{\text{WAIT}}$ indicates that the Z80-SIO is not ready to accept data and that the CPU must extend the output cycle. To a DMA controller, READY indicates that the transmit buffer is empty and that the Z80-SIO is ready to accept the next data character. If the data character is not loaded into the Z80-SIO by the time the transmit shift register is empty, the Z80-SIO enters the Transmit Underrun condition.

Bisync Transmit Underrun. In Bisync protocol, filler characters are inserted to maintain synchronization when the transmitter has no data to send (Transmit Underrun condition). The Z80-SIO has two programmable options for solving this situation: it can insert sync characters or it can send the CRC characters generated so far, followed by sync characters.

These options are under the control of the Reset Transmit Underrun/EOM command in WR0. Following a chip or channel reset, the Transmit Underrun/EOM status bit (RR0, D_6) is in a set condition and allows the insertion of sync characters when there is no data to send. CRC is not calculated on the automatically inserted sync characters. When the CPU detects the end of message, a Reset Transmit Underrun/EOM command can be issued. This allows CRC to be sent when the transmitter has no data. In this case, the Z80-SIO sends CRC, followed by sync characters, to terminate the message.

There is no restriction as to when in the message the Transmit Underrun/EOM bit can be reset. If Reset is issued after the first data character has been loaded, the 16-bit CRC is sent and followed by sync characters the first time the transmitter has no data to send. Because of the Transmit Underrun condition, an External/Status interrupt is generated whenever the Transmit Underrun/EOM bit becomes set.

In the case of sync insertion, an interrupt is generated only after the first automatically inserted sync character has been loaded. The status indicates the Transmit Underrun/EOM bit and the Transmit Buffer Empty bit are set.

In the case of CRC insertion, the Transmit Underrun/EOM bit is set and the Transmit Buffer Empty bit is reset while CRC is being sent. When CRC has been completely sent, the Transmit Buffer Empty status bit is set and an interrupt is generated to indicate to the CPU that another message can begin (this interrupt occurs because CRC has been sent and sync has been loaded). If no more messages are to be sent, the program can terminate transmission by resetting RTS and disabling the transmitter (WR5, D_3).

Pad characters may be sent by setting the Z80-SIO to 8-bits/transmit character and writing FF to the transmitter while CRC is being sent. Alternatively, the sync characters can be redefined as pad characters during this time. The following example is included to clarify this point.

The Z80-SIO interrupts with the Transmit Buffer Empty bit set.

The CPU recognizes that the last character (ETX) of the message has already been sent to the Z80-SIO by examining the internal program status.

To force the Z80-SIO to send CRC, the CPU issues the Reset Transmit Underrun/EOM Latch command (WRO) and satisfies the interrupt with the Reset Transmit Interrupt Pending command. (This command prevents the Z80-SIO from requesting more data.) Because of the transmit underrun caused by this command, the Z80-SIO starts sending CRC. The Z80-SIO also causes an External/Status interrupt with the Transmit Underrun/EOM latch set.

The CPU satisfies this interrupt by loading pad characters into the transmit buffer and issuing the Reset External/Status Interrupt command.

With this sequence, CRC is followed by a pad character instead of a sync character. Note that the Z80-SIO will interrupt with a Transmit Buffer Empty interrupt when CRC is completely sent and that the pad character is loaded into the transmit shift register.

From this point on, the CPU can send more pad characters or sync characters.

Bisync CRC Generation. Setting the Transmit CRC enable bit (WR5, D_0) intiates CRC accumulation when the program sends the first data character to the Z80-SIO. Although the Z80-SIO automatically transmits up to two sync characters (16-bit sync), it is wise to send a few more sync characters ahead of the message (before enabling Transmit CRC) to ensure synchronization at the receiving end.

The transmit CRC Enable bit can be changed on the fly any time in the message to include or exclude a particular data character from CRC accumulation. The Transmit CRC Enable bit should be in the desired state when the data character is loaded from the transmit data buffer into the transmit shift register. To ensure this bit is in the proper state, the Transmit CRC Enable bit must be issued before sending the data character to the Z80-SIO.

Transmit Transparent Mode. Transparent mode (Bisync protocol) operation is made possible by the ability to change Transmit CRC Enable on the fly and by the additional capability of inserting 16-bit sync characters. Exclusion of the DLE characters from CRC calculation can be achieved by disabling CRC calculation immediately preceding the DLE character transfer to the Z80-SIO.

In the case of a Transmit Underrun condition in the Transparent mode, a pair of DLE-SYN characters are sent. The Z80-SIO can be programmed to send the DLE-SYN sequence by loading a DLE character into WR6 and a sync character into WR7.

Transmit Termination. The Z80-SIO is equipped with a special termination that maintains data integrity and validity. If the transmitter is disabled while a data or sync character is being sent, that character is sent as usual, but is followed by a marking line rather than CRC or sync characters. When the transmitter is disabled, a character in the buffer remains in the buffer. If the transmitter is disabled while CRC is being sent, the 16-bit transmission is completed, but sync is sent instead of CRC.

A programmed break is effective as soon as it is written into the control register; characters in the transmit buffer and shift register are lost.

In all modes, characters are sent with the least significant bits first. This requires right-hand justification of transmitted data if the word length is less than eight bits. If the word length is five bits or less, the special technique described in the Write Register 5 discussion (Z80-SIO Programming section) must be used for the data format. The states of any unused bits in a data character are irrelevant, except when in the Five Bits or Less mode.

If the External/Status Interrupt Enable bit is set, transmitter conditions such as "starting to send CRC characters" "starting to send sync characters," and $\overline{CTS}$ changing state cause interrupts that have a unique vector if Status Affects Vector is set. This interrupt mode may be used during block transfers.

All interrupts may be disabled for operation in a Polled mode or to avoid interrupts at inappropriate times during the execution of a program.

SYNCHRONOUS RECEIVE

The system program initiates the Synchronous Receive operation with the following parameters: odd or even parity, 8- or 16-bit sync characters, x1 clock mode, CRC polynomial, receive character length, etc. Sync characters must be loaded into registers WR6 and WR7. The receivers can be enabled only after all receive parameters are set. WR4 parameters must be issued before WR1, WR3, WR5, WR6 and WR7 parameters or commands.

After this is done, the receiver is in the Hunt phase. It remains in this phase until character synchronization is achieved. Note that, under program control, all the leading sync characters of the message can be inhibited from loading the receive buffers by setting the Sync Character Load inhibit bit in WR3.

Data Transfer and Status Monitoring

After character synchronization is achieved, the assembled characters are transferred to the receive data FIFO. The following four interrupt modes are available to transfer the data and its associated status to the CPU.

No Interrupts Enabled. This mode is used for a purely polled operation of for off-line conditions.

Interrupt On First Character Only. This mode is normally used to start a polling loop or a Block Transfer instruction using $\overline{WAIT/READY}$ to synchronize the CPU or the DMA device to the incoming data rate. In this mode, the Z80-SIO interrupts on the first character and thereafter interrupts only if Special

Receive conditions are detected. The mode is reinitialized with the Enable Interrupt on Next Receive Character command to allow the next character received to generate an interrupt. Parity errors do not cause interrupts in this mode, but End Of Frame (SDLC mode) and Receive Overrun do.

If External/Status interrupts are enabled, they may interrupt any time $\overline{DCD}$ changes state.

Interrupt On Every Character. Whenever a character enters the receive buffer, an interrupt is generated. Error and Special Receive conditions generate a special vector if Status Affects Vector is selected. Optionally, a Parity Error may be directed not to generate the special interrupt vector.

Special Receive Condition Interrupts. The Special Receive Condition interrupt can occur only if either the Receive Interrupt On First Character Only or Interrupt On Every Receive Character modes are also set. The Special Receive Condition interrupt is caused by the Receive Overrun error condition. Since the Receive Overrun and Parity error status bits are latched, the error status-when read-reflects an error in the current word in the receive buffer in addition to any Parity or Overrun errors received since the last Error Reset command. These status bits can only be reset by the Error reset command.

CRC Error Checking and Termination. A CRC error check on the receive message can be performed on a per character basis under program control. The Receive CRC Enable bit (WR3, D_3) must be set/reset by the program before the next character is transferred from the receive shift register into the receive buffer register. This ensures proper inclusion or exclusion of data characters in the CRC check.

In the Monosync, Bisync, and External Sync modes, the CRC/Framing Error bit (RR1, D_6) contains the comparison result of the CRC checker 16 bit times (eight bits delay and eight shifts for CRC) after the character has been transferred from the receive shift register to the buffer. The result should be zero, indicating an error-free transmission. (Note that the result is valid only at the end of CRC calculation. If the result is examined before this time, it usually indicates an error.) The comparison is made with each transfer and is valid only as long as the character remains in the receive FIFO.

Following is an example of the CRC checking operation when four characters (A,B,C, and D) are received in that order.
    Character A loaded into buffer
    Character B loaded into buffer

If CRC is disabled before C is in the buffer, CRC is not calculated on B.
    Character C loaded into buffer

After C is loaded, the CRC/Framing Error bit shows the result of the comparison through character A.
    Character D loaded into buffer

After D is in the buffer, the CRC Error bit shows the result of the comparison through character B whether or not B was included in the CRC calculations.

Due to the serial nature of CRC calculation, the Receive Clock (RxC) must cycle 16 times (8-bit delay plus 8-bit CRC shift) after the second CRC character has been loaded into the receive buffer, or 20 times (the previous 16 plus 3-bit buffer delay and 1-bit input delay) after the last bit is at the RxD input, before CRC

Table 7-6. Bisync Receive Mode.

FUNCTION	TYPICAL PROGRAM STEPS	COMMENTS
	REGISTER: INFORMATION LOADED	
	WR0 CHANNEL RESET, RESET RECEIVE CRC CHECKER	Reset SIO, initialize Receive CRC checker
	WR0 POINTER 2	
	WR2 INTERRUPT VECTOR	Channel B only
	WR0 POINTER 4	
	WR4 PARITY INFORMATION, SYNC MODES INFRMATION, x1 CLOCK MODE	Issue receive parameters.
	WR0 POINTER 5, RESET EXTERNAL STATUS INTERRUPT	
	WR5 BISYNC CRC-16 DATA TERMINAL READY	
	WR0 POINTER 3	
INITIALIZE	WR3 SYNC CHARACTER LOAD INHIBIT, RECEIVE CRC ENABLE, ENTER HUNT MODE, AUTO ENABLES, RECEIVE CHARACTER LENGTH	Sync character load inhibit strips all the loading sync characters at the beginning of the message. Auto Enables enables the receiver to accept data only after the $\overline{\text{DCD}}$ input is active
	WR0 POINTER 6	
	WR6 SYNC CHARACTER 1	
	WR0 POINTER 7	
	WR7 SYNC CHARACTER 2	
	WR0 POINTER 1, RESET EXTERNAL/STATUS INTERRUPT	
	WR1 STATUS AFFECTS VECTOR, EXTERNAL INTERRUPT ENABLE, RECEIVE INTERRUPT ON FIRST CHARACTER ONLY	In this interrupt mode, only the first non-sync data character is transferred to the CPU. All subsequent data is transferred on a DMA basis; however, Special Receive Condition interrupts will interrupt the CPU. Status Affects Vector used in Channel B only.
	WR0 POINTER 3, ENABLE INTERRUPT ON NEXT RECEIVE CHARACTER	Resetting this interrupt mode provides simple program loopback entry for the next transaction.
	WR3 RECEIVE ENABLE SYNC CHARACTER LOAD INHIBIT, ENTER HUNT MODE, AUTO ENABLE, RECEIVE WORD LENGTH	WR3 is reissued to enable receiver. Receive CRC Enable must be set after receiving SOH or STX character.
IDLE MODE	EXECUTE HALT INSTRUCTION OR SOME OTHER PROGRAM	Receive mode is fully initialized and the system is waiting for interrupt on first character.

FUNCTION	TYPICAL PROGRAM STEPS	COMMENTS
	WHEN INTERRUPT ON FIRST CHARACTER OCCURS, THE CPU DOES THE FOLLOWING: • TRANSFERS DATA BYTE TO CPU • DETECTS AND SETS APPROPRIATE FLAGS FOR CONTROL CHARACTERS (IN CPU) • INCLUDES/EXCLUDES DATA BYTE IN CRC CHECKER • UPDATES POINTERS AND OTHER PARAMETERS • ENABLES WAIT/READY FOR DMA OPERATION • ENABLES DMA CONTROLLER • RETURNS FOR INTERRUPT	During the Hunt mode, the SIO detects two contiguous characters to establish synchronization. The CPU establishes the DMA mode and all subsequent data characters are transferred by the DMA controller. The controller is also programmed to capture special characters (by examining only the bits that specify ASCII or EBCDIC control characters) and interrupt the CPU upon detection. In response, the CPU examines the status or control characters and takes appropriate action (e.g., CRC Enable Update)
DATA TRANSFER AND STATUS MONITORING	**WHEN WAIT/READY BECOMES ACTIVE, THE DMA CONTROLLER DOES THE FOLLOWING:** • TRANSFERS DATA BYTE TO MEMORY • INTERRUPTS CPU IF A SPECIAL CHARACTER IS CAPTURED BY THE DMA CONTROLLER • INTERRUPTS THE CPU IF THE LAST CHARACTER OF THE MESSAGE IS DETECTED	
	FOR MESSAGE TERMINATION, THE CPU DOES THE FOLLOWING: • TRANSFERS RR1 TO THE CPU • SETS ACK/NAK REPLY FLAG BASED ON CRC RESULT • UPDATES POINTERS AND PARAMETERS • RETURNS FROM INTERRUPT	The SIO interrupts the CPU for error condition and the error routine aborts the present message, clears the error condition and repeats the operation.
TERMINATION	REDEFINE INTERRUPT MODES AND SYNC MODES UPDATE MODEM CONTROLS DISABLES RECEIVE MODE	

calculation is complete. A faster external clock can be gated into the Receive Clock input to supply the required 16 cycles.

The typical program steps that implement a half-duplex Bisync Receive mode are illustrated in Table 7-6. The complete set of command and status bit definitions are explained under "Z80-SIO Programming."

SYNCHRONOUS DATA LINK CONTROL

The Z80-SIO is capable of handling both High-Level Synchronous Data Link Control (HDLC) and IBM Synchronous Data Link Control (SDLC) protocols. In the following discussion, only SDLC is referred to because of the high degree of similarity between SDLC and HDLC. Table 7-7 shows the contents of write Registers 3, 4, and 5 in SDLC modes.

The SDLC mode is considerably different than Synchronous Bisyncund protocol because it is bit oriented rather than character oriented and, therefore, can naturally handle transparent operation. Bit orientation makes SDLC a flexible protocol in terms of message length and bit patterns. The Z80-SIO has several built-in features to handle variable message length. Detailed information concerning SDLC protocol can be found in literature published on this subject, such as IBM document GA27-3093.

The SDLC message, called the frame (Fig. 7-9), is opened and closed by flags that are similar to the sync characters in Bisync protocol. The Z80-SIO handles the transmission and recognition of the flag characters that mark the beginning and end of the frame. Note that the Z80-SIO can receive shared-zero flags, but cannot transmit them. The 8-bit address field of a SDLC frame contains the secondary station address. The Z80-SIO has an Address Search mode that recognizes the secondary station so that it can accept or reject the frame.

Since the control field of the SDLC frame is transparent to the Z80-SIO, it is simply transferred to the CPU. The Z80-SIO handles the Frame Check sequence in a manner that simplifies the program by

Table 7-7. Contents of Write Registers, 3, 4 and 5 in SDLC Modes.

	BIT 7	BIT 6	BIT 5	BIT 4	BIT 3	BIT 2	BIT 1	BIT 0
WR3	00=Rx 5 BITS/CHAR 10=Rx 6 BITS/CHAR 01=Rx 7 BITS/CHAR 11=Rx 8 BITS/CHAR		AUTO ENABLES	ENTER HUNT MODE (IF INCOMING DATA NOT NEEDED)	Rx CRC ENABLE	ADDRESS SEARCH MODE	0	Rx ENABLE
WR4	0	0	1 SELECTS SDLC MODE	0	0	0	0	0
WR5	DTR		00=Tx 5 BITS (OR LESS)/CHAR 10=Tx 6 BITS/CHAR 01=Tx 7 BITS/CHAR 11=Tx 8 BITS/CHAR	0	Tx ENABLE	0 SELECTS SDLC CRC	RTS	Tx CRC ENABLE

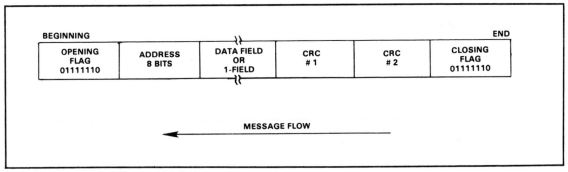

| OPENING FLAG 01111110 | ADDRESS 8 BITS | DATA FIELD OR 1-FIELD | CRC # 1 | CRC # 2 | CLOSING FLAG 01111110 |

END

MESSAGE FLOW

Fig. 7-9. Transmit/receive SDLC/HDLC message format.

incorporating features such as initializing the CRC generator to all 1's, resetting the CRC checker when the opening flag is detected in the Receive mode, and sending the Frame Check/Flag sequence in the Transmit mode. Controller hardware is simplified by automatic zero insertion and deletion logic contained in the Z80-SIO.

Table 7-8 shows the contents of WR3, WR4, and WR5 during SDLC Receive and Transmit modes. WR0 points to other registers and issues various commands. WR1 defines the interrupt modes and WR2 stores the interrupt vector. WR7 stores the flag character and WR6 stores the secondary address.

SDLC TRANSMIT

Like Synchronous operation, the SDLC Transmit mode must be initialized with the following parameters: SDLC mode, SDLC polynomial, Request to Send, Data Terminal Ready, Transmit character length, transmit interrupt modes (or Wait/Ready function), Transmit Enable, Auto Enables and External/Status interrupt.

Selecting the SDLC mode and the SDLC polynomial enables the Z80-SIO to initialize the CRC Generator to all 1's. This is accomplished by issuing the Reset Transmit CRC Generator command (WR0). Refer to the Synchronous Operation section for more details on the interrupt modes.

After reset, or when the transmitter is not enabled, the Transmit Data output is held marking. Break may be programmed to generate a spacing line. With the transmitter fully initialized and enabled, continuous flags are transmitted on the Transmit Data output.

An abort sequence may be sent by issuing the Send Abort command (WR0, CMD$_1$). This causes at least eight, but less than fourteen, 1's to be sent before the line reverts to continuous flags. It is possible that the Abort sequence (eight 1's) could follow up to five continuous 1 bits (allowed by the zero insertion logic) and, thus, cause up to thirteen 1's to be sent. Any data being transmitted and any data in the transmit buffer is lost when an abort is issued.

When required, an extra 0 is automatically inserted when there are five contiguous 1's in the data stream. This does not apply to flags or aborts.

175

Table 7-8. SDLC Transmit Mode.

FUNCTION		TYPICAL PROGRAM STEPS	COMMENTS
		REGISTER: INFORMATION LOADED	
	WR0	CHANNEL RESET	Reset SIO
	WR0	POINTER 2	
	WR2	INTERRUPT VECTOR	Channel B only
	WR0	POINTER 3	
	WR3	AUTO ENABLES	Transmitter sends data only after $\overline{CTS}$ is detected
	WR0	POINTER 4, RESET EXTERNAL STATUS INTERRUPTS	
	WR4	PARITY INFORMATION, SDLC MODE, x1 CLOCK MODE	
	WR0	POINTER 1, RESET EXTERNAL/STATUS INTERRUPTS	
INITIALIZE	WR1	EXTERNAL INTERRUPT ENABLE, STATUS AFFECTS VECTOR, TRANSMIT INTERRUPT ENABLE OR WAIT/READY MODE ENABLE	The External Interrupt Mode monitors the status of the $\overline{CTS}$ and $\overline{DCD}$ inputs, as well as the status of Tx Underrun/EOM latch. Transmit Interrupt interrupts when the Transmit buffer becomes empty; the Wait/Ready mode can be used to transfer data on a DMA or Block Transfer basis. The first interrupt occurs when $\overline{CTS}$ becomes active, at which point flags are transmitted by the Z80-SIO. The first data byte (address field) can be loaded into the Z80-SIO after this interrupt. Flags cannot be sent to the Z80-SIO as data. Status Affects Vector used in Channel B only.
	WR0	POINTER 5	
	WR5	TRANSMIT CRC ENABLE, REQUEST TO SEND, SDLC-CRC, TRANSMIT ENABLE, TRANSMIT WORD LENGTH, DATA TERMINAL READY	Sync mode must be defined before initializing transmit CRC generator.
	WR0	RESET TRANSMIT CRC GENERATOR	Initialize CRC generator to all 1's.
IDLE MODE		EXECUTE HALT INSTRUCTION OR SOME OTHER PROGRAM	Waiting Interrupt or Wait/Ready output to transfer data.
		WHEN INTERRUPT (WAIT/READY) OCCURS, THE CPU DOES THE FOLLOWING: • CHANGES TRANSMIT WORD LENGTH (IF NECESSARY) • TRANSFERS DATA BYTE FROM CPU (MEMORY) TO SIO • RESETS Tx UNDERRUN EOM LATCH WR0	Flags are transmitted by the SIO as soon as Transmit Enable is set and $\overline{CTS}$ becomes active. The $\overline{CTS}$ status change is the first interrupt that occurs and is followed by transmit buffer empty for subsequent transfers.

FUNCTION	TYPICAL PROGRAM STEPS	COMMENTS
	IF LAST CHARACTER OF THE I-FIELD IS SENT, THE SIO DOES THE FOLLOWING: • SENDS CRC • SENDS CLOSING FLAG • INTERRUPTS CPU WITH BUFFER EMPTY STATUS	Word length can be changed on the fly for variable I-field length. The data byte can contain address, control or I-field information (never a flag). It is good practice to reset Tx Underrun/EOM latch in the beginning of the message to avoid a false end-of-frame detection at the receiving end; This ensures that when underrun occurs, CRC is transmitted and underrun interrupt (Tx Underrun/EOM latch active) occurs. Note that "Send Abort" can be issued to the SIO in response to any interrupting continuing to abort the transmission.
DATA TRANSFER AND STATUS MONITORING	CPU DOES THE FOLLOWING: • ISSUES RESET Tx INTERRUPT PENDING COMMAND TO THE Z80-SIO • UPDATES NS COUNT • REPEATS THE PROCESS FOR NEXT MESSAGE, ETC. IF VECTOR INDICATES AN ERROR, THE CPU DOES THE FOLLOWING • SENDS ABORT • EXECUTES ERROR ROUTINE • UPDATES PARAMETERS, MODES, ETC. • RETURNS FROM INTERRUPT	
TERMINATION	REDEFINE INTERRUPT MODES UPDATE MODEM CONTROL OUTPUTS DISABLE TRANSMIT MODE	Terminate gracefully

Data Transfer and Status Monitoring

There are several combinations of interrupts and the Wait/Ready function in the SLDC mode.

Data Transfer Using Interrupts. If the Transmit Interrupt Enable bit is set, an interrupt is generated each time the buffer becomes empty. The interrupt may be satisfied either by writing another character into the transmitter or by resetting the Transmit Interrupt Pending latch with a Reset Transmitter Pending command (WR0, CMD_5). If the interrupt is satisfied with this command and nothing more is written into the transmitter, there are no further transmitter interrupts. The result is a Transmit Underrun condition. When another character is written and sent out, the transmitter can again become empty and interrupt the CPU. Following the flags in an SDLC operation, the 8-bit address field, control field and information field may be sent to the Z80-SIO using the Transmit Interrupt mode. The Z80-SIO transmits the Frame Check sequence using the Transmit Underrun feature.

When the transmitter is first enabled, it is already empty and obviously cannot then become empty. Therefore, no Transmit Buffer Empty interrupts can occur until after the first data character is written.

Data Transfer Using Wait/Ready. If the Wait/Ready function has been selected, WAIT indicates to the CPU that the Z80-SIO is not ready to accept the data and the CPU must extend the I/O cycle. To a DMA controller, READY indicates that the transmitter buffer is empty and that the Z80-SIO is ready to accept the next character. If the data character is not loaded into the Z80-SIO by the time the transmit shift register is empty, the Z80-SIO enters the Transmit Underrun condition. Address, control, and information fields may be transferred to the Z80-SIO with this mode using the Wait/Ready function. The Z80-SIO transmits the Frame Check sequence using the Transmit Underrun feature.

SDLC Transmit Underrun/End of Message. SDLC-like protocols do not have provisions for fill characters within a message. The Z80-SIO therefore automatically terminates an SDLC frame when the transmit data buffer and output shift register have no more bits to send. It does this by first sending the two bytes of CRC and following these with one or more flags. This technique allows very high-speed transmissions under DMA or CPU block I/O control without requiring the CPU to respond quickly to the end of message situation.

The action that the Z80-SIO takes in the underrun situation depends on the state of the Transmit Underrun/EOM command. Following a reset, the Transmit Underrun/EOM status bit is in the set state and prevents the insertion of CRC characters during the time there is no data to send. Consequently, flag characters are sent. The Z80-SIO begins to send the frame as data is written into the transmit buffer. Between the time the first data byte is written and the end of the message, the Reset Transmit Underrun/EOM command must be issued. Thus the Transmit Underrun/EOM status bit is in the reset state at the end of the message (when underrun occurs), which automatically sends the CRC characters. The sending of the CRC again sets the Transmit/Underrun/EOM status bit.

Although there is no restriction as to when the Transmit Underrun/EOM bit can be reset within a message, it is usually reset after the first data character (secondary address) is sent to the Z80-SIO. Resetting this bit allows CRC and flags to be sent when there is no data to send which gives additional time to the CPU for recognizing the fault and responding with an abort command. By resetting it early in the message, the entire message has the maximum amount of CPU response time in an unintentional transmit underrun situation.

When the External/Status interrupt is set and while CRC is being sent, the Transmit Underrun/EOM bit is set and the Transmit Buffer Empty bit is reset to indicate that the transmit register is full of CRC data. When CRC has been completely sent, the Transmit Buffer Empty status bit is set and an interrupt is generated to indicate to the CPU that another message can begin. This interrupt occurs because CRC has been sent and the flag has been loaded. If no more messages are to be sent, the program can terminate transmission by resetting $\overline{RTS}$, and disabling the transmitter.

In the SDLC mode, it is good practice to reset the Transmit Underrun/EOM status bit immediately after the first character is sent to the Z80-SIO. When the Transmit Underrun is detected, this ensures that the transmission time is filled by CRC characters, giving the CPU enough time to issue the Send Abort command. This also stops the flags from going on the line prematurely and eliminates the possibility of the receiver accepting the frame as valid data. The situation can happen because it is possible that—at the receiving end—the data pattern immediately preceding the automatic flag insertion could match the CRC checker, giving a false CRC check result. The External/Status interrupt is generated whenever the Transmit Underrun/EOM bit is set because of the Transmit Underrun condition.

The transmit underrun logic provides additional protection against premature flag insertion if the proper

178

response is given to the Z80-SIO by the CPU interrupt service routine. The following example is given to clarify this point:

The Z80-SIO raises an interrupt with the Transmit Buffer Empty status bit set.

The CPU does not respond in time and causes a Transmit Underrun condition.

The Z80-SIO starts sending CRC characters (two bytes).

The CPU eventually satisfies the Transmit Buffer Empty interrupt with a data character that follows the CRC character being transmitted.

The Z80-SIO sets the External/Status interrupt with the Transmit Underrun/EOM status bit set.

The CPU recognizes the Transmit Underrun/EOM status and determines from its internal program status that the interrupt is not for "end of message."

The CPU immediately issues a Send Abort Command (WR0) to the Z80-SIO.
The Z80-SIO sends the Abort sequence by destroying whatever data (CRC, data or flag) is being sent.

This sequence illustrates that the CPU has a protection of 22 minimum and 30 maximum transmit clock cycles.

SDLC CRC Generation. The CRC generator must be reset to all 1's at the beginning of each frame before CRC accumulation can begin. Actual accumulation begins when the program sends the address field (eight bits) to the Z80-SIO. Although the Z80-SIO automatically transmits one flag character following the Transmit Enable, it may be wise to send a few more flag characters ahead of the message to ensure character synchronization at the receiving end. This can be done by externally timing out after enabling the transmitter and before loading the first character.

The Transmit CRC Enable (WR5, D_0) should be enabled prior to sending the address field. In the SDLC mode all the characters between the opening and closing flags are included in CRC accumulation, and CRC generated in the Z80-SIO transmitter is inverted before it is sent on the line.

Transmit Termination. If the transmitter is disabled while a character is being sent, that character (data or flag) is sent in the normal fashion, but is followed by a marking line rather than CRC or flag characters.

A character in the buffer when the transmitter is disabled remains in the buffer; however, a programmed Abort sequence is effective as soon as it is written into the control register. Characters being transmitted, if any, are lost. In the case of CRC, the 16-bit transmission is completed if the transmitter is disabled; however, flags are sent in place of CRC.

In all modes, characters are sent with the least-significant bits first. This requires right-hand justification of data to be transmitted if the word length is less than eight bits. If the word length is five bits or less, the special technique described in the Write Register 5 section ("Z-80-SIO Programming" chapter; "Write Registers" section) must be used.

Since the number of bits/character can be changed on the fly, the data field can be filled with any number of bits. When used in conjunction with the Receiver Residue codes, the Z80-SIO can receive a message that has a variable I-field and retransmit it exactly as received with no previous information about the character structure of the I-field (if any). A change in the number of bits does not affect the character in the process of being shifted out. Characters are sent with the number of bits programmed at the time that the character is loaded from the transmit buffer to the transmitter.

If the External/Status Interrupt Enable is set, transmitter conditions such as "starting to send CRC characters," "starting to send flag characters," and $\overline{CTS}$ changing state cause interrupts that have a unique vector if Status Affects Vector is set. All interrupts can be disabled for operation in a polled mode.

Table 7-8 shows the typical program steps that implement the half-duplex SDLC Transmit mode.

SDLC RECEIVE

The SDLC Receive mode is initialized by the system with the following parameters: SDLC mode, x1 clock mode, SDLC polynomial, receive word length, etc. The flag characters must also be loaded in WR7 and the secondary address field loaded in WR6. The receiver is enabled only after all the receive parameters have been set. After all this has been done, the receiver is in the Hunt phase and remains in this phase until the first flag is received. While in the SDLC mode, the receiver never re-enters the Hunt phase, unless specifically instructed to do so by the program. The WR4 parameters must be issued prior to the WR1, WR3, WR5, WR6 and WR7 parameters.

Under program control, the receiver can enter the Address Search mode. If the Address Search bit (WR3, D_2) is set, a character following the flag (first non-flag character) is compared against the programmed address in WR6 and the hardwired global address (11111111). If the SDLC frame address field matches either address, data transfer begins.

Since the Z80-SIO is capable of matching only one address character, extended address field recognition must be done by the CPU. In this case, the Z80-SIO simply transfers the additional address bytes to the CPU as if they were data characters. If the CPU determines that the frame does not have the correct address field, it can set the Hunt bit, and the Z80-SIO suspends reception and searches for a new message headed by a flag. Since the control field of the frame is transparent to the Z80-SIO, it is transferred to the CPU as a data character. Extra zeros inserted in the data stream are automatically deleted; flags are not transferred to the CPU.

Data Transfer and Status Monitoring

After receipt of a valid flag, the assembled characters are transferred to the receive data FIFO. The following four interrupt modes are available to transfer this data and its associated status.

No Interrupts Enabled. This mode is used for purely polled operations or for off-line conditions.

Interrupt On First Character Only. This mode is normally used to start a software polling loop or a

Block Transfer instruction using $\overline{\text{WAIT}}/\overline{\text{READY}}$ to synchronize the CPU or DMA device to the incoming data rate. In this mode, the Z80-SIO interrupts on the first character and thereafter only interrupts if Special Receive conditions are detected. The mode is reinitialized with the Enable Interrupt On Next Receive Character Command.

The first character received after this command is issued causes an interrupt. If External/Status interrupts are enabled, they may interrupt any time the $\overline{\text{DCD}}$ input changes state. Special Receive conditions such as End Of Frame and Receiver Overrun also cause interrupts. The End of Frame interrupt can be used to exit the Block Transfer mode.

Interrupt On Every Character. An interrupt is generated whenever the receive FIFO contains a character. Error and Special Receive conditions generate a special vector if Status Affects Vector is selected.

Special Receive Condition Interrupts. The Special Receive Condition interrupt is not, as such, a separate interrupt mode. Before the Special Receive condition can cause an interrupt, either Interrupt On First Receive Character Only or Interrupt On Every Character must be selected. The Special Receive Condition interrupt is caused by a Receive Overrun or End of Frame detection. Since the Receive Overrun status bit is latched, the error status read reflects an error in the current word in the receive buffer in addition to any errors received since the last Error Reset command. The Receive Overrun status bit can only be reset by the Error Reset command. The End Of Frame status bit indicates that a valid ending flag has been received and that the CRC Error and Residue codes are also valid.

Character length may be changed on the fly. If the address and control bytes are processed as 8-bit characters, the receiver may be switched to a shorter character length during the time that the first information character is being assembled. This change must be made fast enough so it is effective before the number of bits specified for the character length have been assembled. For example, if the change is to be from the 8-bit control field to a 7-bit information field, the change must be made before the first seven bits of the I-field are assembled.

SDLC Receive CRC Checking. Control of the receive CRC checker is automatic. It is reset by the leading flag and CRC is calculated up to the final flag. The byte that has the End Of Frame bit set is the byte that contains the result of the CRC check. If the CRC/Framing Error bit is not set, the CRC indicates a valid message. A special check sequence is used for the SDLC check because the transmitted CRC check is inverted. The final check must be 0001110100001111. The 2-byte CRC check characters must be read by the CPU and discarded because the Z80-SIO, while using them for CRC checking, treats them as ordinary data.

SDLC Receive Termination. If enabled, a special vector is generated when the closing flag is received. This signals that the byte with the End Of Frame bit set has been received. In addition to the results of the CRC check, RR1 has three bits of Residue code valid at this time. For those cases in which the number of bits in the I-field is not an integral multiple of the character length used, these bits indicate the boundary between the CRC check bits and the I-field bits. For a detailed description of the meaning of these bits, see the description of the residue codes in RR1 under "Z80-SIO Programming."

Any frame can be prematurely aborted by an Abort Sequence. Aborts are detected if seven or more 1's

Table 7-9. SDLC Receive Mode.

FUNCTION	TYPICAL PROGRAM STEPS		COMMENTS
	REGISTER:	**INFORMATION LOADED**	
	WR0	CHANNEL 2	Reset SIO
	WR0	POINTER 2	
	WR2	INTERRUPT VECTOR	Channel B only
	WR0	POINTER 4	
	WR4	PARITY INFORMATION, SYNC MODE, SDLC MODE, x1 CLOCK MODE	
	WR0	POINTER 5, RESET EXTERNAL/STATUS INTERRUPTS	
	WR5	SDLC-CRC, DATA TERMINAL READY	
	WR0	POINTER 3	
	WR3	RECEIVE CRC ENABLE, ENTER HUNT MODE, AUTO ENABLES RECEIVE CHARACTER LENGTH, ADDRESS SEARCH MODE	"Auto Enables" enables the receiver to accept data only after $\overline{\text{DCD}}$ becomes active. Address Search Mode enables SIO to match the message address with the programmed address or the global address.
INITIALIZE	WR0	POINTER 6	
	WR6	SECONDARY ADDRESS FIELD	This address is matched against the message address in an SDLC poll operation.
	WR0	POINTER 7	
	WR7	SDLC FLAG 01111110	This flag detects the start and end of frame in an SDLC operation.
	WR0	POINTER 1, RESET EXTERNAL/STATUS INTERRUPTS	In this interrupt mode, only the Address Field (1 character only) is transferred to CPU. All subsequent fields (Control, Information, etc.) are transferred on a DMA basis. Status Affects Vector in Channel B only.
	WR1	STATUS AFFECTS VECTOR, EXTERNAL INTERRUPT ENABLE, RECEIVE INTERRUPT ON FIRST CHARACTER ONLY.	
	WR0	POINTER 3, ENABLE INTERRUPT ON NEXT RECEIVE CHARACTER	Used to provide simple loop-back entry point for next transaction. WR3 reissued to enable receiver.
	WR3	RECEIVE ENABLE, RECEIVE CRC ENABLE, ENTER HUNT MODE, AUTO ENABLE, RECEIVER CHARACTER LENGTH, ADDRESS SEARCH MODE	
IDLE MODE		EXECUTE HALT INSTRUCTION OR SOME OTHER PROGRAM	SDLC Receive Mode is fully initialized and SIO is waiting for the opening flag followed by a matching address field to interrupt the CPU.

FUNCTION	TYPICAL PROGRAM STEPS	COMMENTS
	WHEN INTERRUPT ON FIRST CHARACTER OCCURS, THE CPU DOES THE FOLLOWING: • TRANSFERS DATA BYTE (ADDRESS BYTE) TO CPU • DETECTS AND SETS APPROPRIATE FLAG FOR EXTENDED ADDRESS FIELD • UPDATES POINTER AND PARAMETERS • ENABLES DMA CONTROLLER • ENABLES WAIT/READY FUNCTION IN SIO • RETURNS FROM INTERRUPT	During the Hunt phase, the SIO interrupts when the programmed address matches the message address. The CPU establishes the DMA mode and all subsequent data characters are transferred by the DMA controller to memory.
	WHEN THE READY OUTPUT BECOMES ACTIVE, THE DMA CONTROLLER DOES THE FOLLOWING: TRANSFERS THE DATA BYTE TO MEMORY UPDATES THE POINTERS	During the DMA operation, the SIO monitors the $\overline{DCD}$ input and the Abort sequence in the data stream to interrupt the CPU with External Status error. The Special Receive condition interrupt is caused by Receive Overrun error.
DATA TRANSFER AND STATUS MONITORING	WHEN END OF FRAME INTERRUPT OCCURS, THE CPU DOES THE FOLLOWING: • EXITS DMA MODE (DISABLES WAIT/READY) • TRANSFERS RR1 TO THE CPU • CHECKS THE CRC ERROR BIT STATUS AND RESIDUE CODES • UPDATES NR COUNT • ISSUES "ERROR RESET" COMMAND TO SIO	Detection of End of Frame (Flag) causes interrupt and deactiviates the Wait/Ready function. Residue codes indicate the bit structure of the last two bytes of the message, which were transferred to memory under DMA. "Error Reset" is issued to clear the special condition.
	WHEN ABORT SEQUENCE DETECTED INTERRUPT OCCURS, THE CPU DOES THE FOLLOWING: • TRANSFERS RR0 TO THE CPU • EXITS DMA MODE • ISSUES THE RESET EXTERNAL STATUS INTERRUPT COMMAND TO THE SIO • ENTERS THE IDLE MODE	Abort sequence is detected when seven or more 1's are found in the data stream. CPU is waiting for Abort Sequence to terminate. Termination clears the Break/Abort status bit and causes interrupt.
	WHEN THE SECOND ABORT SEQUENCE INTERRUPT OCCURS, THE CPU DOES THE FOLLOWING: • ISSUES THE RESET EXTERNAL STATUS INTERRUPT COMMAND TO THE SIO.	At this point, the program proceeds to terminate this message.
TERMINATION	REDFINE INTERRUPT MODES, SYNC MODE AND SDLC MODES DISABLE RECEIVE MODE	

occur and cause an External/Status interrupt (if enabled) with the Break/Abort bit in RR0 set. After the Reset External/Status interrupts command has been issued a second interrupt occurs when the continuous 1's condition has been cleared. This can be used to distinguish between the Abort and idle line conditions.

Unlike the synchronous mode, CRC calculation in SDLC does not have an 8-bit delay since all the characters are included in CRC calculation. When the second CRC character is loaded into the receive buffer, CRC calculation is complete.

Table 7-9 shows the typical steps required to implement a half-duplex SDLC receive mode.

Chapter 8

SIO Programming

To program the Z80-SIO, the system program first issues a series of commands that initialize the basic mode of operation and the commands that qualify conditions within the selected mode. For example, the Asynchronous mode, character length, clock rate, number of stop bits, even or odd parity are first set, then the interrupt mode, and finally, receiver or transmitter enable. The WR4 parameters must be issued before any other parameters are issued in the initialization routine.

Both channels contain command registers that must be programmed via the system program prior to operation. The Channel Select input ($B/\overline{A}$) and the Control/Data input ($C/\overline{D}$) are the command structure addressing controls, and are normally controlled by the CPU address bus. Figures 8-6 through 8-9 illustrate the timing relationships for programming the write registers, and transferring data and status.

$C/\overline{D}$	$B/\overline{A}$	Function
0	0	Channel A Data
0	1	Channel B Data
1	0	Channel A Commands/Status
1	1	Channel B Commands/Status

WRITE REGISTERS

The Z80-SIO contains eight registers (WR0-WR7) in each channel that are programmed separately by the system program to configure the functional personality of the channels. With the exception of WR0, programming the write registers requires two bytes. The first byte contains three bits (D_0-D_2) that point to the selected register; the second byte is the actual control word that is written into the register to configure the Z80-SIO.

Note that the programmer has complete freedom, after pointing to the selected register, of either reading to test the read register or writing to initialize the write register. By designing software to initialize the Z80-SIO in a modular and structured fashion, the programmer can use powerful block I/O instructions.

WR0 is a special case in that all the basic commands (CMD_0-CMD_2) can be accessed with a single byte. Reset (internal or external) initializes the pointer bits (D_0-D_2) to point to WR0.

The basic commands (CMD_0-CMD_2) and the CRC controls (CRC_0, CRC_1) are contained in the first byte of any write register access. This maintains maximum flexibility and system control. Each channel contains the following control registers. These registers are addressed as commands (not data).

Write Register 0

WR0 is the command register; however, it is also used for CRC reset codes and to point to the other registers.

D_7	D_6	D_5	D_4	D_3	D_2	D_1	D_0
CRC Reset Code 1	CRC Reset Code 0	CMD 2	CMD 1	CMD 0	PTR 2	PTR 1	PTR 0

Pointer Bits (D_0-D_2). Bits D_0-D_2 are pointer bits that determine which other write register the next byte is to be written into or which read register the next byte is to be read from. The first byte written into each channel after a reset (either by a Reset command or by the external reset input) goes into WR0. Following a read or write to any register (except WR0), the pointer will point to WR0.

Command Bits (D_3-D_5). Three bits, D_3-D_5, are encoded to issue the seven basic Z80-SIO commands.

COMMAND	CMD_2	CMD_1	CMD_0	
0	0	0	0	Null Command (no effect)
1	0	0	1	Send Abort (SDLC Mode)
2	0	1	0	Reset External/Status Interrupts
3	0	1	1	Channel Reset
4	1	0	0	Enable Interrupt on next Rx Character
5	1	0	1	Reset Transmitter Interrupt Pending
6	1	1	0	Error Reset (latches)
7	1	1	1	Return from Interrupt (Channel A)

Command 0 (Null). The Null command has no effect. Its normal use is to cause the Z80-SIO to do nothing while the pointers are set for the following byte.

Command 1 (Send Abort). This command is used only with the SDLC mode to generate a sequence of eight to thirteen 1's.

Command 2 (Reset External/Status Interrupts). After an External/Status interrupt (a change on a modem line or a break condition, for example), the status bits of RR0 are latched. This command re-enables them and allows interrupts to occur again. Latching the status bits captures short pulses until the CPU has time to read the change.

Command 3 (Channel Reset). This command performs the same function as an External Reset, but only on a single channel. Channel A Reset also resets the interrupt prioritization logic. All control registers for the channel must be rewritten after a Channel Reset command.

Write Register bit functions are given in Fig. 8-1.

After a Channel Reset, four extra system clock cycles should be allowed for Z80-SIO reset time before any additional commands or controls are written into that channel. This can normally be the time used by the CPU to fetch the next op code.

Command 4 (Enable Interrupt On Next Character). If the Interrupt On First Receive Character mode is selected, this command reactivates that mode after each complete message is received to prepare the Z80-SIO for the next message.

Command 5 (Reset Transmitter Interrupt Pending). The transmitter interrupts when the transmit buffer becomes empty if the Transmit Interrupt Enable mode is selected. In those cases where there are no more characters to be sent (at the end of message, for example), issuing this command prevents further transmitter interrupts until after the next character has been loaded into the transmit buffer or until CRC has been completely sent.

Command 6 (Error Reset). This command resets the error latches. Parity and Overrun errors are latched in RR1 until they are reset with this command. With this scheme, parity errors occurring in block transfers can be examined at the end of the block.

Command 7 (Return From Interrupt). This command must be issued in Channel A and is interpreted by the Z80-SIO in exactly the same way it would interpret a RETI command on the data bus. It resets the interrupt-under-service latch of the highest-priority internal device under service and thus allows lower priority devices to interrupt via the daisy chain. This command allows use of the internal daisy chain even in systems with no external daisy chain or RETI command.

CRC Reset Codes 0 and 1 (D_6 and D_7). Together, these bits select one of the three following reset commands:

CRC Reset Code 1	CRC Reset Code 0	
0	0	Null Code (no effect)
0	1	Reset Receive CRC Checker
1	0	Reset Transmit CRC Generator
1	1	Reset Tx Underrun/End Of Message Latch

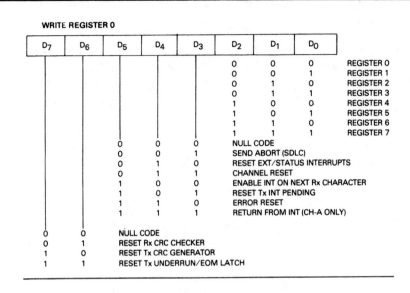

WRITE REGISTER 0

D7	D6	D5	D4	D3	D2	D1	D0	
					0	0	0	REGISTER 0
					0	0	1	REGISTER 1
					0	1	0	REGISTER 2
					0	1	1	REGISTER 3
					1	0	0	REGISTER 4
					1	0	1	REGISTER 5
					1	1	0	REGISTER 6
					1	1	1	REGISTER 7

D5	D4	D3	
0	0	0	NULL CODE
0	0	1	SEND ABORT (SDLC)
0	1	0	RESET EXT/STATUS INTERRUPTS
0	1	1	CHANNEL RESET
1	0	0	ENABLE INT ON NEXT Rx CHARACTER
1	0	1	RESET Tx INT PENDING
1	1	0	ERROR RESET
1	1	1	RETURN FROM INT (CH-A ONLY)

D7	D6	
0	0	NULL CODE
0	1	RESET Rx CRC CHECKER
1	0	RESET Tx CRC GENERATOR
1	1	RESET Tx UNDERRUN/EOM LATCH

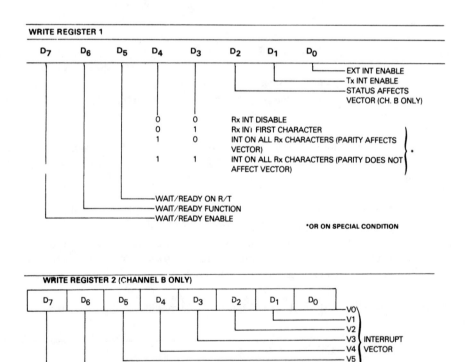

WRITE REGISTER 1

D7	D6	D5	D4	D3	D2	D1	D0

- EXT INT ENABLE
- Tx INT ENABLE
- STATUS AFFECTS VECTOR (CH. B ONLY)

D4	D3	
0	0	Rx INT DISABLE
0	1	Rx INT FIRST CHARACTER
1	0	INT ON ALL Rx CHARACTERS (PARITY AFFECTS VECTOR)
1	1	INT ON ALL Rx CHARACTERS (PARITY DOES NOT AFFECT VECTOR)	*

- WAIT/READY ON R/T
- WAIT/READY FUNCTION
- WAIT/READY ENABLE

*OR ON SPECIAL CONDITION

WRITE REGISTER 2 (CHANNEL B ONLY)

D7	D6	D5	D4	D3	D2	D1	D0

- V0
- V1
- V2
- V3 ⎫ INTERRUPT
- V4 ⎬ VECTOR
- V5
- V6
- V7 ⎭

Fig. 8-1. Write register bit functions.

188

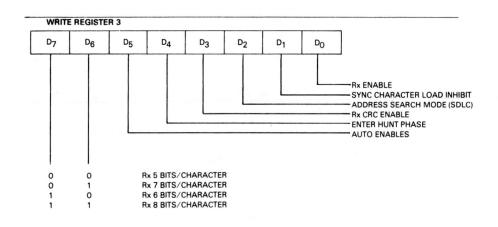

WRITE REGISTER 3

D7	D6	D5	D4	D3	D2	D1	D0

- Rx ENABLE
- SYNC CHARACTER LOAD INHIBIT
- ADDRESS SEARCH MODE (SDLC)
- Rx CRC ENABLE
- ENTER HUNT PHASE
- AUTO ENABLES

0	0	Rx 5 BITS/CHARACTER
0	1	Rx 7 BITS/CHARACTER
1	0	Rx 6 BITS/CHARACTER
1	1	Rx 8 BITS/CHARACTER

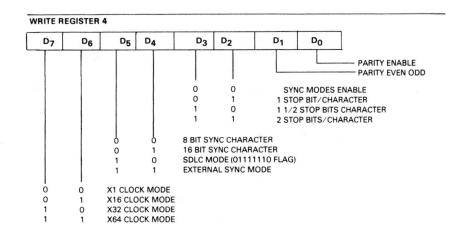

WRITE REGISTER 4

D7	D6	D5	D4	D3	D2	D1	D0

- PARITY ENABLE
- PARITY EVEN ODD

0	0	SYNC MODES ENABLE
0	1	1 STOP BIT/CHARACTER
1	0	1 1/2 STOP BITS CHARACTER
1	1	2 STOP BITS/CHARACTER

0	0	8 BIT SYNC CHARACTER
0	1	16 BIT SYNC CHARACTER
1	0	SDLC MODE (01111110 FLAG)
1	1	EXTERNAL SYNC MODE

0	0	X1 CLOCK MODE
0	1	X16 CLOCK MODE
1	0	X32 CLOCK MODE
1	1	X64 CLOCK MODE

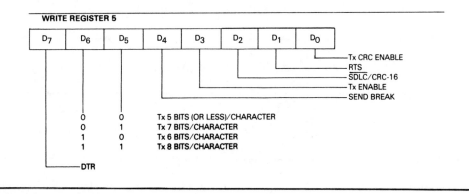

WRITE REGISTER 5

D7	D6	D5	D4	D3	D2	D1	D0

- Tx CRC ENABLE
- RTS
- SDLC/CRC-16
- Tx ENABLE
- SEND BREAK

0	0	Tx 5 BITS (OR LESS)/CHARACTER
0	1	Tx 7 BITS/CHARACTER
1	0	Tx 6 BITS/CHARACTER
1	1	Tx 8 BITS/CHARACTER

- DTR

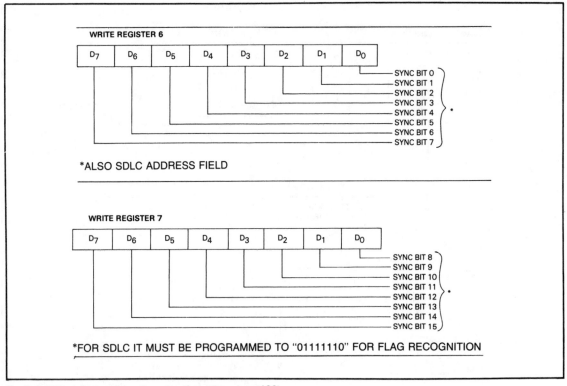

Fig. 8-1. Write register bit functions (continued from page 189).

The Reset Transmit CRC Generator command normally initializes the CRC generator to all 0's. If the SDLC mode is selected, this command initializes the CRC generator to all 1's. The Receive CRC checker is also initialized to all 1's for the SDLC mode.

Write Register 1

WR1 contains the control bits for the various interrupt and Wait/Ready modes.

D_7 Wait/Ready Enable	D_6 Wait Or Ready Function	D_5 Wait/Ready On Receive/Transmit	D_4 Receive Interrupt Mode 1
D_3 Receive Interrupt Mode 0	D_2 Status Affects Vector	D_1 Transmit Interrupt Enable	D_0 External Interrupts Enable

External/Status Interrupt Enable (D_0). The External/Status Interrupt Enable allows interrupts to occur as a result of transitions on the $\overline{DCD}$, $\overline{CTS}$ or $\overline{SYNC}$ inputs, as a result of a Break/Abort detection and

190

termination, or at the beginning of CRC or sync character transmission when the Transmit Underrun/ EOM latch becomes set.

Transmitter Interrupt Enable (D_1). If enabled, the interrupts occur whenever the transmitter buffer becomes empty.

Status Affects Vector (D_2). This bit is active in Channel B only. If this bit is not set, the fixed vector programmed in WR2 is returned from an interrupt acknowledge sequence. If this bit is set, the vector returned from an interrupt acknowledge is variable according to the following interrupt conditions:

	V_3	V_2	V_1	
	0	0	0	Ch B Transmit Buffer Empty
	0	0	1	Ch B External/Status Change
Ch B	0	1	0	Ch B Receive Character Available
	0	1	1	Ch B Special Receive Condition*
	1	0	0	Ch A Transmit Buffer Empty
Ch A	1	0	1	Ch A External/Status Change
	1	1	0	Ch A Receive Character Available
	1	1	1	Ch A Special Receive Condition*

*Special Receive Conditions: Parity Error, Rx Overrun Error, Framing Error, End Of Frame (SDLC).

Receive Interrupt Modes 0 and 1 (D_3 and D_4). Together, these two bits specify the various character-available conditions. In Receive Interrupt modes 1, 2 and 3, a Special Receive Condition can cause an interrupt and modify the interrupt vector.

D_4 Receive Interrupt Mode 1	D_3 Receive Interrupt Mode 0	
0	0	0. Receive Interrupts Disabled
0	1	1. Receive Interrupt On First Character Only
1	0	2. Interrupt On All Receive Characters—parity error is a Special Receive condition
1	1	3. Interrupt On All Receive Characters—parity error is not a Special Receive condition

Wait/Ready Function Selection (D_5-D_7). The Wait and Ready functions are selected by controlling D_5, D_6 and D_7. Wait/Ready function is enabled by setting Wait/Ready Enable (WR1, D_7) to 1. The Ready Function is selected by setting D_6 (Wait/Ready function) to 1. If this bit is 1, the $\overline{\text{WAIT/READY}}$ output switches from High to Low when the Z80-SIO is ready to transfer data. The Wait function is selected by setting D_6 to 0. If this bit is 0, the $\overline{\text{WAIT/READY}}$ output is in the open-drain state and goes Low when active.

Both the Wait and Ready functions can be used in either the Transmit or Receive modes, but not both simultaneously. If D_5 (Wait/Ready or Receive/Transmit) is set to 1, the Wait/Ready function responds to the condition of the receive buffer (empty or full). If D_5 is set to 0, the Wait/Ready function responds to the condition of the transmit buffer (empty or full).

The logic states of the $\overline{\text{WAIT}}/\overline{\text{READY}}$ output when active or inactive depend on the combination of modes selected. Following is a summary of these combinations:

	If $D_7 = 0$	
And $D_6 = 1$		And $D_6 = 0$
$\overline{\text{READY}}$ is High		$\overline{\text{WAIT}}$ is floating
	If $D_7 = 1$	
And $D_5 = 0$		And $D_5 = 1$

$\overline{\text{READY}}$	Is High when transmit buffer is full.	$\overline{\text{READY}}$	Is High when receive buffer is empty.
$\overline{\text{WAIT}}$	Is Low when transmit buffer is full and an SIO data port is selected.	$\overline{\text{WAIT}}$	Is Low when receive buffer is empty and an SIO data port is selected.
$\overline{\text{READY}}$	Is Low when transmit buffer is empty.	$\overline{\text{READY}}$	Is Low when receive buffer is full.
$\overline{\text{WAIT}}$	Is floating when transmit buffer is empty.	$\overline{\text{WAIT}}$	Is Floating when receive buffer is full.

The $\overline{\text{WAIT}}$ output High-to-Low transition occurs when the delay time t_DIC(WR) after the I/O request. The Low-to-High transition occurs with the delay t_DHΦ(WR) from the falling edge of Φ. The $\overline{\text{READY}}$ output High-to-Low transition occurs with the delay t_DLΦ(WR) from the rising edge of Φ. The $\overline{\text{READY}}$ output Low-to-High transition occurs with the delay t_DIC(WR) after $\overline{\text{IORQ}}$ falls.

The Ready function can occur any time the Z80-SIO is not selected. When the $\overline{\text{READY}}$ output becomes active (Low), the DMA controller issues $\overline{\text{IORQ}}$ and the corresponding $\text{B}/\overline{\text{A}}$ and $\text{C}/\overline{\text{D}}$ inputs to the Z80-SIO to transfer data. The Ready output becomes inactive as soon as $\overline{\text{IORQ}}$ and $\overline{\text{CS}}$ become active. Since the Ready function can occur internally in the Z80-SIO whether it is addressed or not, the $\overline{\text{READY}}$ output becomes inactive when any CPU data or command transfer takes place. This does not cause problems because the DMA controller is not enabled when the CPU transfer takes place.

The Wait function—on the other hand—is active only if the CPU attempts to read Z80-SIO data that has not yet been received, which occurs frequently when block transfer instructions are used. The Wait function can also become active (under program control) if the CPU tries to write data while the transmit buffer is still full. The fact that the $\overline{\text{WAIT}}$ output for either channel can become active when the opposite channel is addressed (because the Z80-SIO is addressed) does not affect operation of software loops or block move instructions.

Write Register 2

WR2 is the interrupt vector register; it exists in Channel B only. V_4-V_7 and V_0 are always returned exactly as written; V_1-V_3 are returned as written if the Status Affects Vector (WR1,D_2) control bit is 0. If this bit is 1, they are modified as explained in the previous section.

D_7	D_6	D_5	D_4	D_3	D_2	D_1	D_0
V_7	V_6	V_5	V_4	V_3	V_2	V_1	V_0

Write Register 3

WR3 contains receiver logic control bits and parameters.

D7	D6	D5	D4
Receiver Bits/ Char 1	Receiver Bits/ Char 0	Auto Enables	Enter Hunt Phase
D3	D2	D1	D0
Receiver CRC Enable	Address Search Mode	Sync Char Load Inhibit	Receiver Enable

Receiver Enable (D_0). A 1 programmed into this bit allows receive operations to begin. This bit should be set only after all other receive parameters are set and receiver is completely initialized.

Sync Character Load Inhibit (D_1). Sync characters preceding the message (leading sync characters) are not loaded into the receive buffers if this option is selected. Because CRC calculations are not stopped by sync character stripping, this feature should be enabled only at the beginning of the message.

Address Search Mode (D_2). If SDLC is selected, setting this mode causes messages with addresses not matching the programmed address in WR6 or the global (11111111) address to be rejected. In other words, no receive interrupts can occur in the Address Search mode unless there is an address match.

Receiver CRC Enable (D_3). If this bit is set, CRC calculation starts (or restarts) at the beginning of the last character transferred from the receive shift register to the buffer stack, regardless of the number of characters in the stack. See "SDLC Receive CRC Checking" (SDLC Receive section) and "CRC Error Checking" (Synchronous Receive section) for details regarding when this bit should be set.

Enter Hunt Phase (D_4). The Z80-SIO automatically enters the Hunt phase after a reset; however, it can be re-entered if character synchronization is lost for any reason (Synchronous mode) or if the contents of an incoming message are not needed (SDLC mode). The Hunt phase is re-entered by writing a 1 into bit D_4. This sets the Sync/Hunt bit (D_4) in RR0.

Auto Enables (D_5). If this mode is selected, $\overline{DCD}$ and $\overline{CTS}$ become the receiver and transmitter enables, respectively. If this bit is not set, $\overline{DCD}$ and $\overline{CTS}$ are simply inputs to their corresponding status bits in RR0.

Receiver Bits/Character 1 and 0 (D_7 and D_6). Together, these bits determine the number of serial receive bits assembled to form a character. Both bits may be changed during the time that a character is being assembled, but they must be changed before the number of bits currently programmed is reached.

D7	D6	Bits/Character
0	0	5
0	1	7
1	0	6
1	1	8

Write Register 4

WR4 contains the control bits that affect both the receiver and transmitter. In the transmit and receive initialization routine, these bits should be set before issuing WR1, WR3, WR5, WR6, and WR7.

D_7	D_6	D_5	D_4	D_3	D_2	D_1	D_0
Clock Rate 1	Clock Rate 0	Sync Modes 1	Sync Modes 0	Stop Bits 1	Stop Bits 0	Parity Even/$\overline{\text{Odd}}$	Parity

Parity (D_0). If this bit is set, an additional bit position (in addition to those specified in the bits/character control) is added to transmitted data and is expected in receive data. In the Receive mode, the parity bit received is transferred to the CPU as part of the character, unless 8 bits/character is selected.

Parity Even $\overline{\text{Odd}}$ (D_1). If parity is specified, this bit determines whether it is sent and checked as even or odd (1=even).

Stop Bits 0 and 1 (D_2 and D_3). These bits determine the number of stop bits added to each asynchronous character sent. The receiver always checks for one stop bit. A special mode (00) signifies that a synchronous mode is to be selected.

D_3 Stop Bits 1	D_2 Stop Bits 0	
0	0	Sync modes
0	1	1 stop bit per character
1	0	1½ stop bits per character
1	1	2 stop bits per character

Sync Modes 0 and 1 (D_4 and D_5). These bits select the various options for character synchronization.

Sync Mode 1	Sync Mode 0	
0	0	8-bit programmed sync
0	1	16-bit programmed sync
1	0	SDLC mode (01111110 flag pattern)
1	1	External Sync mode

Clock Rate 0 and 1 (D_6 and D_7). These bits specify the multiplier between the clock ($\overline{\text{T} \times \text{C}}$ and $\overline{\text{R} \times \text{C}}$) and data rates. For synchronous modes, the ×1 clock rate must be specified. Any rate may be specified for asynchronous modes; however, the same rate must be used for both the receiver and transmitter. The system clock in all modes must be at least 5 times the data rate. If the ×1 clock rate is selected, bit synchronization must be accomplished externally.

Clock Rate 1	Clock Rate 0	
0	0	Data Rate x1=Clock Rate
0	1	Data Rate x16=Clock Rate
1	0	Data Rate x32=Clock Rate
1	1	Data Rate x64=Clock Rate

Write Register 5

WR5 contains control bits that affect the operation of transmitter, with the exception of D2, which affects the transmitter and receiver.

D_7	D_6	D_5	D_4	D_3	D_2	D_1	D_0
DTR	Tx Bits/ Char 1	Tx Bits/ Char 0	Send Break	Tx Enable	CRC-16/ SDLC	RTS	Tx CRC Enable

Transmit CRC Enable (D_0). This bit determines if CRC is calculated on a particular transmit character. If it is set at the time the character is loaded from the transmit buffer into the transmit shift register, CRC is calculated on the character. CRC is not automatically sent unless this bit is set when the Transmit Underrun condition exists.

Request To Send (D_1). This is the control bit for the $\overline{RTS}$ pin. When the $\overline{RTS}$ bit is set, the $\overline{RTS}$ pin goes Low; when reset, $\overline{RTS}$ goes High. In the Asynchronous mode, $\overline{RTS}$ goes High only after all the bits of the character are transmitted and the transmitter buffer is empty. In Synchronous modes, the pin directly follows the state of the bit.

CRC-16/$\overline{SDLC}$ (D_2). This bit selects the CRC polynomial used by both the transmitter and receiver. When set, the CRC-16 polynomial ($X^{16}+X^{15}+X^2+1$) is used; when reset, the SDLC polynomial ($X^{16}+X^{12}+X^5+1$) is used. If the SDLC mode is selected, the CRC generator and checker are preset to all 1's and a special check sequence is used. The SDLC CRC polynomial must be selected when the SDLC mode is selected. If the SDLC mode is not selected, the CRC generator and checker are present to all 0's (for both polynomials).

Transmit Enable (D_3). Data is not transmitted until this bit is set and the Transmit Data output is held marking. Data or sync characters in the process of being transmitted are completely sent if this bit is reset after transmission has started. If the transmitter is disabled during the transmission of a CRC character, sync or flag characters are sent instead of CRC.

Send Break (D_4). When set, this bit immediately forces the Transmit Data output to the spacing condition, regardless of any data being transmitted. When reset, T×D returns to marking.

Transmit Bits/Character 0 and 1 (D_5 and D_6). Together, D_6 and D_5 control the number of bits in each byte transferred to the transmit buffer.

D6 Transmit Bits/ Character 1	D5 Transmit Bits/ Character 0	Bits/Character
0	0	Five or less
0	1	7
1	0	6
1	1	8

Bits to be sent must be right justified, least-significant bits first. The Five Or Less mode allows transmission of one to five bits per character; however, the CPU should format the data character as shown in the following table.

D_7	D_6	D_5	D_4	D_3	D_2	D_1	D_0	
1	1	1	1	0	0	0	D	Sends one data bit
1	1	1	0	0	0	D	D	Sends two data bits
1	1	0	0	0	D	D	D	Sends three data bits
1	0	0	0	D	D	D	D	Sends four data bits
0	0	0	D	D	D	D	D	Sends five data bits

Data Terminal Ready (D_7). This is the control bit for the $\overline{DTR}$ pin. When set, $\overline{DTR}$ is active (Low); when reset, $\overline{DTR}$ is inactive (High).

Write Register 6

This register is programmed to contain the transmit sync character in the Monosync mode, the first eight bits of a 16-bit sync character in the Bisync mode or a transmit sync character in the External Sync mode. In the SDLC mode, it is programmed to contain the secondary address field used to compare against the address field of the SDLC frame.

D_7 Sync 7	D_6 Sync 6	D_5 Sync 5	D_4 Sync 4	D_3 Sync 3	D_2 Sync 2	D_1 Sync 1	D_0 Sync 0

Write Register 7

This register is programmed to contain the receive sync character in the Monosync mode, a second byte (last eight bits) of a 16-bit sync character in the Bisync mode and a flag character (01111110) in the SDLC mode. WR7 is not used in the External Sync mode.

D_7 Sync 15	D_6 Sync 14	D_5 Sync 13	D_4 Sync 12	D_3 Sync 11	D_2 Sync 10	D_1 Sync 9	D_0 Sync 8

READ REGISTERS

The Z80-SIO contains three registers, RR0-RR2 (Fig. 8-2), that can be read to obtain the status information for each channel (except for RR2-Channel B only). The status information includes error conditions, interrupt vector and standard communications-interface signals.

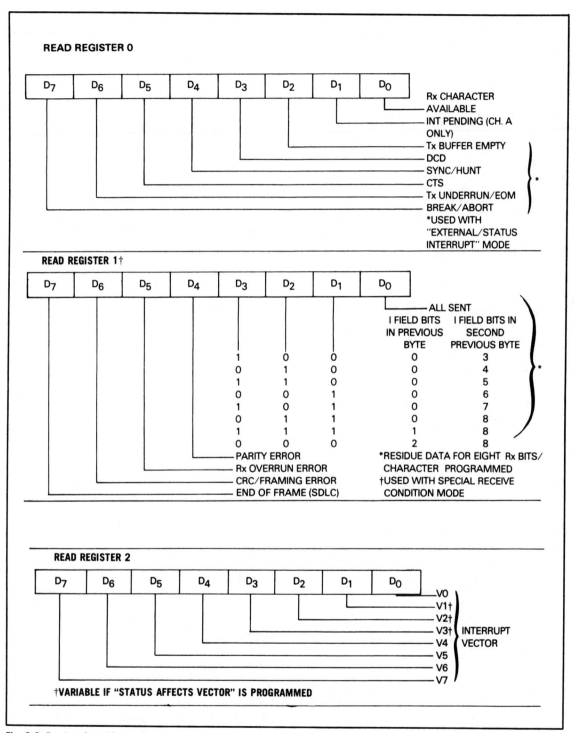

Fig. 8-2. Read register bit functions.

To read the contents of a selected read register other than RR0, the system program must first write the pointer byte to WR0 in exactly the same way as a write register operation. Then, by executing an input instruction, the contents of the addressed read register can be read by the CPU.

The status bits of RR0 and RR1 are carefully grouped to simplify status monitoring. For example, when the interrupt vector indicates that a Special Receive Condition interrupt has occurred, all the appropriate error bits can be read from a single register (RR1).

Read Register 0

This register contains the status of the receive and transmit buffers, the $\overline{DCD}$, $\overline{CTS}$ and $\overline{SYNC}$ inputs, the Transmit Underrun/EOM latch; and the Break/Abort latch.

D_7	D_6	D_5	D_4	D_3	D_2	D_1	D_0
Break Abort	Transmit Underrun/ EOM	CTS	Sync/ Hunt	DCD	Transmit Buffer Empty	Interrupt Pending (Ch. A only)	Receive Character Available

Receive Character Available (D_0). This bit is set when at least one character is available in the receive buffer; it is reset when the receive FIFO is completely empty.

Interrupt Pending (D_1). Any interrupting condition in the Z80-SIO causes this bit to be set; however, it is readable only in Channel A. This bit is mainly used in applications that do not have vectored interrupts available. During the interrupt service routine in these applications, this bit indicates if any interrupt conditions are present in all Z80-SIO. This eliminates the need for analyzing all the bits of RR0 in both Channels A and B. Bit D_1 is reset when all the interrupting conditions are satisfied. This bit is always 0 in Channel B.

Transmit Buffer Empty (D_2). This bit is set whenever the transmit buffer becomes empty, except when a CRC character is being sent in a synchronous or SDLC mode. The bit is reset when a character is loaded into the transmit buffer. This bit is in the set condition after a reset.

Data Carrier Detect (D_3). The DCD bit shows the inverted state of the $\overline{DCD}$ input at the time of the last change of any of the five External/Status bits (DCD, $\overline{CTS}$, Sync/Hunt, Break/Abort or Transmit Underrun/EOM). Any transition of the $\overline{DCD}$ input causes the DCD bit to be latched and causes an External/Status interrupt. To read the current state of the DCD bit, this bit must be read immediately following a Reset External/Status Interrupt command.

Sync/Hunt (D_4). Since this bit is controlled differently in the Asynchronous, Synchronous and SDLC modes, its operation is somewhat more complex than that of the other bits and, therefore, requires more explanation.

In Asynchronous modes, the operation of this bit is similar to the DCD status bit, except that Sync/Hunt shows the state of the $\overline{SYNC}$ input. Any High-to-Low transition on the $\overline{SYNC}$ pin sets this bit and causes an External/Status interrupt (if enabled). The Reset External/Status Interrupt command is issued to clear the interrupt. A Low-to-High transition clears this bit and sets the External/Status interrupt. When the External/Status interrupt is set by the change in state of any other input or condition, this bit shows the inverted state of $\overline{\text{SYNC}}$ pin at the time of the change. This bit must be read immediately following a Reset External/Status Interrupt command to read the current state of the $\overline{\text{SYNC}}$ input.

In the External Sync mode, the Sync/Hunt bit operates in a fashion similar to the Asynchronous mode, except the Enter Hunt Mode control bit enables the external sync detection logic. When the External Sync Mode and Enter Hunt Mode bits are set (for example, when the receiver is enabled following a reset), the $\overline{\text{SYNC}}$ input must be held High by the external logic until external character synchronization is achieved. A High at the $\overline{\text{SYNC}}$ input holds the Sync/Hunt status bit in the reset condition.

When external synchronization is achieved, $\overline{\text{SYNC}}$ must be driven Low on the second rising edge or RxC on which the last bit of the sync character was received. In other words, after the sync pattern is detected, the external logic must wait for two full Receive clock cycles to activate the $\overline{\text{SYNC}}$ input. Once $\overline{\text{SYNC}}$ is forced Low, it is a good practice to keep it Low until the CPU informs the external sync logic that synchronization has been lost or a new message is about to start. The High-to-Low transition of the $\overline{\text{SYNC}}$ input sets the Sync/Hunt bit, which—in turn—sets the External/Status interrupt. The CPU must clear the interrupt by issuing the Reset External/Status Interrupt command.

When the $\overline{\text{SYNC}}$ input goes High again, another External/Status interrupt is generated that must also be cleared. The Enter Hunt Mode control bit is set whenever character synchronization is lost or the end of message is detected. In this case, The Z80-SIO again looks for a High-to-Low transition on the $\overline{\text{SYNC}}$ input and the operation repeats as explained previously. This implies the CPU should also inform the external logic that character synchronization has been lost and that the Z80-SIO is waiting for $\overline{\text{SYNC}}$ to become active.

In the Monosync and Bisync Receive modes, the Sync/Hunt status bit is initially set to 1 by the Enter Hunt Mode bit. The Sync/Hunt bit is reset when the Z80-SIO establishes character synchronization. The High-to-Low transition of the Sync/Hunt bit causes an External/Status interrupt that must be cleared by the CPU issuing the Reset External/Status Interrupt command. This enables the Z80-SIO to detect the next transition of other External/Status bits.

When the CPU detects the end of message of that character synchronization is lost, it sets the Enter Hunt Mode control bit, which—in turn—sets the Sync/Hunt bit to 1. The Low-to-High transition of the Sync/Hunt bit sets the External/Status interrupt, which must also be cleared by the Reset External/Status Interrupt command. Note that the Sync pin acts as an output in this mode and goes Low every time a sync pattern is detected in the data stream.

In the SDLC mode, the Sync/Hunt bit is initially set by the Enter Hunt mode bit or when the receiver is disabled. In any case, it is reset to 0 when the opening flag of the first frame is detected by the Z80-SIO. The External/Status interrupt is also generated and should be handled as discussed previously.

Unlike the Monosync and Bisync modes, once the Sync/Hunt bit is reset in the SDLC mode, it does not need to be set when the end of message is detected. The Z80-SIO automatically maintains synchronization. The only way the Sync/Hunt bit can be set again is by the Enter Hunt Mode bit or by disabling the receiver.

Clear to Send (D$_5$). This bit is similar to the DCD bit, except that it shows the inverted state of the $\overline{\text{CTS}}$ pin.

Transmit Underrun/End of Message (D$_6$). This bit is in a set condition following a reset (internal or external). The only command that can reset this bit is the Reset Transmit Underrun/EOM Latch command (WR0, D$_6$ and D$_7$). When the Transmit Underrun condition occurs, this bit is set; its becoming set causes the External/Status interrupt, which must be reset by issuing the Reset External/Status Interrupt command bits (WR0). This status bit plays an important role in conjunction with other control bits in controlling a transmit operation. Refer to "Bisync Transmit Underrun" and "SDLC Transmit Underrun" for additional details.

Break/Abort (D$_7$). In the Asynchronous Receive mode, this bit is set when a Break sequence (null character plus framing error) is detected in the data stream. The External/Status interrupt, if enabled, is set when Break is detected. The interrupt service routine must issue the Reset External/Status Interrupt command (WR0, CMD$_2$) to the break detection logic so the Break sequence termination can be recognized.

The Break/Abort bit is reset when the termination of the Break sequence is detected in the incoming data stream. The termination of the Break sequence also causes the External/Status interrupt to be set. The Reset External/Status Interrupt command must be issued to enable the break detection logic to look for the next Break sequence. A single extraneous null character is present in the receiver after the termination of a break; it should be read and discarded.

In the SDLC Receive mode, this status bit is set by the detection of an Abort sequence (seven or more 1's). The External/Status Interrupt is handled the same way as in the case of a Break. The Break/Abort bit is not used in the Synchronous Receive mode.

Read Register 1

This register contains the Special Receive condition status bits and Residue codes for the I-field in the SDLC Receive Mode.

D$_7$	D$_6$	D$_5$	D$_4$	D$_3$	D$_2$	D$_1$	D$_0$
End of Frame (SDLC)	CRC/ Framing Error	Receiver Overrun Error	Parity Error	Residue Code 2	Residue Code 1	Residue Code 0	All Sent

All Sent (D$_0$). In Asynchronous modes, this bit is set when all the characters have completely cleared the transmitter. Transitions of this bit do not cause interrupts. It is always set in Synchronous modes.

Residue Codes 0, 1, and 2 (D$_1$-D$_3$). In those cases of the SDLC receive mode where the I-field is not an integral multiple of the character length, these three bits indicate the length of the I-field. These codes are meaningful only for the transfer in which the End Of Frame bit is set (SDLC). For a receive character length of eight bits per character, the codes signify the following:

Residue Code 2	Residue Code 1	Residue Code 0	I-Field Bits In Previous Byte	I-Field Bits In Second Previous Byte
1	0	0	0	3
0	1	0	0	4
1	1	0	0	5
0	0	1	0	6
1	0	1	0	7
0	1	1	0	8
1	1	1	1	8
0	0	0	2	8
I-Field bits are right-justified in all cases				

If a receive character length different from eight bits is used for the I-field, a table similar to the previous one may be constructed for each different character length. For no residue (that is, the last character boundary coincides with the boundary of the I-field and CRC field), the Residue codes are:

Bits per Character	Residue Code 2	Residue Code 1	Residue Code 0
8 Bits per Character	0	1	1
7 Bits per Character	0	0	0
6 Bits per Character	0	1	0
5 Bits per Character	0	0	1

Parity Error (D_4). When parity is enabled, this bit is set for those characters whose parity does not match the programmed sense (even/odd). The bit is latched, so once an error occurs, it remains set until the Error Reset command (WR0) is given.

Receive Overrun Error (D_5). This bit indicates that more than three characters have been received without a read from the CPU. Only the character that has been written over is flagged with this error, but when this character is read, the error condition is latched until reset by the Error Reset command. If Status Affects Vector is enabled, the character that has been overrun interrupts with a Special Receive Condition vector.

CRC/Framing Error (D_6). If a Framing Error occurs (asynchronous modes), this bit is set (and not latched) for the receive character in which the Framing error occurred. Detection of a Framing Error adds an additional one-half of a bit time to the character time so the Framing Error is not interpreted as a new start bit. In Synchronous and SDLC modes, this bit indicates the result of comparing the CRC checker to the appropriate check value. This bit is reset by issuing an Error Reset command. The bit is not latched, so it is always updated when the next character is received. When used for CRC error and status in Synchronous modes, it is usually set since most bit combinations result in a non-zero CRC, except for a correctly completed message.

End of Frame (D_7). This bit is used only with the SDLC mode and indicates that a valid ending flag has been received and that the CRC Error and Residue codes are also valid. This bit can be reset by issuing the Error Reset command. It is also updated by the first character of the following frame.

Read Register 2 (Chapter B only)

This register contains the interrupt vector written into WR2 if the Status Affects Vector control bit is not set. If the control bit is set, it contains the modified vector shown in the Status Affects Vector paragraph of the Write Register 1 section. When this register is read, the vector returned is modified by the highest priority interrupting condition at the time of the read. If no interrupts are pending, the vector is modified with $V_3=0$, $V_2=1$, and $V_1=1$. This register may be read only through Channel B.

D_7	D_6	D_5	D_4	D_3	D_2	D_1	D_0
V_7	V_6	V_5	V_4	V_3	V_2	V_1	V_0

Variable if Status
Affects Vector is
enabled

APPLICATIONS

The flexibility and versatility of the Z80-SIO make it useful for numerous applications, a few of which are included here. These examples show several applications that combine the Z80-SIO with other members of the Z80 family.

Figure 8-3 shows the simple processor-to-processor communication over a direct line. Both remote processors in this system can communicate to the Z80-CPU with different protocols and data rates. Depending on the complexity of the application, other Z80 peripheral circuits (Z80-CTC, for example) may be required. The unused channel of the Z80-SIO can be used to control other peripherals, or they can be connected to other remote processors.

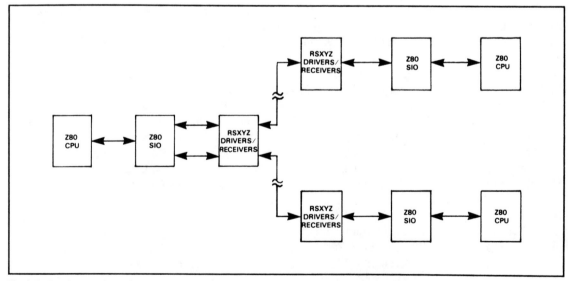

Fig. 8-3. Synchronous/asynchronous processor-to-processor communication (using telephone line).

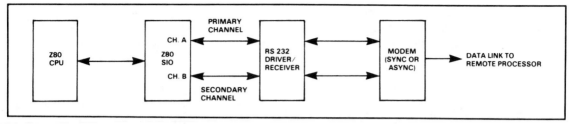

Fig. 8-4. Both channels of a single Z80-SIO.

Figure 8-4 illustrates how both channels of a single Z80-SIO are used with modems that have primary and secondary or reverse channel options. Alternatively, two modems without these options can be connected to the Z80-SIO. A suitable baud-rate generator (Z80-CTC) must be used for Asynchronous modems.

Figure 8-5 shows the Z80-SIO in a data concentrator, a relatively complex application that uses two Z80-SIOs to perform a variety of functions. The data concentrator can be used to collect data from many terminals over low-speed lines and transmit it over a single high-speed line after editing and reformatting.

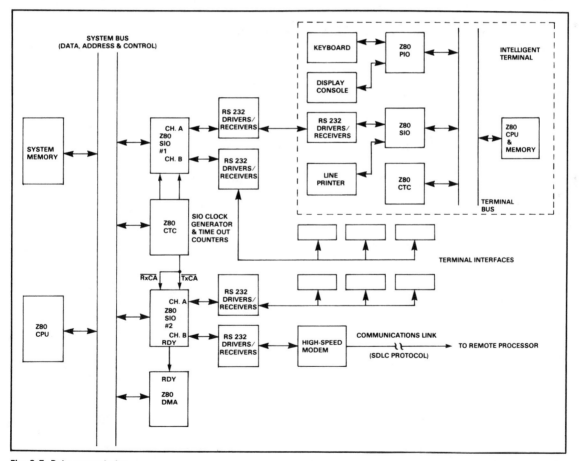

Fig. 8-5. Data concentrator.

The Z80-DMA controller circuit is used with Z80-SIO #2 to transmit the reformatted data at high speed with the required protocol. The high-speed modem provides the transmit clock for this channel. The Z80-CTC counter-timer circuit supplies the transmit and receive clocks for the low-speed lines and is also used as a time-out counter for various functions.

The Z80-SIO #1 controls local or remote terminals. A single intelligent terminal is shown within the dashed lines. The terminal employs a Z80-SIO to communicate to the data concentrator on one channel while providing the interface to a line printer over its second channel. The intelligent terminal shown could be designed to operate interactively with the operator.

Depending on the software and hardware capabilities built into this system, the data concentrator can employ store-and-forward or hold-and-forward methods for regulating information traffic between slow terminals and the high-speed remote processor. If the high-speed channel is provided with a dial-out option, the channel can be connected to a number of remote processors over a switched line.

READ CYCLE

The timing signals generated by a Z80-CPU input instruction to read a Data or Status byte from the Z80-SIO are illustrated in Fig. 8-6.

INTERRUPT ACKNOWLEDGE CYCLE

After receiving an Interrupt Request signal ($\overline{\text{INT}}$ pulled Low,) the Z80-CPU sends an Interrupt Acknowledge signal ($\overline{\text{M1}}$ and $\overline{\text{IORQ}}$ both Low). The daisy-chained interrupt circuits determine the highest priority interrupt requestor. The IEI of the highest priority peripheral is terminated High. For any peripheral that has no interrupt pending or under service, IEO=IEI. Any peripheral that does have an interrupt pending or under service forces its IEO Low. (See Figs. 8-8 and 8-9.)

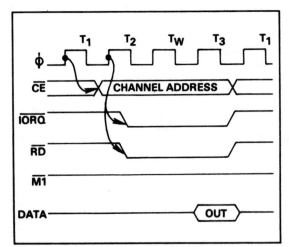

Fig. 8-6. Read cycle.

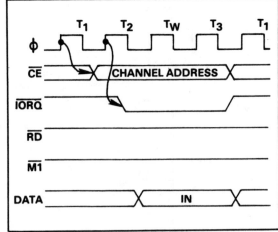

Fig. 8-7. Write cycle.

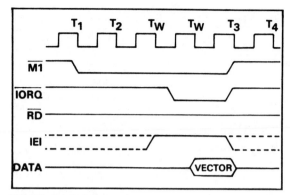

Fig. 8-8. Acknowledge cycle.

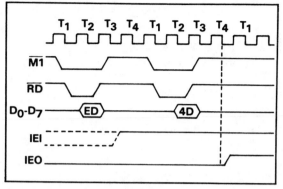

Fig. 8-9. Return from interrupt cycle.

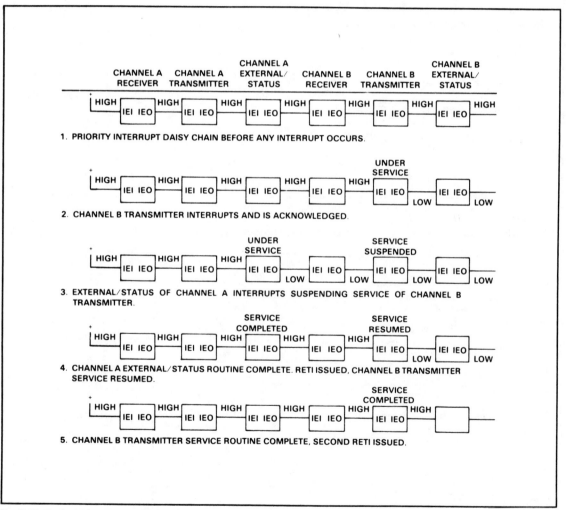

Fig. 8-10. Typical interrupt sequence.

ABSOLUTE MAXIMUM RATING

Voltages on all inputs and outputs with respect to GNE ....−0.3V to +7.0V
Operating Ambient Temperature ....As Specified in Ordering Information
Storage Temperature...−65°C to +150°C

Stresses greater than those listed under Absolute Maximum Ratings may cause permanent damage to the device. This is a stress rating only; operation of the device at any condition above those indicated in the operational sections of these specifications is not implied. Exposure to absolute maximum rating conditions for extended periods may affect device reliability.

STANDARD TEST CONDITIONS

The characteristics below apply for the following standard test conditions, unless otherwise noted. All voltages are referenced to GND. Positive current flows into the referenced pin. Standard conditions are as follows:

- +4.75V ≤ Vcc ≤ +5.25V
- GND = OV
- T_A as specified in Ordering Information

All ac parameters assume a load capacitance of 100 pF max. Timing references between two output signals assume a load difference of 50 pF max.

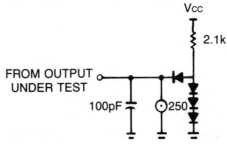

Fig. 8-11. SIO Specifications.

Table 8-1. Dc Characteristics.

SYM	PARAMETER	MIN	MAX	UNIT	TEST CONDITION
V_{ILC}	Clock Input Low Voltage	−0.3	+0.80	V	
V_{IHC}	Clock Input High Voltage	V_{CC} −0.6	+5.5	V	
V_{IL}	Input Low Voltage	−0.3	+0.8	V	
V_{IH}	Input High Voltage	+2.0	+5.5	V	
V_{OL}	Output Low Voltage		+0.4	V	I_{OL} = 2.0mA
V_{OH}	Output High Voltage	+2.4		V	I_{OH} = −250 μA
I_{LI}	Input Leakage Current	−10	± 10	μA	0 < V_{IN} < V_{CC}
I_Z	3-State Output/Data Bus Input Leakage Current	−10	+10	μA	0 < V_{IN} < V_{CC}
$I_{L(SY)}$	SYNC Pin Leakage Current	−40	+10	μA	0 < V_{IN} < V_{CC}
I_{CC}	Power Supply Current		100	mA	

Overall specified temperature and voltage range.

206

Table 8-2. Capacitance.

SYM	PARAMETER	MIN	MAX	UNIT	TEST CONDITION
C	Clock Capacitance		40	pF	Unmeasured
C_{IN}	Input Capacitance		10	pF	pins returned
C_{OUT}	Output Capacitance		10	pF	to ground

Over specified temperature range; f = 1MHz

To insure stable conditions in the daisy chain, all-interrupt status signals are prevented from changing while $\overline{M1}$ is Low. When $\overline{IORQ}$ is Low, the highest priority interrupt requestor (the one with IEI High) places its interrupt vector on the data bus and sets its internal interrupt-under-service latch.

WRITE CYCLE

Figure 8-7 illustrates the timing and data signals generated by a Z80-CPU output instruction to write a Data or Control byte into the Z80-SIO.

RETURN FROM INTERRUPT CYCLE

Normally, the Z80-CPU issues a RETI (Return from interrupt) instruction at the end of an interrupt service routine. RETI is a 2-byte opcode (ED-4D) that resets the interrupt-under-service latch to terminate the interrupt that has just been processed. This is accomplished by manipulating the daisy chain in the following way.

The normal daisy-chain operation can be used to detect a pending interrupt; however, it cannot distinguish between an interrupt under service and a pending unacknowledged interrupt of a higher priority. Whenever "ED" is decoded, the daisy chain is modified by forcing High the IEO of any interrupt that has not yet been acknowledged. Thus, the daisy chain identifies the device presently under service as the only one with an IEI High and an IEO Low. If the next opcode byte is "4D", the interrupt-under-service latch is reset.

The ripple time of the interrupt daisy chain (both the High-to-Low and the Low-to-High transitions) limits the number of devices that can be placed in the daisy chain. Ripple time can be improved with carry-look-read, or by extending the interrupt acknowledge cycle.

DAISY CHAIN INTERRUPT NESTING

Figure 8-10 illustrates the daisy-chain configuration of interrupt circuits and their behavior with nested interrupts (an interrupt that is interrupted by another with a higher priority).

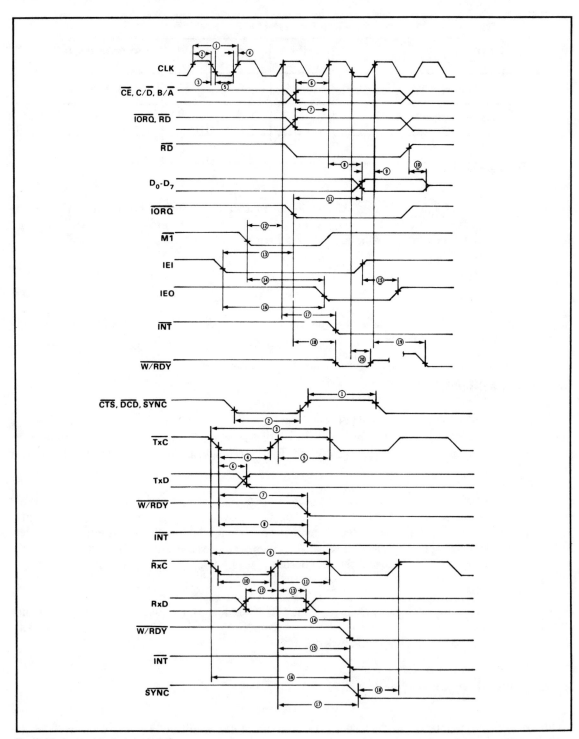

Fig. 8-12. Ac electrical characteristics.

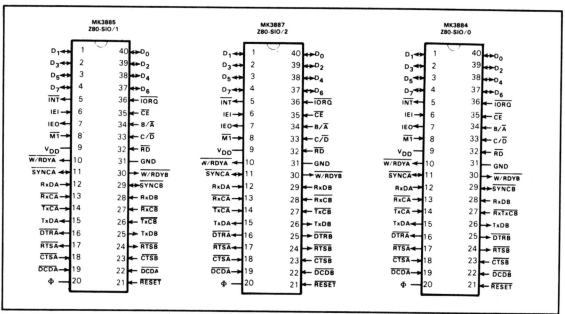

Fig. 8-13. Pin assignments.

PART NO.		PACKAGE TYPE	MAX CLOCK FREQUENCY	TEMPERATURE RANGE
MK3884N	Z80-SIO/0	Plastic	2.5MHz	0°C to +70°C
MK3884P	Z80-SIO/0	Ceramic	2.5MHz	0°C to 70°C
MK3884J	Z80-SIO/0	CERDIP	2.5MHz	0°C to +70°C
MK3884N-10	Z80-SIO/0	Plastic	2.5MHz	-40°C to +85°C
MK3884P-10	Z80-SIO/0	Ceramic	2.5MHz	-40°C to +85°C
MK3884J-10	Z80-SIO/0	CERDIP	2.5MHz	-40°C to +85°C
MK3884N-4	Z80A-SIO/0	Plastic	4MHz	0°C to 70°C
MK3884P-4	Z80A-SIO/0	Ceramic	4MHz	0°C to 70°C
MK3884J-4	Z80A-SIO/0	CERDIP	4MHz	0°C to 70°C
MK3885N	Z80-SIO/1	Plastic	2.5MHz	0°C to +70°C
MK3885P	Z80-SIO/1	Ceramic	2.5MHz	0°C to +70°C
MK3885J	Z80-SIO/1	CERDIP	2.5MHz	0°C to +70°C
MK3885N-10	Z80-SIO/1	Plastic	2.5MHz	-40°C to +85°C
MK3885P-10	Z80-SIO/1	Ceramic	2.5MHz	-40°C to +85°C
MK3885J-10	Z80-SIO/1	CERDIP	2.5MHz	-40°C to +85°C
MK3885N-4	Z80A-SIO/1	Plastic	4MHz	0°C to +70°C
MK3885P-4	Z80A-SIO/1	Ceramic	4MHz	0°C to +70°C
MK3885J-4	Z80A-SIO/1	CERDIP	4MHz	0°C to +70°C
MK3887N	Z80-SIO/2	Plastic	2.5MHz	0°C to +70°C
MK3887P	Z80-SIO/2	Ceramic	2.5MHz	0°C to +70°C
MK3887J	Z80-SIO/2	CERDIP	2.5MHz	0°C to +70°C
MK3887N-10	Z80-SIO/2	Plastic	2.5MHz	-40°C to +85°C
MK3887P-10	Z80-SIO/2	Ceramic	2.5MHz	-40°C to +85°C
MK3887J-10	Z80-SIO/2	CERDIP	2.5MHz	-40°C to +85°C
MK3887N-4	Z80A-SIO/2	Plastic	4MHz	0°C to +70°C
MK3887P-4	Z80A-SIO/2	Ceramic	4MHz	0°C to +70°C
MK3887J-4	Z80A-SIO/2	CERDIP	4MHz	0°C to +70°C

NOTE: Refer to section on Pin Description for explanation of the differences between the MK3884, MK3885, and MK3887.

Fig. 8-14. Ordering information for Mostek chips.

Table 8-3. Ac Electrical Characteristics.

NUMBER	SYM	PARAMETER	MK3884		MK3884-4		UNIT
			MIN	MAX	MIN	MAX	
1	TcC	Clock Cycle Time	400	4000	250	4000	ns
2	TwCh	Clock Width (High)	170	2000	105	2000	ns
3	TfC	Clock Fall Time		30		30	ns
4	TrC	Clock Rise Time		30		30	ns
5	TwC1	Clock Width (Low)	170	2000	105	2000	ns
6	TsAD(C)	$\overline{CE}$, C/$\overline{D}$, B/$\overline{A}$ to Clock ↑ Setup Time	160		145		ns
7	TsCS(C)	$\overline{IORQ}$, $\overline{RD}$ to Clock ↑ Setup Time	240		115		ns
8	TdC(DO)	Clock ↑ to Data Out Delay		240		220	ns
9	TsDI(C)	Data In to Clock ↑ Setup (Write or $\overline{M1}$ Cycle)	50		50		ns
10	TdRD(DOz)	RD ↑ to Data Out Float Delay		230		110	ns
11	TdIO(DOI)	IORQ ↓ to Data Out Delay (INTA Cycle)		340		160	ns
12	TsM1(C)	$\overline{M1}$ to Clock ↑ Setup Time	210		90		ns
13	TsIEI(IO)	IEI to $\overline{IORQ}$ ↓ Setup Time (INTA Cycle)	200		140		ns
14	TdM1(IEO)	$\overline{M1}$ ↓ to IEO ↓ Delay (interrupt before $\overline{M1}$)		300		190	ns
15	TdIEI(IEOr)	IEI ↑ to IEO ↑ Delay (after ED decode)		150		100	ns
16	TdIEI(IEOf)	IEI ↓ to IEO ↓ Delay		150		100	ns
17	TdC(INT)	Clock ↑ to $\overline{INT}$ ↓ Delay		200		200	ns
18	TdIO (W/RWf)	$\overline{IORQ}$ ↓ or $\overline{CE}$ ↓ to $\overline{W/RDY}$ ↓ Delay Wait Mode		300		210	ns
19	TdC (W/RR)	Clock ↑ to $\overline{W/RDY}$ ↓ Delay (Ready Mode)		120		120	ns
20	TdC (W/RWz)	Clock ↓ to $\overline{W/RDY}$ Float Delay (Wait Mode)		150		130	ns
21	Th	Any unspecified Hold when Setup is specified	0		0		ns

NUMBER	SYM	PARAMETER	MK3884		MK3884-4		UNIT
			MIN	MAX	MIN	MAX	
1	TwPh	Pulse Width (High)	200		200		ns
2	TwPl	Pulse Width (Low)	200		200		ns
3	TcTxC	$\overline{TxC}$ Cycle Time	400	∞	400	∞	ns
4	TwTxCl	$\overline{TxC}$ Width (Low)	180	∞	180	∞	ns
5	TwTxCh	$\overline{TxC}$ Width (High)	180	∞	180	∞	ns
6	TdTxC(TxD)	$\overline{TxC}$ ↓ to TxD Delay (x1 Mode)		400		300	ns
7	TdTxC (W/RRf)	$\overline{TxC}$ ↓ to W/RDY ↓ Delay (Ready Mode)	5	9	5	9	Clk Periods*
8	TdTxC(INT)	$\overline{TxC}$ ↓ to INT ↓ Delay	5	9	5	9	Clk Periods*
9	TcRxC	$\overline{RxC}$ Cycle Time	400	∞	400	∞	ns
10	TwRxCl	$\overline{RxC}$ Width (Low)	180	∞	180	∞	ns
11	TwRxCh	$\overline{RxC}$ Width (High)	180	∞	180	∞	ns
12	TsRxD(RxC)	RxD to $\overline{RxC}$ ↑ Setup Time (x1 Mode)	0		0		ns
13	ThRxD(RxC)	$\overline{RxC}$ ↑ to RxD Hold time (x1 Mode)	140		140		ns
14	TdRxC (W/RRf)	$\overline{RxC}$ ↑ to $\overline{W/RDY}$ ↓ Delay (Ready Mode)	10	13	10	13	Clk Periods*
15	TdRxC(INT)	$\overline{RxC}$ ↑ to INT ↓ Delay	10	13	10	13	Clk Periods*
16	TdTxC(INT)	$\overline{TxC}$ ↓ to $\overline{INT}$ ↓ Delay	5	9	5	9	Clk Periods*
17	TdRxC (SYNC)	$\overline{RxC}$ ↑ to $\overline{SYNC}$ ↓ Delay (Output Modes)	4	7	4	7	Clk Periods*
18	TsSYNC (RxC)	$\overline{SYNC}$ ↓ to $\overline{RxC}$ ↑ Setup (External Sync Modes)	–100		–100		ns

In all modes, the System Clock rate must be at least five times the maximum data rate.
RESET must be active a minimum of one complete Clock Cycle.
*System Clock

Each box in the illustration could be a separate external Z80 peripheral circuit with a user-defined order of interrupt priorities. However, a similar daisy-chain structure also exists inside the Z80-SIO, which has six interrupt levels with a fixed order of priorities.

The case illustrated occurs when the transmitter of Channel B interrupts and is granted service. While this interrupt is being serviced, it is interrupted by a higher priority interrupt from Channel A. The second interrupt is serviced and—upon completion—a RETI instruction is executed or a RETI command is written into the Z80-SIO, resetting the interrupt-under-service latch of the Channel A interrupt. At this time, the service routine for Channel B is resumed. When it is completed, another RETI instruction is executed to complete the interrupt service.

SIO SPECIFICATIONS

SIO electrical specifications & ac characteristics, pin assignments and ordering information may be found in Figs. 8-10 through 8-13 and Tables 8-1 through 8-3.

Chapter 9

Fundamental Software Projects

The projects in this chapter can be executed with the basic SD-Z80 Starter Kit (see Chapter 1). No modification has to be made on the BASIC SD-Z80 Starter Kit. For each project you are given a description of the program objective. The programs are broken into three groups: memory information, instruction, and comments.

Within memory information is included address, data, and label. The *address* is the hexadecimal memory location of the data or program. The *label* is a one-word statement describing the data, or what is being executed in the program. For example, the first or starting address is labeled START, and the last program address is usually labeled EXIT. If the word RESULT is listed in the data memory address, one of the results in the program is stored in that data address and is considered data. Most of the one-word statements are self-explanatory. When an explanation is necessary, the one-word statement is defined under comments.

Most programs will begin with the word START in the label column. Most START address locations are the hexadecimal number (2010_{16}. All of the address locations are hexadecimal numbers written in sequence. Next to the address under the *data* column is program information generally to be called *data*; in other words, machine language or object code is given in the data column next to every address location in the program.

The main heading instruction includes the subheadings opcode and operand. The instruction portion of the programming form is the assembly-language statements or mnemonics of the program. The subheading opcode defines the Z80 Instruction Set that is employed in the program.

The operand column is the register location, memory location or data required in the program. Also, any combination of the register, memory location or data required can be included in the Operand column.

The comment column clarifies the execution of the programs. The last comment of each program is usually the statement "Return to monitor routine." This comment is listed in a few programs; where it is not listed, it is to be understood as the last program statement.

PROJECT 10: COMPLEMENT OF A NUMBER IN THE ACCUMULATOR

This program will take the contents of memory location 2000 and load it into the accumulator. It will take that number and complement it and store the results in memory location 2001. The program will then go back to the monitor program where you can use the substitute memory key to examine memory locations one at a time.

MEMORY INFORMATION			INSTRUCTION		COMMENT
ADDRESS	DATA	LABEL	OPCODE	OPERAND	
2000	DATA				LOCATION OF DATA TO BE COMPLEMENTED.
2001					LOCATION OF RESULT.
2010	3A	START	LD	A,2000	LOAD ACCUMULATOR WITH DATA FOUND AT
2011	00				MEMORY LOCATION 2000.
2012	20				
2013	2F		CPL		COMPLEMENT ACCUMULATOR.
2014	32		LD	2001,A	LOAD MEMORY LOCATION 2001 WITH DATA
2015	01				FOUND IN ACCUMULATOR.
2016	20				
2017	C7		RST	00	RETURN TO MONITOR ROUTINE.

Example

The following example shows you how to load the data and program into the SD-Z80 and then check to see if the program has executed properly. Each keystroke on the SD-Z80 is listed under the column head Key. The next two columns in the example, ADDR and DATA, tell you what characters you will see on the LED display of the SD-Z80. The ADDR characters will be seen in the Address Field of the LED display, and the DATA characters will be seen in the Data Field of the LED display after the reader has pressed the proper KEY instruction. The comments provide special remarks about the execution of the program.

Step-by-step keystroking is not provided for the other projects in this book. If you need reinforcement in the proper keystrokes for future programs, refer to this example and your SD-Z80 User's Manual, which provides simple keystroke examples. Keystroke confidence is obtained from practice, practice, practice. Special keystroke requirements are given when needed in the following programs.

To execute Project 10 follow the keystrokes listed below, after the dc supply has been connected to the Z80-Kit.

214

The table below provides a few hexadecimal numbers, their complements, and their additive inverse. You can use this information to check the programs in Projects 10 and 11.

Number	Complement	Additive Inverse = Complement + 1
00	FF	00 (FF + 1)
01	FE	FF (FE + 1)
02	FD	FE (FD + 1)
03	FC	FD (FC + 1)

KEY	ADDR	DATA	COMMENTS
RESET	-		THE MONITOR IS READY TO ACCEPT A COMMAND.
2	2		
0	20		
0	200		
0	2000		
MEM EXAM	2000	??	THE SYMBOL ? MEANS THAT ANY CHARACTER ON THE KEYBOARD COULD BE DISPLAYED IN THE DATA FIELD.
0	2000	??	
1	2000	01	DATA WILL NOT CHANGE TO NEW DATA UNTIL BOTH NUMBERS HAVE BEEN KEYED IN.
NEXT	2001	??	ADDRESS FIELD ADVANCES ONE POSITION, AND DISPLAYS WHATEVER (??) IS CONTAINED IN THAT LOCATION.
0	2001	??	
0	2001	00	
MON	-		PRESSING "MON" KEY WILL RETURN YOU TO THE MONITOR ROUTINE. NOW THE FIRST ADDRESS OF THE PROGRAM MAY BE KEYED IN. THIS METHOD IS MUCH QUICKER THAN PRESSING THE "NEXT" KEY UNTIL THE ADDRESS YOU WISH TO MONITOR APPEARS.
2	2		
0	20		
1	201		
0	2010		
MEM EXAM	2010	??	
3	2010	??	
A	2010	3A	
NEXT	2011	??	
0	2011	??	
0	2011	00	
NEXT	2012	??	
2	2912	??	
0	2012	20	

KEY	ADDR	DATA	COMMENTS
NEXT	2013	??	
2	2013	??	
F	2013	2F	
NEXT	2014	??	
3	2014	??	
2	2014	32	
NEXT	2015	??	
0	2015	??	
1	2015	01	
NEXT	2016	??	
2	2016	??	
0	2016	20	
NEXT	2017	??	
C	2017	??	
7	2017	C7	
MON	-		
2	2		
0	20		
0	200		
0	2000		
Mem			
EXAM	2000	01	
NEXT	2001	00	
MON	-		
2	2		
0	20		
1	201		
0	2010		
MEM			
EXAM	2010	3A	
NEXT	2011	00	
NEXT	2012	20	
NEXT	2013	2F	
NEXT	2014	32	
NEXT	2015	01	

KEY	ADDR	DATA	COMMENTS
NEXT	2016	20	
NEXT	2017	C7	IF THE PROGRAM IS CORRECT PROCEED AS FOLLOWS.
MON	-		
2 0 1 0	2 20 201 2010		
EXEC	-		IF THE MINUS SIGN APPEARS IN THE DISPLAY, THE PROGRAM HAS BEEN PROPERLY EXECUTED.

PROJECT 11: FINDING THE ADDITIVE INVERSE OF A NUMBER IN THE ACCUMULATOR

This program will take the contents of location 2000, find its additive inverse, and then store it in 2001. The program will then go back to the monitor program where you can examine memory locations one at a time.

MEMORY INFORMATION			INSTRUCTION		COMMENT
ADDRESS	DATA	LABEL	OPCODE	OPERAND	
2000	DATA				LOCATION OF DATA.
2001					LOCATION OF RESULT.
2010	3A	START	LD	A,2000	LOAD ACCUMULATOR WITH DATA FOUND AT
2011	00				MEMORY LOCATION 2000.
2012	20				
2013	06		LD	B,01	LOAD REGISTER B IMMEDIATELY.
2014	01				WITH DATA 01.
2015	2F		CPL		COMPLEMENT ACCUMULATOR.
2016	80		ADD	A,B	ADD REGISTER B TO ACCUMULATOR.
2017	32		LD	2001,A	LOAD MEMORY LOCATION 2001 WITH DATA
2018	01				FOUND IN ACCUMULATOR.
2019	20				
201A	C7		RST	00	RETURN TO MONITOR ROUTINE.

PROJECT 12: THE ADDITIVE INVERSE TEST

This program will prove that the additive inverse is generated by adding it back to the original number and storing the result in 2001.

MEMORY INFORMATION			INSTRUCTION		COMMENT
ADDRESS	DATA	LABEL	OPCODE	OPERAND	
2000					LOCATION OF DATA TO BE TESTED.
2001					LOCATION OF RESULT.
2010	21		LD	HL,2000	LOAD REG. PAIR HL WITH DATA 2000.
2011	00				
2012	20				
2013	7E		LD	A,(HL)	LOAD ACCUM. WITH DATA FOUND IN ADD. 2000.
2014	ED		NEG		GENERATE 2'S COMPLEMENT.
2015	44				
2016	86	ADD	A,(HL)	ADD	DATAFOUND ADD. 2000 TO ACCUM.
2017	23		INC	HL	INCREMENT REG. PAIR H&L.
2018	77		LD	(HL),A	LOAD ADD. 2001 WITH DATA FOUND IN ACCUM.
2019	C7		RST	00	RETURN TO MONITOR ROUTINE.

PROJECT 13: SUBTRACTION EMPLOYING ADDITIVE INVERSE

This program will subtract the number in address 2000 from the number in address 2001 by adding the complement of the number to be subtracted. The result will be stored in address 2002.

Example

2000	02	Subtrahend
2001	05	Minuend
2002	03	Answer (5-2)

MEMORY INFORMATION			INSTRUCTION		COMMENT
ADDRESS	DATA	LABEL	OPCODE	OPERAND	
2000	DATA				
2001	DATA				NUMBER TO BE SUBTRACTED FROM.
2002					LOCATION OF RESULT.
2010	3A	START	LD	A,2001	LOAD ACCUMULATOR WITH DATA FOUND IN
2011	01				ADD. 2001.
2012	20				
2013	47		LD	B,A	LOAD REG. B WITH DATA FOUND IN ACCUM.
2014	3A		LD	A,2000	LOAD ACCUM. WITH DATA FOUND IN
2015	00				ADD. 2000.
2016	20				
2017	2F		CPL		COMPLEMENT ACCUMULATOR.
2018	3C		INC	A	INCREMENT ACCUM.
2019	80		ADD	A,B	ADD REG. B TO ACCUM.
201A	32		LD	2002,A	LOAD MEM. LOC. 2002 WITH DATA FOUND
201B	02				IN ACCUM.
201C	20				
201D	C7	EXIT	RST	00	RETURN TO MONITOR ROUTINE.

PROJECT 14: HEXADECIMAL ADDITION OF TWO NUMBERS

This program will take the contents of location 2000, add it to 2001, store the result in location 2002, and then return to the monitor program.

MEMORY INFORMATION			INSTRUCTION		COMMENT
ADDRESS	DATA	LABEL	OPCODE	OPERAND	
2000	DATA				FIRST NUMBER TO BE ADDED.
2001	DATA				SECOND NUMBER TO BE ADDED.
2002					RESULT.
2010	01		LD	BC,2000	LOAD REG. PAIR BC WITH DATA 2000.
2011	00				
2012	20				
2013	11		LD	DE,2002	LOAD REG. PAIR DE WITH DATA 2002
2014	02				
2015	20				
2016	21		LD	HL,2001	LOAD REG. PAIR HL WITH DATA 2001
2017	01				
2018	20				
2019	0A		LD	A,(BC)	LOAD ACCUM. WITH DATA FOUND IN ADD. 2000.
201A	86		ADD	A,(HL)	ADD DATA FOUND IN ADD. 2001 TO ACCUM.
201B	12		LD	(DE),A	LOAD ADD. 2002 WITH DATA FOUND IN ACCUM.
201C	C7		RST	00	RETURN TO MONITOR ROUTINE.

PROJECT 15: DECOMAL ADDITION OF TWO NUMBERS

This program will add the decimal numbers in 2000 and 2001 and store the result in decimal from address 2002.

Example

ADDR   DATA

2000   10
2001   20
2002   30

MEMORY INFORMATION			INSTRUCTION		COMMENT
ADDRESS	DATA	LABEL	OPCODE	OPERAND	
2000	DATA				TWO DECIMAL NUMBERS TO BE ADDED.
2001	DATA				
2002					RESULT.

MEMORY INFORMATION			INSTRUCTION		COMMENT
ADDRESS	DATA	LABEL	OPCODE	OPERAND	
2010	3A		LD	A,2000	LOAD ACCUM. WITH DATA FOUND IN
2011	00				ADD. 2000.
2012	20				
2013	47		LD	B,A	LOAD REG. B WITH DATA FOUND IN ACCUM.
2014	3A		LD	A,2001	LOAD ACCUM. WITH DATA FOUND IN ADD.
2015	01				2001.
2016	20				
2017	80		ADD	A,B	ADD REG. B TO ACCUM.
2018	27		DAA		CONVERT DATA IN ACCUM. TO DECIMAL.
2019	32		LD	2002,A	LOAD MEM. LOC. 2002 WITH DATA FOUND
201A	02				IN ACCUM.
201B	20				
201C	C7		RST	00	RETURN TO MONITOR ROUTINE.

PROJECT 16: ADD TWO NUMBERS IN HEXADECIMAL AND CONVERT THE ANSWER TO DECIMAL

This program adds two numbers that are stored in memory at addresses 2000 and 2001. The numbers are hexadecimal and the resulting addition is stored in address 2003 as a hexadecimal number. Also, the resulting addition is stored in address 2004 as a decimal. No carry is recorded in this program.

MEMORY INFORMATION			INSTRUCTION		COMMENT
ADDRESS	DATA	LABEL	OPCODE	OPERAND	
2000	DATA				NUMBERS TO BE ADDED.
2001	DATA				
2002					
2003					RESULT IN HEXIDECIMAL FORM.
2004					RESULT IN DECIMAL FORM.
2010	01		LD	BC,2000	LOAD REG. PAIR BC WITH DATA 2000.
2011	00				
2012	20				
2013	0A		LD	A,(BC)	LOAD ACCUM. WITH DATA FOUND IN ADD. 2000.
2017	80		ADD	A,B	ADD REG. B TO ACCUM.
2018	32		LD	2003,A	LOAD MEM. LOC. 2003 WITH DATA FOUND
2019	03				IN ACCUM.
201A	20				
201B	27		DAA		CONVERT DATA IN ACCUM. TO DECIMAL.
201C	32		LD	2004,A	LOAD MEM. LOC. 2004 WITH DATA FOUND
201D	04				IN ACCUM.
201E	20				
201F	C7		RST	00	RETURN TO MONITOR ROUTINE.

220

PROJECT 17: SIXTEEN-BIT ADDITION

This program will add two sixteen-bit numbers and store the answer in addresses 2004 and 2005. The program also sets the carry flag if the result is greater than the hexadecimal number FFFF.

Example

ADDR DATA

2000 04   LSB1

2001 02   MSB1

2002 10   LSB2

2003 30   MSB2

2004 14   LSB1 + LSB2 (04 + 10)

2005 32   MSB1 + MSB2 (02 + 30)

MEMORY INFORMATION			INSTRUCTION		COMMENT
ADDRESS	DATA	LABEL	OPCODE	OPERAND	
2000	DATA	LSB			FIRST 16-BIT NUMBER.
2001	DATA	MSB			
2002	DATA	LSB			SECOND 16-BIT NUMBER.
2003	DATA	MSB			
2004	LSB				
2005	MSB				RESULT OF ADDITION.
2010	2A		LD	HL,(2000)	LOAD REG. PAIR HL WITH DATA FOUND
20011	00				IM MEM. LOC. 2000 & 2001 (NO OVERFLOW).
2012	20				
2013	ED		LD	B,,(2002)	LOAD REG. PAIR BC WITH DATA FOUND
2014	4B				IN MEM. LOC. 2002 & 2003 (NO OVERFLOW).
2015	02				
2016	20				
2017	09		ADD	HL,BC	ADD REG. PAIR BC TO HL.
2018	22		LD	(2004),HL	LOAD MEM. LOC. 2004 & 2005 WITH DATA
2019	04				FOUND IN REG. PAIR HL.
201A	20				
201B	C7		RST	00	RETURN TO MONITOR ROUTINE.

PROJECT 18: COUNTING DECIMAL NUMBER DISPLAY (00 to 99)

This program begins by keystroking the beginning address, then the EXEC key is pressed and a two-digit decimal number will begin the counting. To stop the two-digit decimal number from counting, press the monitor key marked MON.

MEMORY INFORMATION			INSTRUCTION		COMMENT
ADDRESS	DATA	LABEL	OPCODE	OPERAND	
2000	31		LD	SP, 2390	INITIALIZE STACK POINTER.
2001	90				
2002	23				
2003	ED		1M	1	ENABLE MODE 1 INTERRUPT.
2004	56				
2005	FB		EI		
2006	3E		LD	A,00	INITIALIZE DECIMAL COUNT.
2007	00				
2008	CD	LOOP	CALL	DISPLAY	DISPLAY COUNT.
2009	40				
200A	20				
200B	3C		INC	A	INCREMENT COUNT AND
200C	B7		OR	A	ADJUST TO DECIMAL.
200D	27		DAA		
200E	C3		JMP	LOOP	
200F	08				
2010	20				
					Display Routine
2040	F5		PUSH	AF	SAVE ACCUM. & FLAGS ON STACK.
2041	47		LD	B,A	
2042	E6		AND	F0	MASK OUT LOWER BITS.
2043	F0				
2044	1F		RRA		SHIFT UPPER FOUR BITS TO
2045	1F		RRA		
2046	1F		RRA		LOWER FOUR BITS.
2047	1F		RRA		
2048	21		LD	HL,2090	INITIALIZE COMPARISON TABLE
2049	90				POINTER.
204A	20				
204B	11		LD	DE,07A6	INITIALIZE DISPLAY CODE
204C	A6				TABLE POINTER.
204D	07				
204E	BE	CONTINUE	CP	(HL)	COMPARE ACCUM. TO MEMORY.
204F	CA		JP	Z,CODE	JUMP IF ZERO TO "CODE."
2050	57				
2051	20				
2052	23		INC	HL	IF NOT ZERO INCREMENT
2053	13		INC	DE	COMPARISON TABLE AND CODE
2054	C3		JP	CONTINUE	TABLE POINTERS, THEN
2055	4E				CONTINUE.
2056	20				
2057	1A	CODE	LD	A,(DE)	LOAD DISPLAY CODE IN ACCUM.
2058	4F		LD	C,A	THEN TRANSFER TO REG. C.
2059	78		LD	A,B	RELOAD ACCUM. WITH NUMBER TO
205A	E6		AND	0F	BE DISPLAYED. THEN MASK OUT
205B	0F				UPPER FOUR BITS.

MEMORY INFORMATION			INSTRUCTION		COMMENT
ADDRESS	DATA	LABEL	OPCODE	OPERAND	
205C	21		LD	HL,2090	REINITIALIZE TABLE POINTERS.
205D	90				
205E	20				
205F	11		LD	DE,07A6	
2060	A6				
2061	07				
2062	BE	RETURN	CP	(HL)	COMPARE ACCUM. TO DATA IN TABLE.
2063	CA		JP	Z,LOAD	IF ZERO JUMP TO "LOAD."
2064	6B				
2065	20				
2066	23		INC	HL	IF NOT ZERO INCREMENT
2067	13		INC	DE	TABLE POINTERS AND JUMP
2068	C3		JP	RETURN	TO "RETURN."
2069	62				
206A	20				
206B	1A	LOAD	LD	A,(DE)	LOAD DISPLAY CODE IN ACCUM.
206C	47		LD	B,A	THEN TRANSFER TO REG.B.
206D	1E		LD	E,	
206E					
206F	79		LD	A,C	
2070	D3		OUT	(88),A	OUTPUT UPPER FOUR BIT
2071	88				CODE TO DISPLAY.
2072	3E		LD	A,02	
2073	02				
2074	D3		OUT	(8C),A	
2075	8C				
2076	CD		CALL	DELAY	DELAY 20 MSEC.
2077	4F				
2078	06				
2079	78		LD	A,B	
207A	D3		OUT	(88),A	OUTPUT LOWER FOUR BIT CODE
207B	88				TO DISPLAY.
207C	3E		LD	A,01	
207D	01				
207E	D3		OUT	(8C),A	
207F	8C				
2080	CD		CALL	DELAY	DELAY 20 MSEC.
2081	4F				
2082	06				
2083	1D		DEC	E	CONTINUE TO OUTPUT NUMBER
2084	C2		JP	NZ	UNTIL REG E GOES TO ZERO.
2085	6F				
2086	20				
2087	F1		POP	AF	
2088	C9		RET		RETURN TO MAIN PROGRAM.

MEMORY INFORMATION			INSTRUCTION		COMMENT
ADDRESS	DATA	LABEL	OPCODE	OPERAND	
2090	00				Compare Table
2091	01				
2092	02				
2093	03				
2094	04				
2095	05				
2096	06				
2097	07				
2098	08				
2099	09				
					INTERRUPT SERVICE ROUTINE.
20A0	F5		PUSH	AF	SAVES CONTENTS OF ACCUMULATOR
20A1	3E		LD	A,7F	ON STACK POINTER THEN BLANKS
20A2	7F				OUT DISPLAY AND WAITS FOR
20A3	D3		OUT	(88),A	A KEY TO BE DEPRESSED.
20A4	88				IF A KEY IS DEPRESSED, THEN
20A5	3E		LD	A,3F	CONTROL IS RETURNED TO MAIN
20A6	3F				PROGRAM. IF NO KEY IS PRESSED
20A7	D3		OUT	(8C),A	THEN LOOP UNTIL ONE IS PRESSED.
20A8	8C				
20A9	DB		IN	A,(90)	
20AA	90				
20AB	E6		AND	1F	
20AC	1F				
20AD	FE		CP	1F	
20AE	1F				
20AF	CA		JP	Z	
20B0	A9				
20B1	20				
20B2	FB		EI		
20B3	ED		RET1		
20B4	4D				
23D3	C3		JP		JUMP TO INTERRUPT SERVICE
23D4	A0				ROUTINE.
23D5	20				

PROJECT 19: MULTI-BYTE ADDITION

This program will add two hexadecimal numbers that are n-bytes long and store the result starting at address 2001. The lowest address location should contain the least significant byte.

Example

2000	07	Program adjusted for 7 places.
2001	15	LSB1

224

2002 23

2003 46   MSB1

2008 4C   LSB2

2009 2F

200A 1A   MSB2

After Execution

2001 61   LSB of answer.

2002 52

2003 60   MSB of answer.

MEMORY INFORMATION			INSTRUCTION		COMMENT
ADDRESS	DATA	LABEL	OPCODE	OPERAND	
2000					NUMBER OF BYTES TO BE ADDED (1-7)
2001	DATA				
2002	DATA				FIRST NUMBER (MAY BE 1→7 BYTES
2003	DATA				LONG).
2004					
2008	DATA				
2009	DATA				SECOND NUMBER (MAY BE 1→7
200A	DATA				BYTES LONG).
200B					
2010	21		LD	HL,2001	LOAD REG. PAIR HL WITH DATA 2001.
2011	01				
2012	20				
2013	11		LD	DE,2008	LOAD REG. PAIR DE WITH DATA 2008.
2014	08				
2015	20				
2016	3A		LD	A,2000	LOAD ACCUM. WITH DATA FOUND IN
2017	00				ADD. 2000.
2018	20				
2019	47		LD	B,A	LOAD REG. B WITH DATA IN ACCUM.
201A	AF		XOR	A	CLEAR ACCUM. AND FLAGS.
201B	1A	LOOP	LD	A,(DE)	LOAD ACCUM. WITH DATA IN ADD. (DE).
201C	4E		LD	C,(HL)	LOAD REG. C WITH DATA IN ADD. (HL).
201D	89		ADC	A,C	ADD REG. C & CARRY TO ACCUM.
201E	12		LD	(DE),A	LOAD ADD. (DE) WITH DATA IN ACCUM.
201F	23		INC	HL	INCREMENT REG. PAIR HL.
2020	13		INC	DE	INCREMENT REG. PAIR DE.
2021	05		DEC	B	DECREMENT REG.B.
2022	C2		JP	NZ,201B	JUMP TO LOOP IF REG B IS NOT ZERO.
2023	1B				
2024	20				
2025	C7		RST	00	RETURN TO MONITOR ROUTINE.

PROJECT 20: ADDITION OF 8-BIT NUMBER SERIES

This program will add a variable number of hexadecimal numbers and place the result in address 2000. At the start of the program, address 2000 will hold the total of the numbers to be added. Care should be taken that the sum does not exceed the hexadecimal number FF.

MEMORY INFORMATION			INSTRUCTION		COMMENT
ADDRESS	DATA	LABEL	OPCODE	OPERAND	
2000					NO. OF BYTES TO BE ADDED & STORAGE OF RESULTS
2001					
2002					NUMBERS TO BE ADDED.
2003					
2004					
2010	21		LD	HL,2000	LOAD REG. PAIR HL WITH DATA 2000.
2011	00				
2012	20				
2013	46		LD	B,(HL)	LOAD REG. B WITH DATA FOUND IN ADD. (HL).
2014	AF		XOR	A	CLEAR ACCUM.
2015	23	LOOP	INC	HL	INCREMENT HL.
2016	86		ADD	A,(HL)	ADD ADDM (HL) TO ACCUM.
2017	05		DEC	B	DECREMENT B.
2018	C2		JP	NZ,2015	JUMP TO LOOP IF REG B IS NOT ZERO.
2019	15				
201A	20				
201B	32		LD	2000,A	LOAD ADD. 2000 WITH DATA IN ACCUM.
201C	00				
201D	20				
201E	C7		RST	00	RETURN TO MONITOR ROUTINE.

PROJECT 21: FINDING THE LARGER OF TWO NUMBERS

This program will compare the contents of locations 2000 and 2001 and store the larger of the two numbers in address 2002.

MEMORY INFORMATION			INSTRUCTION		COMMENT
ADDRESS	DATA	LABEL	OPCODE	OPERAND	
2000					ANY TWO NUMBER'S TO BE COMPARED.
2001					
2002					LARGER OF THE TWO NUMBERS
2010	3A		LD	A,(2001)	LOAD ACCUM. WITH DATA IN ADD. 2001.
2011	01				
2012	20				
2013	47		LD	B,A	LOAD REG. B WITH DATA IN ACCUM.

MEMORY INFORMATION			INSTRUCTION		COMMENT
ADDRESS	DATA	LABEL	OPCODE	OPERAND	
2014	3A		LD	A,(2000)	LOAD ACCUM. WITH DATA IN ADD. 2000.
2015	00				
2016	20				
2017	B8		CP	B	COMPARE REG B WITH ACCUM.
2018	D2		JP	NC,201C	JUMP TO EXIT IF NO CARRY.
2019	1C				
201A	20				
201B	78		LD	A,B	LOAD ACCUM. WITH DATA IN REG. B.
201C	32	EXIT	LD	(2002),A	LOAD ADD. 2002 WITH DATA IN ACCUM.
201D	02				
201E	20				
201F	C7		RST	00	RETURN TO MONITOR ROUTINE.

PROJECT 22: SEPARATION OF HEXADECIMAL NUMBERS INTO TWO DIGITS (HEX-ITS)

This program will take the contents in location 2000, separate the least and most significant four bits, and then store them in locations 2001 and 2002 respectively.

Example

2000   AF

2001   00

2002   00

After Execution:

2001   0F

2002   A0

MEMORY INFORMATION			INSTRUCTION		COMMENT
ADDRESS	DATA	LABEL	OPCODE	OPERAND	
2000					NUMBER TO BE SEPARATED.
2001					RESULT LSB.
2002					RESULT MSB
2010	01		LD	BC,2000	LOAD REG. PAIR BC WITH DATA 2000.
11	00				
12	20				
13	11		LD	DE,2001	LOAD REG. PAIR DE WITH DATA 2001.
14	01				

MEMORY INFORMATION			INSTRUCTION		COMMENT
ADDRESS	DATA	LABEL	OPCODE	OPERAND	
15	20				
16	0A		LD	A,(BC)	LOAD ACCUM. WITH DATA IN ADD. (BC).
17	E6		AND	0F	"AND" DATA OF$_H$ WITH ACCUM.
18	0F		LD	(DE),A	LOAD ADD. (DE) WITH DATA IN ACCUM.
19	12		LD	A,(BC)	LOAD ACCUM. WITH DATA IN ADD. (BC).
1A	0A		AND	F0	"AND" DATA F0$_H$ WITH ACCUM.
1B	E6				
1C	F0			DE	INCREMENT REG. PAIR DE.
1D	13		INC	(DE),A	LOAD ADD. (DE) WITH A DATA IN ACCUM.
1E	12		LD	00	RETURN TO MONITOR ROUTINE.
1F	C7		RST		

PROJECT 23: COMBINING HEX-ITS INTO A HEXADECIMAL NUMBER (GAME PROGRAM PREREQUISITE)

This program will put two single digit hexadecimal (00-0F) numbers together. The first single digit hexadecimal or HEX-IT would be the most significant byte (MSB), and the second HEX-IT would be the least significant byte (LSB).

Example

ADDR   DATA

2000   04   MSB

2001   05   LSB

2002   00

After Execution

2000   04

2001   05

2002   45

MEMORY INFORMATION			INSTRUCTION		COMMENT
ADDRESS	DATA	LABEL	OPCODE	OPERAND	
2000					DATA FOR MSB (00→0F).
2001					DATA FOR LSB (00→0F).
2002					RESULT.
2010	11		LD	DE,2000	LOAD REG. PAIR DE WITH DATA 2000$_H$.

MEMORY INFORMATION			INSTRUCTION		COMMENT
ADDRESS	DATA	LABEL	OPCODE	OPERAND	
2011	00				
2012	20				
2013	06		LD	B,04	LOAD REG. B WITH DATA 04$_H$.
2014	04				
2015	1A		LD	A,(DE)	LOAD ACCUM. WITH DATA FOUND IN ADD. (DE).
2016	17	LOOP	RLA		ROTATE ACCUM. LEFT THROUGH CARRY.
2017	05		DEC	B	DECREMENT REG. B
2018	C2		JP	NZ,2016	JUMP TO LOOP UNTIL REG. B GOES TO
2019	16				ZERO.
201A	20				
201B	13		INC	DE	INCREMENT REG. PAIR DE.
201C	47		LD	B,A	LOAD REG. B WITH DATA IN ACCUM.
201D	1A		LD	A,(DE)	LOAD ACCUM. WITH DATA IN ADD. (DE).
201E	B0		OR	B	"OR" REG. B WITH ACCUM.
201F	13		INC	DE	INCREMENT REG. PAIR DE.
2020	12		LD	(DE),A	LOAD ADD. (DE) WITH DATA IN ACCUM.
2021	C7		RST	00	RETURN TO MONITOR ROUTINE.

PROJECT 24: TESTING FOR THE CONDITION (HIGH OR LOW STATE) OF BIT THREE OF AN 8-BIT (HEX-IT) NUMBER

This program will test bit-3 of a Hex-It number with the location of Bit-3 in 2000. If Bit-3 is High ("1"), the number in 2000 will be stored in 2001. If Bit-3 is Low ("0"), no action is taken and the data address locations will be in the null state.

MEMORY INFORMATION			INSTRUCTION		COMMENT
ADDRESS	DATA	LABEL	OPCODE	OPERAND	
2000	DATA				NUMBER TO BE TESTED.
2001					DATA COPIED IF BIT 3 IS HIGH.
2010	06		LD	B,04	LOAD REG. B WITH DATA 04.
2011	04				
2012	3A		LD	A,(2000)	LOAD ACCUM. WITH DATA IN ADD. 2000.
2013	00				
2014	20				
2015	1F	LOOP	RRA		ROTATE ACCUM. RIGHT THROUGH CARRY.
2016	05		DEC	B	DECREMENT REG. B.
2017	C2		JP	NZ,2015	JUMP TO LOOP IF REG. B IS NOT ZERO.
2018	15				
2019	20				
201A	D2		JP	NC,2023	JUMP TO EXIT IF CARRY IS NOT SET.
201B	23				
201C	20				
201D	3A		LD	A,(2000)	LOAD ACCUM. WITH DATA IN ADD. 2000.

MEMORY INFORMATION			INSTRUCTION		COMMENT
ADDRESS	DATA	LABEL	OPCODE	OPERAND	
201E	00				
201F	20				
2020	32		LD	(2001),A	LOAD ADD. 2001 WITH DATA IN ACCUM.
2021	01				
2022	20				
2023	C7	EXIT	RST	00	RETURN TO MONITOR ROUTINE.

BIT-3

```
| 7 | 6 | 5 | 4 | 3 | 2 | 1 | 0 |  ← BIT-No.
   8   7   6   5   4   3   2   1   ← BIT-Position
```

8-BIT (HEX-IT) Number Diagram

PROJECT 25: NEW AND IMPROVED BIT TESTING PROGRAM OF BIT THREE OF AN 8-BIT NUMBER

This program does exactly the same thing as Project 24, except that it does it faster and with less memory using the BIT instruction. Please refer to Project 24 for the details of the program objective.

MEMORY INFORMATION			INSTRUCTION		COMMENT
ADDRESS	DATA	LABEL	OPCODE	OPERAND	
2000	DATA				NUMBER TO BE TESTED.
2001					DATA COPIED IF BIT 3 IS HIGH.
2010	3A		LD	A,(2000)	LOAD ACCUM. WITH DATA IN ADD. 2000.
2011	00				
2012	20				
2013	CB		BIT	3,A	TEST BIT 3 OF ACCUM.
2014	5F				
2015	CA		JP	Z,201B	JUMP TO EXIT IF BIT 3 IS NOT
2016	1B				HIGH.
2017	20				
2018	32		LD	(2001), A	LOAD ADD. 2001 WITH DATA IN ACCUM.
2019	01				
201A	20				
201B	C7	EXIT	RST	00	RETURN TO MONITOR ROUTINE.

PROJECT 26: TESTING FOR THE CONDITION (HIGH OR LOW STATE) OF BIT ZERO OF AN 8-BIT (HEX-IT) NUMBER

This program does exactly the same thing as Project 25, except that it tests the condition of the initial bit position of an 8-Bit number, that is, bit 0. In many microprocessor applications it is necessary to test bit conditions (high or low) and store this information for reference. We believe you should know the exact bit testing programs for each bit of a Hex-It number, although only minor program changes occur in each of the bit testing programs. Refer to Projects 24 and 25 for the details of the program objectives.

230

MEMORY INFORMATION			INSTRUCTION		COMMENT
ADDRESS	DATA	LABEL	OPCODE	OPERAND	
2000 2001	DATA				NUMBER TO BE TESTED. DATA COPIED IF BIT 0 IS HIGH.
2010 2011 2012	3A 00 20		LD	A,(2000)	LOAD ACCUM. WITH DATA IN ADD. 2000.
2013 2014	CB 47		BIT	0,A	TEST BIT 0 OF ACCUM.
2015 2016 2017	CA 1B 20		JP	Z,201B	JUMP TO EXIT IF BIT 0 IS NOT HIGH.
2018 2019 201A	32 01 20		LD	(2001),A	LOAD ADD. 2001 WITH DATA IN ACCUM.
201B	C7	EXIT	RST	00	RETURN TO MONITOR ROUTINE.

PROJECT 27: TESTING FOR THE CONDITION (HIGH OR LOW STATE) OF BIT ONE OF AN 8-BIT (HEX-IT) NUMBER

This program does exactly the same thing as Project 25, except that it tests the condition of the initial bit position of an 8-Bit number, in this case bit 1. You should refer to Projects 24 and 25 for the details of the program objectives.

MEMORY INFORMATION			INSTRUCTION		COMMENT
ADDRESS	DATA	LABEL	OPCODE	OPERAND	
2000 2001	DATA				NUMBER TO BE TESTED. DATA COPIED IF BIT 1 IS HIGH.
2010 2011 2012	3A 00 20		LD	A,(2000)	LOAD ACCUM. WITH DATA IN ADD. 2000.
2013 2014	CB 4F		BIT	1,A	TEST BIT 1 OF ACCUM.
2015 2016 2017	CA 1B 20		JP	Z,201B	JUMP TO EXIT IF BIT 1 IS NOT HIGH.
2018 2019 201A	32 01 20		LD	(2001),A	LOAD ADD. 2001 WITH DATA IN ACCUM.
201B	C7	EXIT	RST	00	RETURN TO MONITOR ROUTINE.

PROJECT 28: TESTING FOR THE CONDITION (HIGH OR LOW STATE) OF BIT TWO OF AN 8-BIT (HEX-IT) NUMBER

This program does exactly the same thing as Project 25, except that it tests the condition of the initial bit position of an 8-Bit number; this time bit 2.

Refer to Projects 24 and 25 for the details of program objectives.

MEMORY INFORMATION			INSTRUCTION		COMMENT
ADDRESS	DATA	LABEL	OPCODE	OPERAND	
2000	DATA				NUMBER TO BE TESTED.
2001					DATA COPIED IF BIT 2 IS HIGH.
2010	3A		LD	A,(2000)	LOAD ACCUM. WITH DATA IN ADD. 2000.
2011	00				
2012	20				
2013	CB		BIT	2,A	TEST BIT 2 OF ACCUM.
2014	57				
2015	CA		JP	Z,201B	JUMP TO EXIT IF BIT 2 IS NOT
2016	1B				HIGH.
2017	20				
2018	32		LD	(2001),A	LOAD ADD. 2001 WITH DATA IN ACCUM.
2019	01				
201A	20				
201B	C7	EXIT	RST	00	RETURN TO MONITOR ROUTINE.

PROJECT 29: TESTING FOR THE CONDITION (HIGH OR LOW STATE) OF BIT FOUR OF AN 8-BIT (HEX-IT) NUMBER

This program does exactly the same thing as Project 25, except that it tests the condition of the initial bit position of an 8-Bit number that is, bit 4.

Refer to Projects 24 and 25 for the details of the program objectives.

MEMORY INFORMATION			INSTRUCTION		COMMENT
ADDRESS	DATA	LABEL	OPCODE	OPERAND	
2000	DATA				NUMBER TO BE TESTED.
2001					DATA COPIED IF BIT 4 IS HIGH.
2010	3A		LD	A,(2000)	LOAD ACCUM. WITH DATA IN ADD. 2000.
2011	00				
2012	20				
2013	CB		BIT	4,A	TEST BIT 4 OF ACCUM.
2014	67				

MEMORY INFORMATION			INSTRUCTION		COMMENT
ADDRESS	DATA	LABEL	OPCODE	OPERAND	
2015	CA		JP	Z,201B	JUMP TO EXIT IF BIT 4 IS NOT
2016	1B				HIGH.
2017	20				
2018	32		LD	(2001),A	LOAD ADD. 2001 WITH DATA IN ACCUM.
2019	01				
201A	20				
201B	C7	EXIT	RST	00	RETURN TO MONITOR ROUTINE.

PROJECT 30: TESTING FOR THE CONDITION (HIGH OR LOW STATE) OF BIT FIVE OF AN 8-BIT (HEX-IT) NUMBER

This program does exactly the same thing as Project 25, except that it tests the condition of the initial bit position of an 8-Bit number, that is, bit 5.

Refer to Projects 24 and 25 for the details of the program objectives.

MEMORY INFORMATION			INSTRUCTION		COMMENT
ADDRESS	DATA	LABEL	OPCODE	OPERAND	
2000	DATA				NUMBER TO BE TESTED.
2001					DATA COPIED IF BIT 5 IS HIGH.
2010	3A		LD	A,(2000)	LOAD ACCUM. WITH DATA IN ADD. 2000.
2011	00				
2012	20				
2013	CB		BIT	5,A	TEST BIT 5 OF ACCUM.
2014	6F				
2015	CA		JP	Z,201B	JUMP TO EXIT IF BIT 5 IS NOT
2016	1B				HIGH.
2017	20				
2018	32		LD	(2001),A	LOAD ADD. 2001 WITH DATA IN ACCUM.
2019	01				
201A	20				
201B	C7	EXIT	RST	00	RETURN TO MONITOR ROUTINE.

PROJECT 31: TESTING FOR THE CONDITION (HIGH OR LOW STATE) OF BIT SIX OF AN 8-BIT (HEX-IT) NUMBER

This program does exactly the same thing as Project 25, except that it tests the condition of the initial bit position of an 8-Bit number, that is bit 6.

Refer to Projects 24 and 25 for the details of the program objectives.

MEMORY INFORMATION			INSTRUCTION		COMMENT
ADDRESS	DATA	LABEL	OPCODE	OPERAND	
2000	DATA				NUMBER TO BE TESTED.
2001					DATA COPIED IF BIT 6 IS HIGH.
2010	3A		LD	A,(2000)	LOAD ACCUM. WITH DATA IN ADD. 2000.
2011	00				
2012	20				
2013	CB		BIT	6,A	TEST BIT 6 OF ACCUM.
2014	77				
2015	CA		JP	Z,201B	JUMP TO EXIT IF BIT 6 IS NOT
2016	1B				HIGH.
2017	20				
2018	32		LD	(2001),A	LOAD ADD. 2001 WITH DATA IN ACCUM.
2019	01				
201A	20				
201B	C7	EXIT	RST	00	RETURN TO MONITOR ROUTINE.

PROJECT 32: TESTING FOR THE CONDITION
(HIGH OR LOW STATE) OF BIT SEVEN OF AN 8-BIT (HEX-IT) NUMBER

This program does exactly the same thing as Project 25, except that it tests the condition of the initial bit position of an 8-Bit number, that is, bit 7.

Refer to Projects 24 and 25 for the details of the program objectives.

MEMORY INFORMATION			INSTRUCTION		COMMENT
ADDRESS	DATA	LABEL	OPCODE	OPERAND	
2000	DATA				NUMBER TO BE TESTED.
2001					DATA COPIED IF BIT 7 IS HIGH.
2010	3A		LD	A,(2000)	LOAD ACCUM WITH DATA IN ADD. 2000.
2011	00				
2012	20				
2013	CB		BIT	7,A	TEST BIT 7 OF ACCUM.
2014	7F				
2015	CA		JP	Z,201B	JUMP TO EXIT IF BIT 7 IS NOT
2016	1B				HIGH.
2017	20				
2018	32		LD	(2001),A	LOAD ADD. 2001 WITH DATA IN ACCUM.
2019	01				
201A	20				
201B	C7	EXIT	RST	00	RETURN TO MONITOR ROUTINE.

PROJECT 33: COMPARISON OF TWO NUMBERS TO TEST FOR EQUALITY

This program will compare the contents of data locations 2000 and 2001 and test the numbers in these locations to see if they are equal. If the numbers are equal they will be put into memory location 2002. If they are not, the number 00 will be stored in location 2002.

ADDRESS	DATA	LABEL	OPCODE	OPERAND	COMMENT
2000	DATA				FIRST NUMBER.
2001	DATA				SECOND NUMBER.
2002		RESULT			IF NUMBERS ARE EQUAL STORE NUMBER: IF NOT STORE 00.
2010	3A		LD	A,(2000)	LOAD ACCUM. WITH DATA IN ADD. 2000.
2011	00				
2012	20				
2013	47		LD	B,A	LOAD REG. B WITH DATA IN ACCUM.
2014	3A		LD	A,(2001)	LOAD ACCUM. WITH DATA IN ADD. 2001.
2015	01				
2016	20				
2017	B8		CP	B	COMPARE REG. B TO ACCUM.
2018	CA		JP	Z,2010	JUMP TO EQUAL IF REG. B IS EQUAL
2019	1D				TO ACCUM.
201A	20				
201B	3E		LD	A,00	LOAD ACCUM. WITH DATA 00.
201C	00				
201D	32	EQUAL	LD	(2002),A	LOAD ADD. 2002 WITH DATA IN ACCUM.
201E	02				
201F	20				
2020	C7		RST	00	RETURN TO MONITOR ROUTINE.

PROJECT 34: ODD OR EVEN PARITY CHECK

This program will determine if the parity of the number in memory location 2000 is odd or even. If the number is odd a 00 will be stored in 2001; if the number is even, an EE will be stored in location 2001.

ADDRESS	DATA	LABEL	OPCODE	OPERAND	COMMENT
2000					NUMBER TO BE TESTED.
2001					RESULT. IF EVEN PARITY STORE EE; IF ODD STORE 00.
2010	3A		LD	A,(2000)	LOAD ACCUM. WITH DATA IN ADD. 2000.
2011	00				
2012	20				

235

MEMORY INFORMATION			INSTRUCTION		COMMENT
ADDRESS	DATA	LABEL	OPCODE	OPERAND	
2013	B7		OR	A	SET FLAGS.
2014	EA		JP	PE,201F	JUMP TO EVEN IF PARITY EVEN.
2015	1F				
2016	20				
2017	3E		LD	A,00	LOAD ACCUM. WITH DATA 00.
2018	00				
2019	32		LD	(2001),A	LOAD ADD. 2001 WITH DATA IN ACCUM.
201A	01				
201B	20				
201C	C3		JP	2024	JUMP TO EXIT.
201D	24				
201E	20				
201F	3E	EVEN	LD	A,EE	LOAD ACCUM. WITH DATA EE.
2020	EE				
2021	32		LD	(2001),A	LOAD ADD. 2001 WITH DATA IN ACCUM.
2022	01				
2023	20				
2024	C7	EXIT	RST	00	RETURN TO MONITOR ROUTINE.

PROJECT 35: MULTIPLICATION BY TWO, EMPLOYING BIT ROTATION

This program will take the contents of location 2000 and shift it to the left, which is the same as multiplying the number by 2. The results will be stored in address 2001. If the number is greater than hexidecimal FF, the carry flag will be set.

MEMORY INFORMATION			INSTRUCTION		COMMENT
ADDRESS	DATA	LABEL	OPCODE	OPERAND	
2000	DATA				NUMBER TO BE MULTIPLIED BY 2.
2001					RESULT.
2010	3A		LD	A,(2000)	LOAD ACCUM. WITH DATA IN ADD. 2000.
2011	00				
2012	20				
2013	B7		OR	A	CLEAR CARRY FLAG.
2014	17		RLA		ROTATE ACCUM. LEFT.
2015	32		LD	(2001),A	LOAD ADD. 2001 WITH DATA IN ACCUM.
2016	01				
2017	20				
2018	C7		RST	00	RETURN TO MONITOR ROUTINE.

Chapter 10

Intermediate Software Projects

Some of the projects in this chapter can be executed with the purchase of the SD-Z80 Kit; however, we suggest that you now modify the SD-Z80 Kit so that all of the projects in this chapter can be executed. You must refer to Chapter 1 and perform all of the hardware projects in order to expand the trainer. The expansion of the trainer requires the purchase of additional IC chips, LEDs and switches from Mostek. The details of purchase are given in Chapter 1.

The program format for the projects in this chapter correspond to the format of the previous one. Sometimes obvious data statements are eliminated where appropriate.

PROJECT 36: MULTIPLICATION OF TWO EIGHT-BIT NUMBERS BY REPETITIVE ADDITION

This program will multiple two numbers together from the contents of data locations 2000 and 2001, and then determine the quickest method of multiplication and store the result in addresses 2002 and 2003.

MEMORY INFORMATION			INSTRUCTION		COMMENT
ADDRESS	DATA	LABEL	OPCODE	OPERAND	
2000					LOCATION OF VARIABLES FOR
2001					MULTIPLICATION.
2002					LSB } LOCATION OF RESULT.
2003					MSB }

MEMORY INFORMATION			INSTRUCTION		COMMENT
ADDRESS	DATA	LABEL	OPCODE	OPERAND	
2010	3A		LD	A,2000	LOAD FIRST NUMBER INTO REG. B
2011	00				
2012	20				
2013	47		LD	B,A	
2014	3A		LD	A,2001	LOAD SECOND NUMBER INTO ACCUM.
2015	01				
2016	20				
2017	B8		CP	B	COMPARE REG. B TO ACCUM. TO
2018	DA		JP	C,SET-A	FIND THE SMALLER OF THE TWO.
2019	IE				IF A IS SMALLER JUMP TO
201A	20				SET-A.
201B	C2		JP	NZ,SET-B	IF B IS SMALLER JUMP TO
201C	23				SET-B.
201D	20				
201E	4F	SET-A	LD	C,A	SET COUNTER TO SMALLER
201F	78		LD	A,B	VALUE IN ACCUM.
2020	C3		JP		
2021	25				
2022	20				
2023	48	SET-B	LD	C,B	SET COUNTER TO SMALLER
2024	47		LD	B,A	VALUE IN REG. B.
2025	0D		DEC	C	
2026	80	LOOP	ADD	B	
2027	DA		JP	C,	ADD REG. B TO ACCUM.
2028	32				UNTIL COUNTER GOES
2029	20				TO ZERO.
202A	0D	DECREASE	DEC	C	
202B	C2		JP	NZ,LOOP	
202C	26				
202D	20				
202E	32		LD	2002,A	STORE LSB IN ADDRESS 2002.
202F	02				
2030	20				
2031	C7		RST	00	RETURN TO MONITOR ROUTINE
2032	21		LD	HL,2003	STORE MSB IN ADDRESS 2003.
2033	03				
2034	20				
2035	34		INC	(HL)	
2036	C3		JP	DECREASE	RETURN TO DECREASE AFTER
2037	2A				STORAGE OF MSB.
2038	20				

PROJECT 37: THE DIVISION OF TWO EIGHT-BIT NUMBERS BY REPETITIVE SUBTRACTION

This program will divide the number in data location 2000 by the number in data location 2001. The result will be rounded off and stored in location 2002.

MEMORY INFORMATION			INSTRUCTION		COMMENT
ADDRESS	DATA	LABEL	OPCODE	OPERAND	
2000					NUMBER TO BE DIVIDED.
2001					DIVISOR.
2002					RESULT.
2010	21		LD	HL,2000	POINT TO FIRST NUMBER.
2011	00				
2012	20				
2013	0E		LD	C,00	CLEAR COUNTER.
2014	00				
2015	7E		LD	A,(HL)	GET FIRST NUMBER.
2016	2C		INC	L	
2017	46		LD	B,(HL)	GET SECOND NUMBER.
2018	B8	LOOP	CP	B	TEST IF A>B AND JUMP IF
2019	DA		JP	C,ROUND	NOT.
201A	24				
201B	20				
201C	90		SUB	B	SUBTRACT B FROM A.
201D	CA		JP	Z,	JUMP IF RESULT IS ZERO.
201E	29				
201F	20				
2020	0C		INC	C	INCREMENT COUNTER.
2021	C3		JP	LOOP	JUMP TO LOOP.
2022	18				
2023	20				
2024	07	ROUND	RLCA		MULTIPLY REMAINDER BY TWO.
2025	90		SUB	B	SUBTRACT B FROM A. IF A<B.
2026	DA		JP	C,DONE	JUMP TO "DONE".
2027	2A				
2028	20				
2029	0C		INC	C	IF A>B INCREMENT COUNTER.
202A	2C	DONE	INC	L	INCREMENT POINTER.
202B	71		LD	(HL),C	STORE RESULT.
202C	C7		RST	00	

PROJECT 38: MEMORY COPY

This program will move a block of data from one place in memory to another. The source will be pointed to by HL registers, the destination will be the DE registers, and the BC registers will contain the number of bytes. See the following example before loading the program.

Example

Copy this program between memory locations 2050 and 205F. In other words the destination address of this program is 2050, hence the ending address of the copied program must be 205F.

1. Before loading the program into memory, make all memory locations between 2050 and 205F have 00 for data.
2. Load the program in Project 38 and execute.
3. If the program has executed properly, it will be copied in locations 2050 and 205F.

The memory copy doesn't have to be this program. The memory copy can be from any start address to any destination address.

MEMORY INFORMATION			INSTRUCTION		COMMENT
ADDRESS	DATA	LABEL	OPCODE	OPERAND	
2000	21		LD	HL,2020	FIRST ADDRESS OF MEMORY TO BE
2001	20				TRANSFERRED (ADD. CAN BE CHANGED.)
2002	20				
2003	11		LD	DE,2050	DESTINATION OF TRANSFERRED
2004	50				MEMORY (ADD. CAN BE CHANGED).
2005	20				
2006	01		LD	BC,000F	NUMBER OF BYTES TO BE
2007	0F				TRANSFERRED.
2008	00				
2009	ED		LDIR		TRANSFERS MEMORY, INCREMENTS LOC.
200A	B0				(DE) & (HL), DECREMENTS BC & REPEATS
200B	C7		RST	00	UNTIL BC=0. THEN RETURN TO MONITOR ROUTINE.

PROJECT 39: FINDING THE SQUARE OF A NUMBER EMPLOYING A LOOK-UP TABLE

This program will look up a value in a table and return the value to location 2000. Values should be between the decimal numbers 1 and 9, because of the length of words for this trainer.

MEMORY INFORMATION			INSTRUCTION		COMMENT
ADDRESS	DATA	LABEL	OPCODE	OPERAND	
2000					NUMBER TO BE SQUARED.
2001	01				
2002	04				
2003	09				
2004	16				
2005	25				DECIMAL VALUES FOR
2006	36				SQUARES.
2007	49				
2008	64				
2009	81				
2010	21		LD	HL,2000	SET POINTER.
2011	00				
2012	20				

MEMORY INFORMATION			INSTRUCTION		COMMENT
ADDRESS	DATA	LABEL	OPCODE	OPERAND	
2013	6E		LD	L,(HL)	FORM ADD. TO LOOK-UP TABLE.
2014	7E		LD	A,(HL)	GET ANSWER FROM TABLE.
2015	32		LD	(2000),A	STORE ANSWER.
2016	00				
2017	20				
2018	C7		RST	00	

PROJECT 40: ECHO KEYBOARD TO DISPLAY

This program will accept an input from the keyboard and display it on the LEDs. When the program has been executed properly no characters appear in the Address Field, and at least one zero will appear in the Data Field.

MEMORY INFORMATION			INSTRUCTION		COMMENT
ADDRESS	DATA	LABEL	OPCODE	OPERAND	
2000	31		LD	SP,2390	SET STACK POINTER.
2001	90				
2002	23				
2003	3E	START	LD	A,7F	TURN OFF DISPLAY.
2004	7F				
2005	D3		OUT	(88),A	
2006	88				
2007	3E		LD	A,3F	OUTPUT ALL ROWS LOW.
2008	3F				
2009	D3		OUT	(8C),A	
200A	8C				
200B	DB		IN	A,(90)	
200C	90				
200D	E6		AND	1F	
200E	1F				CHECK TO SEE IF KEY IS DOWN.
200F	FE		CP	1F	
2010	1F				
2011	CA		JP	Z,DISPLAY	IF NOT CONTINUE WITH
2012	46				DISPLAY.
2013	20				
2014	06		LD	B,01	
2015	01				
2016	78	LOOP-2	LD	A,B	PLACE SELECTED ROW LOW.
2017	D3		OUT	(8C),A	
2018	8C				
2019	DB		IN	A,(90)	
201A	90				CHECK TO SEE IF A KEY IS
201B	E6		AND	1F	DOWN IN SELECTED ROW.
201C	1F				
201D	FE		CP	1F	
201E	1F				

MEMORY INFORMATION			INSTRUCTION		COMMENT
ADDRESS	DATA	LABEL	OPCODE	OPERAND	
201F	C2		JP	NZ,LOOP-1	JUMP OUT OF LOOP IF A KEY
2020	27				IS FOUND DOWN.
2021	20				
2022	CB		RLC	B	SELECT NEXT ROW TO BE
2023	00				CHECKED.
2024	C3		JP	LOOP-2	CONTINUE TO CHECK KEYS.
2025	16				
2026	20				
2027	0E	LOOP-1	LD	C,00	
2028	00				
2029	0D	LOOP-3	DEC	C	
202A	CB		SBL	B	
202B	38				
202C	20		JR	NZ,LOOP-3	LOOP BACK UNTIL B IS ZERO.
202D	FB				
202E	CB		SLA	C	
202F	21				
2030	CB		SLA	C	
2031	21				SHIFT VALUE TO HIGH BYTE.
2032	CB		SLA	C	
2033	21				
2034	CB		SLA	C	
2035	21				
2036	81		ADD	A,C	FORM KEY CODE.
2037	11		LD	DE,07A6	SET DISPLAY CODE POINTER.
2038	A6				
2039	07				
203A	21		LD	HL,07B9	SET KEY CODE POINTER.
203B	B9				
203C	07				
203D	BE	LOOP-4	CP	(HL)	FIND KEY.
203E	CA		JP	Z,DISPLAY	
203F	46				
2040	20				
2041	13		INC	DE	ADVANCE POINTERS.
2042	23		INC	HL	
2043	C3		JP	LOOP-4	CONTINUE UNTIL KEY IS FOUND.
2044	3D				
2045	20				
2046	1A	DISPLAY	LD	A,(DE)	
2047	D3		OUT	(88),A	
2048	88				
2049	3E		LD	A,01	DISPLAY NO. PRESSED IN
204A	01				LSB OF DATA FIELD.
204B	D3		OUT	(8C),A	
204C	8C				
204D	CD		CALL	DELAY	
204E	4F				
204F	06				
2050	3E		LD	A,40	

MEMORY INFORMATION			INSTRUCTION		COMMENT
ADDRESS	DATA	LABEL	OPCODE	OPERAND	
2051	40				
2052	D3		OUT	(88),A	
2053	88				
2054	3E		LD	A,02	DISPLAY A ZERO IN MSB
2055	02				OF DATA FIELD.
2056	D3		OUT	(8C),A	
2057	8C				
2058	CD		CALL	DELAY	
2059	4F				
205A	06				
205B	C3		JP	START	CONTINUE WITH PROGRAM.
205C	03				
205D	20				

PROJECT 41: TWO-CHARACTER KEYBOARD DISPLAY

This program is similar to the previous project, except that it takes two characters from the keyboard and displays them in the data field.

MEMORY INFORMATION			INSTRUCTION		COMMENT
ADDRESS	DATA	LABEL	OPCODE	OPERAND	
2010	31		LD	SP,2390	SET STACK POINTER.
2011	90				
2012	23				
2013	06	START	LD	B,02	NO. OF CHAR. TO BE DISPLAYED.
2014	02				
2015	11		LD	DE,2000	SET DISPLAY POINTER.
2016	00				
2017	20				
2018	1A	DISPLAY	LD	A,(DE)	
2019	D3		OUT	(88),A	
201A	88				
201B	78		LD	A,B	DISPLAY CHARACTER.
201C	D3		OUT	(8C),A	
201D	8C				
201E	21		LD	HL,01FF	SET TIME DELAY.
201F	FF				
2020	01				
2021	CD		CALL	DELAY	
2022	52				
2023	06				
2024	13		INC	DE	ADVANCE DISPLAY POINTER.
2025	05		DEC	B	DECREASE NO. OF CHAR. TO BE
2026	20		JR	NZ, DISPLAY	DISPLAYED. IF ALL CHAR. NOT
2027	F0				DISPLAYED CONTINUE UNTIL DONE.
2028	CD		CALL	DECODE	

MEMORY INFORMATION			INSTRUCTION		COMMENT
ADDRESS	DATA	LABEL	OPCODE	OPERAND	
2029	2D				
202A	20				
202B	18		JR	START	
202C	E6				
202D	3E	DECODE	LD	A,7F	
202E	7F				
202F	D3		OUT	(88),A	TURN OFF DISPLAY.
2030	88				
2031	3E		LD	A,3F	
2032	3F				
2033	D3		OUT	(8C),A	OUTPUT ALL ROWS LOW.
2034	8C				
2035	DB		IN	A,(90)	INPUT DATA FROM KEYBOARD.
2036	90				
2037	E6		AND	1F	MASK OUT UNWANTED INPUTS.
2038	1F				
2039	FE		CP	1F	CHECK TO SEE IF KEY DOWN.
203A	1F				
203B	C8		RET	Z	IF NOT RETURN TO MAIN PROGRAM.
203C	CD		CALL	DELAY	DEBOUNCE KEY.
203D	4F				
203E	06				
203F	06		LD	B,01	
2040	01				
2041	78	LOOP	LD	A,B	PLACE SELECTED ROW LOW.
2042	DE		OUT	(8C),A	
2043	8C				
2044	DB		IN	A,(90)	
2045	90				
2046	E6		AND	1F	CHECK TO SEE IF KEY DOWN
2047	1F				IN SELECTED ROW.
2048	FE		CP	1F	
2049	1F				
204A	20		JR	NZ,KEY	JUMP OUT OF LOOP IF A KEY IS
204B	08				FOUND DOWN.
204C	CB		RLC	B	
204D	00				
204E	3E		LD	A,10	SELECT NEXT ROW. IF ALL
204F	10				ROWS HAVE BEEN CHECKED
2050	B8		CP	B	THEN RETURN TO MAIN
2051	20		JR	NZ,LOOP	PROGRAM.
2052	EE				
2053	C9		RET		
2054	0E	KEY	LD	C,00	
2055	00				
2056	0D	KEY-1	DEC	C	
2057	CB		SRL	B	
2058	38				
2059	20		JR	NZ,KEY-1	LOOP BACK UNTIL B IS ZERO.
205A	FB				

MEMORY INFORMATION			INSTRUCTION		COMMENT
ADDRESS	DATA	LABEL	OPCODE	OPERAND	
205B	CB		SLA	C	SHIFT VALUE TO HIGH BYTE.
205C	21				
205D	CB		SLA	C	
205E	21				
205F	CB		SLA	C	
2060	21				
2061	CB		SLA	C	
2062	21				
2063	81		ADD	A,C	
2064	21		LD	HL,0789	SET POINTER FOR KEY VALUE. LOOK UP TABLE.
2065	B9				
2066	07				
2067	BE	KEY-3	CP	(HL)	FIND KEY.
2068	28		JR	Z,KEY-2	
2069	04				
206A	23		INC	HL	ADVANCE POINTER.
206B	04		INC	B	ADVANCE COUNTER.
206C	18		JR	KEY-3	CONTINUE UNTIL KEY IS FOUND.
206D	F9				
206E	DB	KEY-2	IN	A,(90)	CHECK FOR KEY RELEASE. LOOP UNTIL KEY IS UP.
206F	90				
2070	E6		AND	1F	
2071	1F				
2072	FE		CP	1F	
2073	1F				
2074	20		JR	NZ,KEY-2	
2075	F8				
2076	CD		CALL	DELAY	DEBOUNCE KEY.
2077	4F				
2078	06				
2079	3A		LD	A,(2000)	CHECK FOR BLANK DISPLAY PATTERN IN MSB OF DATA FIELD.
207A	00				
207B	20				
207C	FE		CP	7F	
207D	7F				
207E	28		JR	Z,KEY-4	IF BLANK THEN JUMP AHEAD.
207F	14				
2080	3E		LD	A,7F	IF NOT BLANK LOAD BLANK DISPLAY CODE IN MSB.
2081	7F				
2082	32		LD	(2000),A	
2083	00				
2084	20				
2085	78	KEY-5	LD	A,B	
2086	32		LD	(208F),A	GET AND STORE DISPLAY CODE FOR NUMBER TO BE DISPLAYED IN LSB OF DATA FIELD.
2087	8F				
2088	20				
2089	DD		LD	IX,07A6	
208A	21				
208B	A6				
208C	07				

MEMORY INFORMATION			INSTRUCTION		COMMENT
ADDRESS	DATA	LABEL	OPCODE	OPERAND	
208D	DD		LD	A,(IX+d)	GET AND STORE DISPLAY
208E	7E				CODE FOR NUMBER TO BE
208F	00				DISPLAYED IN LSB OF
2090	32		LD	(2001),A	DATA FIELD.
2091	01				
2092	20				RETURN TO MAIN PROGRAM.
2093	C9		RET		
2094	3A	KEY-4	LD	A,(2001)	
2095	01				SHIFT LSB OF DATA FIELD
2096	20				TO MSB.
2097	32		LD	(2000),A	
2098	00				
2099	20				
209A	18		JR	KEY-5	
209B	E9				

PROJECT 42: ADD TWO HEXIDECIMAL NUMBERS FROM THE KEYBOARD USING CALCULATOR STYLE

This program should function as a simple Hex calculator by adding only 1 byte with no overflow error message.

After the program is executed, no character will appear in the Address Field. The following examples will illustrate how this project can be used as a Hex calculator by adding two 1-byte numbers but with no overflow message.

Example 1: Adding 01 + 02 = 03.

KEY	ADDR	DATA	COMMENTS
0	Blank	0	FIRST KEYSTROKE.
1	Blank	01	SECOND KEYSTROKE.
0	Blank	00	THIRD KEYSTROKE.
2	Blank	03	FOURTH KEYSTROKE YIELDS ANSWER IN DATA FIELD.

To clear the Data Field the following keystrokes must be made: MON, 2010, EXEC.

When the preceding keystrokes are made, no character will appear in the Address Field.

Example 2: Adding 1F + 01 = 20.

KEY	ADDR	DATA	COMMENTS
1	Blank	1	
F	Blank	1F	
0	Blank	00	
1	Blank	20	FOURTH KEYSTROKE YIELDS ANSWER.

246

MEMORY INFORMATION			INSTRUCTION		COMMENT
ADDRESS	DATA	LABEL	OPCODE	OPERAND	
2010	31		LD	SP,2390	SET STACK POINTER.
2011	90				
2012	23				
2013	3E		LD	A,00	
2014	00				SET DIGIT COUNTER.
2015	ED		LD	1,A	
2016	47				
2017	FD		LD	1Y,2005	
2018	21				
2019	05				
201A	20				
201B	06	START	LD	B,02	NO. OF CHAR. TO BE DISPLAYED.
201C	02				
201D	11		LD	DE,2000	SET DISPLAY POINTER.
201E	00				
201F	20				
2020	1A	DISPLAY	LD	A,(DE)	
2021	D3		OUT	(88),A	
2022	88				DISPLAY CHARACTER.
2023	78		LD	A,B	
2024	D3		OUT	(8C),A	
2025	8C				
2026	21		LD	HL,01FF	SET TIME DISPLAY.
2027	FF				
2028	01				
2029	CD		CALL	DELAY	
202A	52				
202B	06				
202C	13		INC	DE	ADVANCE DISPLAY POINTER.
202D	05		DEC	B	DECREASE NO. OF CHAR.
202E	20		JR	NZ,DISPLAY	CONTINUE UNTIL B IS ZERO.
202F	F0				
2030	CD		CALL	DECODE	
2031	35				
2032	20				
2033	18		JR	START	
2034	E6				
2035	3E	DECODE	LD	A,7F	
2036	7F				TURN OFF DISPLAY.
2037	D3		OUT	(88),A	
2038	88				
2039	3E		LD	A,3F	
203A	3F				OUTPUT ALL ROWS LOW.
203B	D3		OUT	(8C),A	
203C	8C				
203D	DB		IN	A,(90)	INPUT DATA FROM KEYBOARD.
203E	90				
203F	E6		AND	1F	MASK OUT UNWANTED INPUTS.
2040	1F				
2041	FE		CP	1F	CHECK TO SEE IF KEY DOWN.

MEMORY INFORMATION			INSTRUCTION		COMMENT
ADDRESS	DATA	LABEL	OPCODE	OPERAND	
2042	1F				
2043	C8		RET	Z	IF NOT RETURN TO MAIN PROGRAM.
2044	CD		CALL	DELAY	DEBOUNCE KEY.
2045	4F				
2046	06				
2047	06		LD	B,01	
2048	01				
2049	78	LOOP-1	LD	A,B	PLACE SELECTED ROW LOW.
204A	D3		OUT	(8C),A	
204B	8C				
204C	DB		IN	A,(90)	
204D	90				
204E	E6		AND	1F	CHECK TO SEE IF KEY IS
204F	1F				DOWN IN SELECTED ROW.
2050	FE		CP	1F	
2051	1F				
2052	20		JR	NZ,LOOP-2	IF KEY IS DOWN JUMP AHEAD.
2053	08				
2054	CB		RLC	B	
2055	00				
2056	3E		LD	A,10	SELECT NEXT ROW. IF ALL
2057	10				ROWS HAVE BEEN CHECKED
2058	B8		CP	B	THEN RETURN TO MAIN
2059	20		JR	NZ,LOOP-1	PROGRAM.
205A	EE				
205B	C9		RET		
205C	0E	LOOP-2	LD	C,00	
205D	00				
205E	0D	LOOP-3	DEC	C	
205F	CB		SRL	B	
2060	38				
2061	20		JR	NZ,LOOP-3	LOOP BACK UNTIL B IS ZERO.
2062	FB				
2063	CB		SLA	C	
2064	21				
2065	CB		SLA	C	SHIFT VALUE TOO HIGH
2066	21				BYTE.
2067	CB		SLA	C	
2068	21				
2069	CB		SLA	C	
206A	21				
206B	81		ADD	A,C	
206C	21		LD	HL,07B9	SET POINTER FOR KEY VALUE.
206D	B9				LOOK UP TABLE.
206E	07				
206F	BE	LOOP-4	CP	(HL)	FIND KEY.
2070	28		JR	Z,LOOP-5	
2071	04				
2072	23		INC	HL	ADVANCE POINTER AND
2073	04		INC	B	COUNTER.

MEMORY INFORMATION			INSTRUCTION		COMMENT
ADDRESS	DATA	LABEL	OPCODE	OPERAND	
2074	18		JR	LOOP-4	CONTINUE UNTIL KEY IS FOUND.
2075	F9				
2076	DB	LOOP-5	IN	A,(90)	
2077	90				
2078	E6		AND	1F	
2079	1F				CHECK FOR KEY RELEASE.
207A	FE		CP	1F	LOOP UNTIL KEY IS UP.
207B	1F				
207C	20		JR	NZ,LOOP-5	
207D	F8				
207E	CD		CALL	DELAY	DEBOUNCE KEY.
207F	4F				
2080	06				
2081	3A		LD	A,(2000)	
2082	00				CHECK FOR BLANK DISPLAY
2083	20				CODE IN MSB OF DATA
2084	FE		CP	7F	FIELD.
2085	7F				
2086	28		JR	Z,LOOP-6	IF BLANK THEN JUMP.
2087	23				
2088	3E		LD	A,7F	
2089	7F				
208A	32		LD	(2000),A	IF NOT BLANK LOAD BLANK
208B	00				DISPLAY CODE IN MSB.
208C	20				
208D	ED	LOOP-7	LD	A,1	
208E	57				
208F	32		LD	(2094),A	
2090	94				
2091	20				
2092	FD		LD	(IY+d),B	STORE DIGIT.
2093	70				
2094	00				
2095	3C		INC	A	ADVANCE DIGIT COUNTER.
2096	ED		LD	1,A	STORE COUNT.
2097	47				
2098	FE		CP	04	CHECK TO SEE IF FOUR DIGITS
2099	04				HAVE BEEN STORED.
209A	28		JR	Z,ANSWER	IF YES THEN GET ANSWER.
209B	17				
209C	78		LD	A,B	
209D	32	LOOP-8	LD	(20A6),A	
209E	A6				
209F	20				
20A0	DD		LD	IX,07A6	
20A1	21				GET AND STORE DISPLAY
20A2	A6				CODE FOR NUMBER TO BE
20A3	07				DISPLAYED IN LSB OF DATA
20A4	DD		LD	A,(IX+d)	FIELD.
20A5	7E				

MEMORY INFORMATION			INSTRUCTION		COMMENT
ADDRESS	DATA	LABEL	OPCODE	OPERAND	
20A6	00				GET AND STORE DISPLAY
20A7	32		LD	(2001),A	CODE FOR NUMBER TO BE
20A8	01				DISPLAYED IN LSB OF DATA FIELD.
20A9	20				
20AA	C9		RET		RETURN TO MAIN PROGRAM.
20AB	3A	LOOP-6	LD	A,(2001)	
20AC	01				
20AD	20				SHIFT LSB OF DATA FIELD
20AE	32		LD	(2000),A	DISPLAY TO MSB.
20AF	00				
20B0	20				
20B1	18		JR	LOOP-7	
20B2	DA				
20B3	FD	ANSWER	LD	A,(IY+0)	GET FIRST DIGIT.
20B4	7E				
20B5	00				
20B6	CB		SLA	A	
20B7	27				
20B8	CB		SLA	A	
20B9	27				
20BA	CB		SLA	A	MOVE TO HIGH BYTE.
20BB	27				
20BC	CB		SLA	A	
20BD	27				
20BE	FD		OR	(IY+1)	GET SECOND DIGIT AND "OR"
20BF	B6				TOGETHER WITH FIRST DIGIT.
20C0	01				
20C1	47		LD	B,A	STORE NO. FORMED.
20C2	FD		LD	A,(IY+2)	GET THIRD DIGIT.
20C3	7E				
20C4	02				
20C5	CB		SLA	A	
20C6	27				
20C7	CB		SLA	A	
20C8	27				
20C9	CB		SLA	A	MOVE TO HIGH BYTE.
20CA	27				
20CB	CB		SLA	A	
20CC	27				
20CD	FD		OR	(IY+3)	GET FOURTH DIGIT AND "OR"
20CE	B6				WITH THIRD DIGIT.
20CF	03				
20D0	80		ADD	A,B	ADD NO.'S FORMED TO GET ANSWER.
20D1	47		LD	B,A	STORE NO.
20D2	CB		SRL	A	
20D3	3F				MOVE HIGH TO LOW BYTE.
20D4	CB		SRL	A	
20D5	3F				
20D6	CB		SRL	A	
20D7	3F				

MEMORY INFORMATION			INSTRUCTION		COMMENT
ADDRESS	DATA	LABEL	OPCODE	OPERAND	
20D8	CB		SRL	A	MOVE HIGH TO LOW BYTE.
20D9	3F				
20DA	32		LD	(20DF),A	
20DB	DF				
20DC	20				
20DD	DD		LD	A,(IX+d)	GET AND STORE DISPLAY
20DE	7E				CODE FOR NO. TO BE
20DF	00				DISPLAYED IN MSB OF
20E0	32		LD	(2000),A	DATA FIELD.
20E1	00				
20E2	20				
20E3	78		LD	A,B	GET ANSWER.
20E4	E6		AND	OF	MASK OUT HIGH BYTE.
20E5	0F				
20E6	18		JR	LOOP-8	
20E7	B5				

PROJECT 43: ADD TWO DECIMAL NUMBERS FROM THE KEYBOARD USING CALCULATOR STYLE

This program should function as a simple decimal calculator by adding only 1 byte with another byte. No overflow error message is given.

MEMORY INFORMATION			INSTRUCTION		COMMENT
ADDRESS	DATA	LABEL	OPCODE	OPERAND	
2010	31		LD	SP,2390	SET STACK POINTER.
2011	90				
2012	23				
2013	3E		LD	A,00	SET DIGIT COUNTER.
2014	00				
2015	ED		LD	1,A	
2016	47				
2017	FD		LD	1Y,2005	
2018	21				
2019	05				
201A	20				
201B	06	START	LD	B,02	NO OF CHAR. TO BE DISPLAYED.
201C	02				
201D	11		LD	DE,2000	SET DISPLAY POINTER.
201F	00				
201F	20				
2020	1A	DISPLAY	LD	A,(DE)	DISPLAY CHARACTER.
2021	D3		OUT	(88),A	
2022	88				
2023	78		LD	A,B	
2024	D3		OUT	(8C),A	
2025	8C				
2026	21		LD	HL,01FF	SET TIME DISPLAY.

MEMORY INFORMATION			INSTRUCTION		COMMENT
ADDRESS	DATA	LABEL	OPCODE	OPERAND	
2027	FF				
2028	01				
2029	CD		CALL	DELAY	
202A	52				
202B	06				
202C	13		INC	DE	ADVANCE DISPLAY POINTER.
202D	05		DEC	B	DECREASE NO. OF CHAR.
202E	20		JR	NZ,DISPLAY	CONTINUE UNTIL B IS ZERO.
202F	F0				
2030	CD		CALL	DECODE	
2031	35				
2032	20				
2033	18		JR	START	
2034	E6				
2035	3E	DECODE	LD	A,7F	TURN OFF DISPLAY.
2036	7F				
2037	D3		OUT	(88),A	
2038	88				
2039	3E		LD	A,3F	OUTPUT ALL ROWS LOW.
203A	3F				
203B	D3		OUT	(8C),A	
203C	8C				
203D	DB		IN	A,(90)	INPUT DATA FROM KEYBOARD.
203E	90				
203F	E6		AND	IF	MASK OUT UNWANTED INPUTS.
2040	1F				
2041	FE		CP	1F	CHECK TO SEE IF KEY DOWN.
2042	1F				
2043	C8		RET	Z	IF NOT RETURN TO MAIN PROGRAM.
2044	CD		CALL	DELAY	DEBOUNCE KEY.
2045	4F				
2046	06				
2047	06		LD	B,01	PLACE SELECTED ROW LOW.
2048	01				
2049	78	LOOP-1	LD	A,B	
204A	D3		OUT	(8C),A	
204B	8C				
204C	DB		IN	A,(90)	
204D	90				
204E	E6		AND	IF	CHECK TO SEE IF KEY IS DOWN IN SELECTED ROW.
204F	1F				
2050	FE		CP	1F	
2051	1F				
2052	20		JR	NZ,LOOP-2	IF KEY IS DOWN JUMP AHEAD.
2053	08				
2054	CB		RLC	B	SELECT NEXT ROW. IF ALL ROWS HAVE BEEN CHECKED THEN RETURN TO MAIN PROGRAM.
2055	00				
2056	3E		LD	A,10	
2057	10				
2058	B8		CP	B	

MEMORY INFORMATION			INSTRUCTION		COMMENT
ADDRESS	DATA	LABEL	OPCODE	OPERAND	
2059	20		JR	NZ,LOOP-1	SELECT NEXT ROW IF ALL
205A	EE				ROWS HAVE BEEN CHECKED
205B	C9		RET		THEN RETURN TO MAIN
205C	0E	LOOP-2	LD	C,00	PROGRAM.
205D	00				
205E	0D	LOOP-3	DEC	C	
205F	CB		SRL	B	
2060	38				
2061	20		JR	NZ,LOOP-3	LOOP BACK UNTIL B IS ZERO.
2062	FB				
2063	CB		SLA	C	
2064	21				
2065	CB		SLA	C	SHIFT VALUE TO HIGH
2066	21				BYTE.
2067	CB		SLA	C	
2068	21				
2069	CB		SLA	C	
206A	21				
206B	81		ADD	A,C	
206C	21		LD	HL,07B9	SET POINTER FOR KEY VALUE.
206D	B9				LOOK UP TABLE.
206E	07				
206F	BE	LOOP-4	CP	(HL)	FIND KEY.
2070	28		JR	Z,LOOP-5	
2071	04				
2072	23		INC	HL	ADVANCE POINTER AND
2073	04		INC	B	COUNTER.
2074	18		JR	LOOP-4	CONTINUE UNTIL KEY IS FOUND.
2075	F9				
2076	DB	LOOP-5	IN	A,(90)	
2077	90				
2078	E6		AND	1F	
2079	1F				
207A	FE		CP	1F	CHECK FOR KEY RELEASE.
207B	1F				LOOP UNTIL KEY IS UP.
207C	20		JR	NZ,LOOP-5	
207D	F8				
207E	CD		CALL	DELAY	DEBOUNCE KEY.
207F	4F				
2080	06				
2081	3A		LD	A,(2000)	
2082	00				CHECK FOR BLANK DISPLAY.
2083	20				CODE IN MSB OF DATA
2084	FE		CP	7F	FIELD.
2085	7F				
2086	28		JR	Z,LOOP-6	IF BLANK THEN JUMP.
2087	23				
2088	3E		LD	A,7F	IF NOT BLANK LOAD BLANK
2089	7F				DISPLAY CODE IN MSB.
208A	32		LD	(2000),A	

MEMORY INFORMATION			INSTRUCTION		COMMENT
ADDRESS	DATA	LABEL	OPCODE	OPERAND	
208B	00				IF NOT BLANK LOAD BLANK
208C	20				DISPLAY CODE IN MSB.
208D	ED	LOOP-7	LD	A,1	
208E	57				
208F	32		LD	(2094),A	
2090	94				
2091	20				
2092	FD		LD	(IY+d),B	STORE DIGIT.
2093	70				
2094	00				
2095	3C		INC	A	ADVANCE DIGIT COUNTER.
2096	ED		LD	1,A	STORE COUNT.
2097	47				
2098	FE		CP	04	CHECK TO SEE IF FOUR DIGITS
2099	04				HAVE BEEN STORED.
209A	28		JR	Z,ANSWER	IF YES THEN GET ANSWER.
209B	17				
209C	78		LD	A,B	
209D	32	LOOP-8	LD	(20A6),A	
209E	A6				
209F	20				
20A0	DD		LD	IX,07A6	
20A1	21				
20A2	A6				
20A3	07				
20A4	DD		LD	A,(IX+d)	GET AND STORE DISPLAY
20A5	7E				CODE FOR NUMBER TO BE
20A6	00				DISPLAYED IN LSB OF DATA
20A7	32		LD	(2001),A	FIELD.
20A8	01				
20A9	20				
20AA	C9		RET		RETURN TO MAIN PROGRAM.
20AB	3A	LOOP-6	LD	A,(2001)	
20AC	01				
20AD	20				
20AE	32		LD	(2000),A	SHIFT LSB OF DATA FIELD
20AF	00				DISPLAY TO MSB.
20B0	20				
20B1	18		JR	LOOP-7	
20B2	DA				
20B3	FD	ANSWER	LD	A,(IY+0)	GET FIRST DIGIT.
20B4	7E				
20B5	00				
20B6	CB		SLA	A	
20B7	27				
20B8	CB		SLA	A	
20B9	27				MOVE TO HIGH BYTE.
20BA	CB		SLA	A	
20BB	27				
20BC	CB		SLA	A	
20BD	27				

MEMORY INFORMATION			INSTRUCTION		COMMENT
ADDRESS	DATA	LABEL	OPCODE	OPERAND	
20BE	FD		OR	(IY+1)	GET SECOND DIGIT AND "OR"
20BF	B6				TOGETHER WITH FIRST DIGIT.
20C0	01				
20C1	47		LD	B,A	STORE NO. FORMED.
20C2	FD		LD	A,(IY+2)	GET THIRD DIGIT.
20C3	7E				
20C4	02				
20C5	CB		SLA	A	
20C6	27				
20C7	CB		SLA	A	
20C8	27				MOVE TO HIGH BYTE.
20C9	CB		SLA	A	
20CA	27				
20CB	CB		SLA	A	
20CC	27				
20CD	FD		OR	(IY+3)	GET FOURTH DIGIT AND "OR"
20CE	B6				WITH THIRD DIGIT.
20CF	03				
20D0	80		ADD	A,B	ADD NO.'S FORMED TO GET ANSWER
20D1	27		DAA		DECIMAL ADJUST ANSWER.
20D2	47		LD	B,A	STORE NO.
20D3	CB		SRL	A	
20D4	3F				
20D5	CB		SRL	A	
20D6	3F				MOVE HIGH TO LOW BYTE.
20D7	CB		SRL	A	
20D8	3F				
20D9	CB		SRL	A	
20DA	3F				
20DB	32		LD	(20E0),A	
20DC	E0				
20DD	20				
20DE	DD		LD	A,(IX+d)	GET AND STORE DISPLAY
20DF	7E				CODE FOR NO. TO BE
20E0	00				DISPLAYED IN MSB OF
20E1	32		LD	(2000),A	DATA FIELD.
20E2	00				
20E3	20				
20E4	78		LD	A,B	GET ANSWER.
20E5	E6		AND	0F	MASK OUT HIGH BYTE.
20E6	0F				
20E7	18		JR	LOOP-8	
20E8	B4				

PROJECT 44: COMBINATION LOCK

This program will turn the SD-Z80 Kit into a combination lock. The 6-digit combination is stored in location 20C5 through 20CA.

After the program is executed properly, no character will appear in the Address Field. You can now press any 6-digit combination. If the wrong six digits are pressed the message LOCH will appear on the LED display. If the 6 digit combination is pressed as appears in the memory, the message OPEN will appear on the LED display.

MEMORY INFORMATION			INSTRUCTION		COMMENT
ADDRESS	DATA	LABEL	OPCODE	OPERAND	
2010	31		LD	SP-2390	SET STACK POINTER.
2011	90				
2012	23				
2013	AF	START	XOR	A	SET TO ZERO AND CLEAR FLAGS.
2014	32		LD	(209F),A	RESET MESSAGE POINTER.
2015	9F				
2016	20				
2017	21		LD	HL,20C5	SET COMBINATION POINTER.
2018	C5				
2019	20				
201A	3E	DECODE	LD	A,7F	
201B	7F				TURN OFF DISPLAY.
201C	D3		OUT	(88),A	
201D	88				
201E	3E		LD	A,3F	
201F	3F				
2020	D3		OUT	(8C),A	OUTPUT ALL ROWS LOW.
2021	8C				
2022	DB		IN	A,(90)	INPUT DATA FROM KEYBOARD.
2023	90				
2024	E6		AND	1F	MASK OUT UNWANTED INPUTS.
2025	1F				
2026	FE		CP	1F	CHECK TO SEE IF KEY DOWN.
2027	1F				
2028	28		JR	Z,DISPLAY	IF NOT JUMP TO DISPLAY.
2029	4E				
202A	06		LD	B,01	
202B	01				PLACE SELECTED ROW LOW.
202C	78	LOOP-1	LD	A,B	
202D	D3		OUT	(8C),A	
202E	8C				
202F	DB		IN	A,(90)	
2030	90				
2031	E6		AND	1F	CHECK TO SEE IF KEY STILL DOWN.
2032	1F				
2033	FE		CP	1F	
2034	1F				
2035	20		JR	NZ,KEY	IF NOT JUMP TO "KEY."
2036	04				
2037	CB		RLC	B	SELECT NEXT ROW.
2038	00				
2039	18		JR	LOOP-1	CONTINUE TO SCAN KEYBOARD.
203A	F1				
203B	0E	KEY	LD	C,00	
203C	00				

256

MEMORY INFORMATION			INSTRUCTION		COMMENT
ADDRESS	DATA	LABEL	OPCODE	OPERAND	
203D	0D	LOOP-2	DEC	C	
203E	CB		SRL	B	
203F	38				
2040	20		JR	NZ,LOOP-2	LOOP BACK UNTIL B IS ZERO.
2041	FB				
2042	CB		SLA	C	
2043	21				
2044	CB		SLA	C	
2045	21				SHIFT VALUE TO HIGH
2046	CB		SLA	C	BYTE.
2047	21				
2048	CB		SLA	C	
2049	21				
204A	81		ADD	A,C	
204B	FD		LD	IY,07B9	SET POINTER FOR KEY VALUE.
204C	21				LOOK UP TABLE.
204D	B9				
204E	07				
204F	FD	LOOP-3	CP	(IY)	FIND KEY.
2050	BE				
2051	00				
2052	28		JR	Z,CHECK	IF FOUND JUMP TO "CHECK."
2053	05				
2054	04		INC	B	ADVANCE COUNTER.
2055	FD		INC	IY	ADVANCE POINTER.
2056	23				
2057	18		JR	LOOP-3	CONTINUE UNTIL KEY IS FOUND.
2058	F6				
2059	DB	CHECK	IN	A,(90)	
205A	90				
205B	E6		AND	1F	CHECK TO SEE IF KEY IS
205C	1F				UP. IF NOT LOOP BACK
205D	FE		CP	1F	UNTIL IT IS.
205E	1F				
205F	20		JR	NZ,CHECK	
2060	F8				
2061	78		LD	A,B	
2062	BE		CP	(HL)	COMPARE NO. WITH COMBINATION.
2063	28		JR	Z,ADVANCE	IF CORRECT JUMP "ADVANCE."
2064	05				
2065	3E		LD	A,04	
2066	04				IF NOT LOAD OFFSET.
2067	32		LD	(209F),A	
2068	9F				
2069	20				
206A	23	ADVANCE	INC	HL	
206B	3E		LD	A,CB	ADVANCE POINTER.
206C	CB				CHECK IF END OF COMBINATION.
206D	BD		CP	L	
206E	28		JR	Z,MESSAGE	IF SO GO DISPLAY MESSAGE.

MEMORY INFORMATION			INSTRUCTION		COMMENT
ADDRESS	DATA	LABEL	OPCODE	OPERAND	
206F	25				
2070	78		LD	A,B	
2071	32		LD	(207A),A	
2072	7A				
2073	20				
2074	FD		LD	IY,07A6	
2075	21				
2076	A6				
2077	07				
2078	FD	DISPLAY	LD	A,(IY+d)	
2079	7E				
207A	00				
207B	D3		OUT	(88),A	DISPLAY NO. PRESSED ON
207C	88				KEYBOARD IN DATA FIELD.
207D	3E		LD	A,01	
207E	01				
207F	D3		OUT	(8C),A	
2080	8C				
2081	E5		PUSH	HL	
2082	CD		CALL	DELAY	
2083	4F				
2084	06				
2085	EI		POP	HL	
2086	3E		LD	A,40	
2087	40				
2088	D3		OUT	(88),A	
2089	88				DISPLAY A ZERO IN HIGH
208A	3E		LD	A,02	BYTE OF DATA FIELD.
208B	02				
208C	D3		OUT	(8C),A	
208D	8C				
208E	E5		PUSH	HL	
208F	CD		CALL	DELAY	
2090	4F				
2091	06				
2092	EI		POP	HL	
2093	18		JR	DECODE	GO CHECK KEYBOARD.
2094	85				
2095	06	MESSAGE	LD	B,20	
2096	20				
2097	0E		LD	C,04	
2098	04				SET UP POINTERS & COUNTER
2099	DD		LD	IX,20CB	TO DISPLAY MESSAGE.
209A	21				
209B	CB				
209C	20				
209D	DD	LOAD	LD	A,(IX+d)	
209E	7E				DISPLAY MESSAGE.
209F	00				
20A0	D3		OUT	(88),A	

258

MEMORY INFORMATION			INSTRUCTION		COMMENT
ADDRESS	DATA	LABEL	OPCODE	OPERAND	
20A1	88				
20A2	78		LD	A,B	
20A3	D3		OUT	(8C),A	DISPLAY MESSAGE.
20A4	8C				
20A5	21		LD	HL,01FF	SET UP TIME DELAY.
20A6	FF				
20A7	01				
20A8	CD		CALL	DELAY	PAUSE BETWEEN CHARACTERS.
20A9	52				
20AA	06				
20AB	CB		SRL	B	
20AC	38				MOVE POINTERS.
20AD	DD		INC	IX	
20AE	23				
20AF	0D		DEC	C	DECREMENT COUNTER.
20B0	20		JR	NZ,LOAD	DISPLAY NEXT CHARACTER IF NOT
20B1	EB				DONE.
20B2	3E		LD	A,7F	
20B3	7F				
20B4	D3		OUT	(88),A	
20B5	88				
20B6	3E		LD	A,3F	TURN OFF DISPLAY.
20B7	3F				
20B8	D3		OUT	(8C),A	
20B9	8C				
20BA	DB		IN	A,(90)	
20BB	90				
20BC	E6		AND	1F	CHECK TO SEE IF KEY
20BD	1F				HAS BEEN PRESSED.
20BE	FE		CP	1F	
20BF	1F				
20C0	28		JR	Z,MESSAGE	IF NOT CONTINUE TO DISPLAY
20C1	D3				MESSAGE.
20C2	C3		JP	START	IF SO GO DECODE KEY.
20C3	13				
20C4	20				
20C5	00				
20C6	01				
20C7	02				
20C8	03				COMBINATION.
20C9	04				
20CA	05				
20CB	40	0			
20CC	0C	P			
20CD	06	E			
20CE	48	N			
20CF	47	L			DISPLAY CODE FOR
20D0	40	O			MESSAGES.
20D1	46	C			
20D2	09	H			

PROJECT 45: RANDOM NUMBER GENERATOR

This program is executed by going to location 2010 and pressing the interrupt button, which will cause a random number to appear between the hexadecimal numbers 00 and FF. Remember the interrupt button was wired onto the wire wrap area in Chapter 1.

MEMORY INFORMATION			INSTRUCTION		COMMENT
ADDRESS	DATA	LABEL	OPCODE	OPERAND	
2000					LOCATION OF RANDOM NO.
2002					LOCATION OF DATA TO BE
2003					DISPLAYED.
2010	31		LD	SP,2390	SET STACK POINTER.
2011	90				
2012	23				
2013	ED		IM	I	SET INTERRUPT MODE ONE.
2014	56				
2015	FB		EI		ENABLE INTERRUPT.
2016	11	GENERATE	LD	DE,2002	SET DISPLAY POINTER.
2017	02				
2018	20				
2019	3C		INC	A	ADVANCE COUNT.
201A	18		JR	GENERATE	
201B	FA				
201C	32	BEGIN	LD	(2000),A	STORE NUMBER GENERATED.
201D	00				
201E	20				
201F	0E		LD	C,02	LOAD COUNTER.
2020	02				
2021	E6		AND	F0	MASK OUT LOW BYTE.
2022	F0				
2023	1F		RRA		
2024	1F		RRA		MOVE HIGH BYTE TO LOW
2025	1F		RRA		BYTE.
2026	1F		RRA		
2027	DD	REPEAT	LD	IX,2070	SET INDEX TABLE POINTER.
2028	21				
2029	70				
202A	20				
202B	21		LD	HL,07A6	SET POINTER FOR 7-SEGMENT
202C	A6				DISPLAY PATTERNS TABLE.
202D	07				
202E	DD	LOOP	CP	(IX+d)	FIND NO.
202F	BE				
2030	00				
2031	CA		JP	Z,LOAD	IF FOUND EXIT LOOP.
2032	3A				
2033	20				
2034	DD		INC	IX	ADVANCE POINTERS.
2035	23				
2036	23		INC	HL	

MEMORY INFORMATION			INSTRUCTION		COMMENT
ADDRESS	DATA	LABEL	OPCODE	OPERAND	
2037	C3		JP	LOOP	CONTINUE UNTIL NO. IS FOUND.
2038	2E				
2039	20				
203A	7E	LOAD	LD	A,(HL)	GET DISPLAY PATTERN.
203B	12		LD	(DE),A	STORE DISPLAY PATTERN.
203C	3A		LD	A,(2000)	GET RANDOM NO.
203D	00				
203E	20				
203F	E6		AND	0F	MASK OUT HIGH BYTE.
2040	0F				
2041	13		INC	DE	ADVANCE DISPLAY POINTER.
2042	0D		DEC	C	DECREMENT COUNTER.
2043	C2		JP	NZ,REPEAT	CONTINUE UNTIL COUNTER IS
2044	27				ZERO.
2045	20				
2046	0E		LD	C,30	RELOAD COUNTER.
2047	30				
2048	11	OUTPUT	LD	DE,2002	LOAD DISPLAY POINTER.
2049	02				
204A	20				
204B	1A		LD	A,(DE)	GET DISPLAY PATTERN.
204C	D3		OUT	(88),A	
204D	88				
204E	3E		LD	A,02	OUTPUT IT TO DISPLAY.
204F	02				
2050	D3		OUT	(8C),A	
2051	8C				
2052	CD		CALL	DELAY	PAUSE BEFORE DISPLAYING
2053	4F				NEXT NO.
2054	06				
2055	13		INC	DE	ADVANCE POINTER.
2056	1A		LD	A(DE)	GET DISPLAY PATTERN.
2057	D3		OUT	(88),A	
2058	88				
2059	3E		LD	A,01	SEND IT TO DISPLAY.
205A	01				
205B	D3		OUT	(8C),A	
205C	8C				
205D	CD		CALL	DELAY	PAUSE BEFORE DISPLAYING NEXT
205E	4F				NO.
205F	06				
2060	0D		DEC	C	DECREMENT COUNTER.
2061	C2		JP	NZ,OUTPUT	CONTINUE WITH DISPLAY UNTIL
2062	48				COUNTER IS ZERO.
2063	20				
2064	FB		EI		ENABLE INTERRUPTS.
2065	3E		LD	A,7F	CLEAR DISPLAY.
2066	7F				
2067	D3		OUT	(88),A	
2068	88				

MEMORY INFORMATION			INSTRUCTION		COMMENT
ADDRESS	DATA	LABEL	OPCODE	OPERAND	
2069	ED		RETI		RETURN TO MAIN PROGRAM.
206A	4D				
2070	00				
2071	01				
2072	02				
2073	03				
2074	04				
2075	05				
2076	06				
2077	07				INDEX TABLE
2078	08				
2079	09				
207A	0A				
207B	0B				
207C	0C				
207D	0D				
207E	0E				
207F	0F				
23D3	C3		JP	BEGIN	JUMP TO SUBROUTINE.
2304	1C				
23D5	20				

PROJECT 46: NUMBER GUESS GAME

This program is a game between you and the computer. To start the game you must go to location 2009, EXEC then press the interrupt button and enter your guess of a hexadecimal number between 00 and FF.

After the program is loaded into memory, no character will appear in the Address Field. The game is ready to play. The following example will illustrate a few keystrokes that will help you play the game.

Example

KEY	ADDR	DATA	COMMENTS
INTR BUTT	BLANK	BLANK	THE FIRST KEYSTROKE TO PLAY THE GAME WILL NOT CHANGE THE DISPLAY.
00	10 LO	00	THE FIRST GUESS WE PUT IN IS PURPOSELY LOW IN ORDER TO ILLUSTRATE THE DISPLAY OF A LOW GUESS. WE KNOW WE HAVE GUESSED LOW, THEREFORE OUR NEXT GUESS MUST BE HIGHER THAN OUR LOW GUESS.
FF	HI	FF	THE SECOND GUESS IS PURPOSELY HIGH TO ILLUSTRATE THE DISPLAY OF A HIGH GUESS.

262

KEY	ADDR	DATA	COMMENTS
			AS INDICATED IN THE FIRST TWO GUESSES, THE ADDRESS FIELD SHOWS WHETHER YOU ARE LOWER (LO) OR HIGHER (HI) THAN THE RANDOM NUMBER STORED IN LOCATION 2000 FOR THIS GAME. THE DATA FIELD SHOWS YOUR GUESS.
XX	RITE	XX	KEEP ENTERING A GUESS UNTIL THE CORRECT NUMBER (XX) IS ENTERED AND MATCHES THE RANDOM NUMBER STORED IN LOCATION 2000. THE ADDRESS FIELD WILL DISPLAY RITE WHEN THE GUESS IS CORRECT.

To start another game press RESET 2009 EXEC and the interrupt button.

MEMORY INFORMATION			INSTRUCTION		COMMENT
ADDRESS	DATA	LABEL	OPCODE	OPERAND	
2000		ADD. FIELD	MSB		LOCATION OF DATA TO BE OUTPUTED TO DISPLAY.
2001		ADD. FIELD			
2002		ADD. FIELD			
2003		ADD. FIELD	LSB		
2004		DATA FIELD	MSB		
2005		DATA FIELD	LSB		
2006					
2007					
2008					
2009	31		LD	SP,2390	INITIALIZE STACK POINTER.
200A	90				
200B	23				
200C	ED		1M	1	SET INTERRUPT MODE ONE.
200D	56				
200E	FB		EI		ENABLE INTERRUPT.
200F	21		LD	HL,2000	
2010	00				
2011	20				
2012	3E		LD	A,7F	
2013	7F				
2014	77		LD	(HL),A	CLEAR ADDRESS FIELD OF DISPLAY.
2015	2C		INC	L	
2016	77		LD	(HL),A	
2017	2C		INC	L	
2018	77		LD	(HL),A	
2019	2C		INC	L	
201A	77		LD	(HL),A	
201B	AF		XOR	A	RESET DIGIT COUNTER.
201C	ED		LD	I,A	
201D	47				
201E	08		EX	AF,AF'	RESET GUESS COUNTER.
201F	FD		LD	IY,2006	
2020	21				
2021	06				

MEMORY INFORMATION			INSTRUCTION		COMMENT
ADDRESS	DATA	LABEL	OPCODE	OPERAND	
2022	20				
2023	3C	ADVANCE	INC	A	COUNT UNTIL INTERRUPTED.
2024	18		JR	ADVANCE	
2025	FD				
2026	32	BEGIN	LD	(2008),A	STORE NUMBER.
2027	08				
2028	20				
2029	0E	START	LD	C,06	NUMBER OF CHARACTERS TO BE
202A	06				DISPLAYED.
202B	06		LD	B,20	
202C	20				
202D	11		LD	DE,2000	INITIALIZE DISPLAY POINTER.
202E	00				
202F	20				
2030	1A	DISPLAY	LD	A,(DE)	
2031	D3		OUT	(88),A	
2032	88				DISPLAY CHARACTER.
2033	78		LD	A,B	
2034	D3		OUT	(8C),A	
2035	8C				
2036	21		LD	HL,01FF	INITIALIZE DELAY COUNTER.
2037	FF				
2038	01				
2039	CD		CALL	DELAY	
203A	52				
203B	06				
203C	CB		SRL	B	
203D	38				
203E	13		INC	DE	ADVANCE DISPLAY DATA POINTER.
203F	0D		DEC	C	DECREASE NO. OF CHAR. TO BE
2040	20		JR	NZ,DISPLAY	DISPLAYED. IF ALL CHAR. NOT
2041	EE				DISPLAYED JUMP TO DISPLAY.
2042	CD		CALL	DECODE	
2043	47				
2044	20				
2045	18		JR	START	
2046	E2				
2047	3E	DECODE	LD,	A,7F	
2048	7F				TURN OFF DISPLAY.
2049	D3		OUT	(88),A	
204A	88				
204B	3E		LD	4,3F	
204C	3F				
204D	D3		OUT	(8C),A	OUTPUT ALL ROWS LOW
204E	8C				
204F	DB		IN	A,(90)	INPUT DATA FROM KEYBOARD.
2050	90				
2051	E6		AND	1F	MASK OUT UNWANTED INPUTS.
2052	1F				
2053	FE		CP	1F	CHECK TO SEE IF KEY DOWN.

MEMORY INFORMATION			INSTRUCTION		COMMENT
ADDRESS	DATA	LABEL	OPCODE	OPERAND	
2054	1F				IF NOT RETURN TO MAIN PROGRAM.
2055	C8		RET	Z	DEBOUNCE KEY.
2056	CD		CALL	DELAY	
2057	4F				
2058	06				
2059	06		LD	B,01	
205A	01				
205B	78	LOOP-1	LD	A,B	PLACE SELECTED ROW LOW.
205C	D3		OUT	(8C),A	
205D	8C				
205E	DB		IN	A,(90)	
205F	90				CHECK TO SEE IF KEY
2060	E6		AND	1F	DOWN IN SELECTED ROW.
2061	1F				
2062	FE		CP	1F	
2063	1F				
2064	20		JR	NZ,LOOP-2	JUMP OUT OF LOOP IF A KEY IS
2065	08				FOUND DOWN.
2066	CB		RLC	B	
2067	00				
2068	3E		LD	A,10	
2069	10				SELECT NEXT ROW.
206A	B8		CP	B	IF DONE RETURN TO MAIN
206B	20		JR	NZ,LOOP-1	PROGRAM.
206C	EE				
206D	C9		RET		
206E	0E	LOOP-2	LD	C,00	
206F	00				
2070	0D	LOOP-3	DEC	C	
2071	CB		SRL	B	
2072	38				
2073	20		JR	NZ,LOOP-3	LOOP BACK UNTIL B IS ZERO.
2074	FB				
2075	CB		SLA	C	
2076	21				
2077	CB		SLA	C	SHIFT VALUE TO HIGH
2078	21				BYTE.
2079	CB		SLA	C	
207A	21				
207B	CB		SLA	C	
207C	21				
207D	81		ADD	A,C	
207E	21		LD	HL,07B9	SET POINTER FOR KEY VALUE.
207F	B9				LOOKUP TABLE.
2080	07				
2081	BE	LOOP-4	CP	(HL)	FIND KEY.
2082	28		JR	Z,LOOP-5	
2083	04				
2084	23		INC	HL	ADVANCE POINTER.
2085	04		INC	B	ADVANCE COUNTER.

MEMORY INFORMATION			INSTRUCTION		COMMENT
ADDRESS	DATA	LABEL	OPCODE	OPERAND	
2086	18		JR	LOOP-4	CONTINUE UNTIL KEY IS FOUND.
2087	F9				
2088	DB	LOOP-5	IN	A,(90)	
2089	90				
208A	E6		AND	1F	CHECK FOR KEY RELEASE.
208B	1F				LOOP UNTIL KEY IS UP.
208C	FE		CP	1F	
208D	1F				
208E	20		JR	NZ,LOOP-5	
208F	F8				
2090	CD		CALL	DELAY	DEBOUNCE KEY.
2091	4F				
2092	06				
2093	3A		LD	A,(2004)	CHECK FOR BLANK DISPLAY
2094	04				PATTERN IN MSB OF
2095	20				DATA FIELD.
2096	FE		CP	7F	
2097	7F				
2098	28		JR	Z,LOOP-6	IF BLANK THEN JUMP AHEAD.
2099	23				
209A	3E		LD	A,7F	IF NOT BLANK LOAD BLANK
209B	7F				DISPLAY PATTERN IN MSB.
209C	32		LD	(2004),A	
209D	04				
209E	20				
209F	ED	LOOP-7	LD	A,1	
20A0	57				
20A1	32		LD	(20A6),A	
20A2	A6				
20A3	20				
20A4	FD		LD	(IY+d),B	STORE YOUR GUESS.
20A5	70				
20A6	00				
20A7	3C		INC	A	ADVANCE DIGIT COUNTER.
20A8	ED		LD	I,A	STORE COUNT.
20A9	47				
20AA	FE		CP	02	CHECK TO SEE IF GUESS IS
20AB	02				COMPLETE.
20AC	28		JR	Z,ANSWER	IF COMPLETE THEN SHOW
20AD	17				ANSWER.
20AE	78		LD	A,B	
20AF	32	LOOP-8	LD	(20B8),A	
20B0	B8				
20B1	20				
20B2	DD		LD	IX,07A6	
20B3	21				GET AND STORE DISPLAY
20B4	A6				PATTERN FOR NUMBER TO
20B5	07				BE DISPLAYED IN LSB,
20B6	DD		LD	A,(IX+d)	OF DATA FIELD.
20B7	7E				

MEMORY INFORMATION			INSTRUCTION		COMMENT
ADDRESS	DATA	LABEL	OPCODE	OPERAND	
20B8	00				GET AND STORE DISPLAY
20B9	32		LD	(2005),A	PATTERN FOR NUMBER TO
20BA	05				BE DISPLAYED IN LSB
20BB	20				OF DATA FIELD.
20BC	C9		RET		
20BD	3A	LOOP-6	LD	A,(2005)	RETURN TO MAIN PROGRAM.
20BE	05				
20BF	20				SHIFT LSB OF DATA FIELD
20C0	32		LD	(2004),A	DISPLAY TO MSB.
20C1	04				
20C2	20				
20C3	18		JR	LOOP-7	
20C4	DA				
20C5	08	ANSWER	EX	AF,AF'	
20C6	3C		INC	A	INCREMENT GUESS COUNTER.
20C7	08		EX	AF,AF'	
20C8	FD		LD	A,(IY+0)	GET FIRST DIGIT OF GUESS.
20C9	7E				
20CA	00				
20CB	CB		SLA	A	
20CC	27				
20CD	CB		SLA	A	
20CE	27				MOVE TO HIGH BYTE.
20CF	CB		SLA	A	
20D0	27				
20D1	CB		SLA	A	
20D2	27				
20D3	FD		OR	(IY+1)	GET SECOND DIGIT OF GUESS
20D4	B6				AND "OR" TOGETHER WITH
20D5	01				FIRST DIGIT.
20D6	47		LD	B,A	
20D7	3A		LD	A,(2008)	GET RANDOM NUMBER.
20D8	08				
20D9	20				
20DA	B8		CP	B	TEST IF GUESS IS CORRECT.
20DB	28		JR	Z,CORRECT	
20DC	1C				
20DD	38		JR	C, HI	
20DE	36				
20DF	3E		LD	A,7F	
20E0	7F				
20E1	32		LD	(2000),A	
20E2	00				
20E3	20				
20E4	32		LD	(2001),A	GUESS IS LOW. DISPLAY
20E5	01				"LO" MESSAGE.
20E6	20				
20E7	3E		LD	A,47	
20E8	47				
20E9	32		LD	(2002),A	

MEMORY INFORMATION			INSTRUCTION		COMMENT
ADDRESS	DATA	LABEL	OPCODE	OPERAND	
20EA	02				
20EB	20				
20EC	3E		LD	A,40	GUESS IS LOW. DISPLAY
20ED	40				"LO" MESSAGE.
20EE	32		LD	(2003),A	
20EF	03				
20F0	20				
20F1	AF		XOR	A	RESET DIGIT COUNTER.
20F2	ED		LD	1,A	
20F3	47				
20F4	FD		LD	A,(IY+1)	
20F5	7E				
20F6	01				
20F7	18		JR	LOOP-8	
20F8	B6				
20F9	3E	CORRECT	LD	A,4E	
20FA	4E				
20FB	32		LD	(2000),A	
20FC	00				
20FD	20				
20FE	3E		LD	A,4F	
20FF	4F				
2100	32		LD	(2001),A	
2101	01				
2102	20				GUESS IS CORRECT.
2103	3E		LD	A,07	DISPLAY "RITE" MESSAGE
2104	07				
2105	32		LD	(2002),A	
2106	02				
2107	20				
2108	3E		LD	A,06	
2109	06				
210A	32		LD	(2003),A	
210B	03				
210C	20				
210D	AF		XOR	A	RESET DIGIT COUNTER.
210E	ED		LD	1,A	
210F	47				
2110	FD		LD	A,(IY+1)	
2111	7E				
2112	01				
2113	18		JR	LOOP-8	
2114	9A				
2115	3E	HI	LD	A,7F	
2116	7F				
2117	32		LD	(2000),A	GUESS IS HIGH. DISPLAY
2118	00				"HI" MESSAGE.
2119	20				
211A	32		LD	(2001),A	
211B	01				

MEMORY INFORMATION			INSTRUCTION		COMMENT
ADDRESS	DATA	LABEL	OPCODE	OPERAND	
211C	20				
211D	3E		LD	A,09	
211E	09				
211F	32		LD	(2002),A	
2120	02				GUESS IS HIGH. DISPLAY
2121	20				"HI" MESSAGE.
2122	3E		LD	A,79	
2123	79				
2124	32		LD	(2003),A	
2125	03				
2126	20				
2127	AF		XOR	A	
2128	ED		LD	1,A	RESET DIGIT COUNTER.
2129	47				
212A	FD		LD	A,(IY+1)	
212B	7E				
212C	01				
212D	18		JR	LOOP-8	
212E	80				
23D3	C3		JP	BEGIN	
23D4	26				
23D5	20				

PROJECT 47: A GAME CALLED 21 MATCHES

This program is a game that you can play against the computer. The computer has 21 decimal (15 hexadecimal) matches. You and the computer will take away 1, 2, or 3 matches per turn, until there are no matches remaining. The player who takes away the last match wins.

After the program is executed, no character will appear in the Address Field, and the hexadecimal number 15 (equivalent to decimal 21) will appear in the Data Field. The game is ready to be played. You can now pick one of three numbers, 1, 2, or 3 by pressing one of those keys. Your number pick will appear for one second in the Data Field. Then your pick will be subtracted from 15 along with the computer's selection. In other words, two numbers will be subtracted from 15, yours and the computer's. At this point, you must make another selection. The above procedure will be repeated by the program. The selection process continues until there are no matches remaining. The player or computer taking away the last match wins. The word GOOD is displayed if you win, and the word LOSE is displayed if the computer wins. When the game is over 15 will appear in the Data Field with either the word LOSE or GOOD appearing in the Address Field. At this point a new game can be played.

MEMORY INFORMATION			INSTRUCTION		COMMENT
ADDRESS	DATA	LABEL	OPCODE	OPERAND	
2000					MEMORY LOCATION OF DATA TO BE
2001					OUTPUTTED TO DISPLAY.

MEMORY INFORMATION			INSTRUCTION		COMMENT
ADDRESS	DATA	LABEL	OPCODE	OPERAND	
2002					MEMORY LOCATION OF DATA TO BE
2003					OUTPUTTED TO DISPLAY.
2004					
2005					
2006	31		LD	SP,2390	SET STACK POINTER.
2007	90				
2008	23				
2009	21		LD	HL,2000	SET DISPLAY POINTER.
200A	00				
200B	20				
200C	3E		LD	A,7F	
200D	7F				
200E	77		LD	(HL),A	TURN OFF FIRST FOUR
200F	2C		INC	L	DISPLAYS BY LOADING
2010	77		LD	(HL),A	"BLANK" CODE IN DISPLAY'S
2011	2C		INC	L	FIRST FOUR MEMORY LOC.
2012	77		LD	(HL),A	
2013	2C		INC	L	
2014	77		LD	(HL),A	
2015	IE		LD	E,15	STORE NUMBER OF MATCHES.
2016	15				
2017	3E		LD	A,79	
2018	79				
2019	2C		INC	L	LOAD NUMBER OF
201A	77		LD	(HL,),A	MATCHES TO BE DISPLAYED IN
201B	3E		LD	A,12	DISPLAY'S MEMORY.
201C	12				
201D	2C		INC	L	
201E	77		LD	(HL),A	
201F	0E	START	LD	C,06	LOAD NO. OF CHARACTERS TO
2020	06				BE DISPLAYED IN COUNTER.
2021	06		LD	B,20	
2022	20				
2023	21		LD	HL,2000	RESET DISPLAY POINTER.
2024	00				
2025	20				
2026	7E	DISPLAY	LD	A,(HL)	
2027	D3		OUT	(88),A	
2028	88				DISPLAY CHARACTER.
2029	78		LD	A,B	
202A	D3		OUT	(8C),A	
202B	8C				
202C	E5		PUSH	HL	
202D	21		LD	HL,01FF	SET TIME DELAY.
202E	FF				
202F	01				
2030	CD		CALL	DELAY	
2031	52				
2032	06				
2033	EI		POP	HL	

MEMORY INFORMATION			INSTRUCTION		COMMENT
ADDRESS	DATA	LABEL	OPCODE	OPERAND	
2034	CB		SRL	B	
2035	38				
2036	23		INC	HL	ADVANCE POINTER.
2037	0D		DEC	C	DECREASE COUNTER.
2038	20		JR	NZ,DISPLAY	IF COUNTER NOT ZERO
2039	EC				CONTINUE UNTIL IT IS.
203A	CD		CALL	DECODE	
203B	4A				
203C	20				
203D	15		DEC	D	GENERATE THE COMPUTER'S
203E	7A		LD	A,D	NUMBER OF MATCHES TO
203F	E6		AND	03	BE TAKEN AWAY.
2040	03				
2041	20		JR	NZ,LOAD	
2042	04				
2043	16		LD	D,03	
2044	03				
2045	18		JR	START	CONTINUE WITH DISPLAY.
2046	D8				
2047	57	LOAD	LD	D,A	
2048	18		JR	START	
2049	D5				
204A	3E	DECODE	LD	A,7F	TURN OFF DISPLAY.
204B	7F				
204C	D3		OUT	(88),A	
204D	88				
204E	3E		LD	A,3F	OUTPUT ALL ROWS LOW.
204F	3F				
2050	D3		OUT	(8C),A	
2051	8C				
2052	DB		IN	A,(90)	
2053	90				
2054	E6		AND	1F	CHECK TO SEE IF A KEY
2055	1F				IS DOWN.
2056	FE		CP	1F	
2057	1F				
2058	C8		RET	Z	IF NOT RETURN TO MAIN PROGRAM.
2059	CD		CALL	DELAY	DEBOUNCE KEY.
205A	4F				
205B	06				
205C	06		LD	B,01	PLACE SELECTED ROW LOW.
205D	01				
205E	78	LOOP-1	LD	A,B	
205F	D3		OUT	(8C),A	
2060	8C				
2061	DB		IN	A,(90)	
2062	90				
2063	E6		AND	1F	CHECK TO SEE IF KEY IS
2064	1F				DOWN IN SELECTED ROW.
2065	FE		CP	1F	
2066	1F				

MEMORY INFORMATION			INSTRUCTION		COMMENT
ADDRESS	DATA	LABEL	OPCODE	OPERAND	
2067	20		JR	NZ,LOOP-2	JUMP OUT OF LOOP IF A KEY IS
2068	08				FOUND DOWN.
2069	CB		RLC	B	
206A	00				
206B	3E		LD	A,10	SELECT NEXT ROW. IF ALL
206C	10				ROWS HAVE BEEN CHECKED
206D	B8		CP	B	THEN RETURN TO MAIN
206E	20		JR	NZ,LOOP-1	PROGRAM.
206F	EE				
2070	C9		RET		
2071	0E	LOOP-2	LD	C,00	
2072	00				
2073	0D	LOOP-3	DEC	C	
2074	CB		SRL	B	
2075	38				
2076	20		JR	NZ,LOOP-3	LOOP BACK UNTIL B IS ZERO.
2077	FB				
2078	CB		SLA	C	
2079	21				
207A	CB		SLA	C	
207B	21				SHIFT VALUE TO HIGH BYTE.
207C	CB		SLA	C	
207D	21				
207E	CB		SLA	C	
207F	21				
2080	81		ADD	A,C	FORM KEY CODE.
2081	21		LD	HL,07B9	SET KEY CODE POINTER.
2082	B9				
2083	07				
2084	BE	LOOP-4	CP	(HL)	FIND KEY.
2085	28		JR	Z,LOOP-5	
2086	04				
2087	23		INC	HL	ADVANCE POINTER.
2088	04		INC	B	ADVANCE COUNTER.
2089	18		JR	LOOP-4	CONTINUE UNTIL KEY IS FOUND.
208A	F9				
208B	DB	LOOP-5	IN	A, (90)	
208C	90				
208D	E6		AND	1F	CHECK FOR KEY RELEASE.
208E	1F				LOOP UNTIL KEY IS UP.
208F	FE		CP	1F	
2090	1F				
2091	20		JR	NZ,LOOP-5	
2092	F8				
2093	CD		CALL	DELAY	DEBOUNCE KEY.
2094	4F				
2095	06				
2096	21		LD	HL,2000	RESET DISPLAY POINTER.
2097	00				

MEMORY INFORMATION			INSTRUCTION		COMMENT
ADDRESS	DATA	LABEL	OPCODE	OPERAND	
2098	20				
2099	3E		LD	A,7F	
209A	7F				
209B	77		LD	(HL),A	
209C	23		INC	HL	LOAD "BLANK" CODE IN
209D	77		LD	(HL),A	DISPLAY'S FIRST FOUR
209E	23		INC	HL	MEMORY LOCATIONS.
209F	77		LD	(HL),A	
20A0	23		INC	HL	
20A1	77		LD	(HL),A	
20A2	78		LD	A,B	GET YOUR NUMBER.
20A3	E6		AND	03	MAKE IT A LEGAL NUMBER IF
20A4	03				IT ISN'T.
20A5	47		LD	B,A	
20A6	7B		LD	A,E	
20A7	B8		CP	B	
20A8	28		JR	Z,WIN	TEST FOR WIN.
20A9	45				
20AA	90		SUB	B	TAKE AWAY MATCHES.
20AB	FE		CP	03	CHECK TO SEE HOW MANY
20AC	03				MATCHES ARE LEFT. IF
20AD	28		JR	Z,SUB	THREE OR LESS THEN JUMP
20AE	06				TO "SUB."
20AF	38		JR	C,SUB	
20B0	04				
20B1	92		SUB	D	SUBTRACT COMPUTER'S MATCHES.
20B2	5F		LD	E,A	STORE REMAINDER.
20B3	18		JR	SHIFT	
20B4	03				
20B5	97	SUB	SUB	A	TAKE AWAY REMAINING MATCHES.
20B6	18		JR	LOST	JUMP TO "LOST."
20B7	52				
20B8	CB	SHIFT	SRL	A	
20B9	3F				
20BA	CB		SRL	A	GET REMAINING MATCHES.
20BB	3F				SAVE HIGH BYTE AND SHIFT
20BC	CB		SRL	A	IT TO LOW BYTE.
20BD	3F				
20BE	CB		SRL	A	
20BF	3F				
20C0	32		LD	(20C9),A	
20C1	C9				
20C2	20				
20C3	DD		LD	IX,07A6	
20C4	21				GET DISPLAY CODE FOR
20C5	A6				NUMBER.
20C6	07				
20C7	DD		LD	A,(IX+d)	
20C8	7E				
20C9	00				

MEMORY INFORMATION			INSTRUCTION		COMMENT
ADDRESS	DATA	LABEL	OPCODE	OPERAND	
20CA	32		LD	(2004),A	STORE DISPLAY CODE.
20CB	04				
20CC	20				
20CD	7B		LD	A,E	GET REMAINING MATCHES.
20CE	E6		AND	0F	SAVE LOW BYTE.
20CF	0F				
20D0	32		LD	(20D5),A	
20D1	D5				
20D2	20				GET DISPLAY CODE FOR
20D3	DD		LD	A,(IX+d)	NUMBER.
20D4	7E				
20D5	00				
20D6	32		LD	(2005),A	STORE DISPLAY CODE.
20D7	05				
20D8	20				
20D9	78		LD	A,B	GET YOUR NUMBER OF MATCHES.
20DA	32		LD	(20DF),A	
20DB	DF				
20DC	20				
20DD	DD		LD	A,(IX+d)	GET DISPLAY CODE.
20DE	7E				
20DF	00				
20E0	D3		OUT	(88),A	
20E1	88				
20E2	3E		LD	A,01	
20E3	01				DISPLAY NUMBER OF
20E4	D3		OUT	(8C),A	MATCHES PLAYER IS TAKING
20E5	8C				AWAY.
20E6	0E		LD	C,32	
20E7	32				
20E8	CD	DELAY	CALL	DELAY	
20E9	4F				
20EA	06				DISPLAY FOR ONE SECOND.
20EB	0D		DEC	C	
20EC	20		JR	NZ,DELAY	
20ED	FA				
20EE	C9		RET		RETURN TO MAIN PROGRAM.
20EF	21	WIN	LD	HL,2000	
20F0	00				
20F1	20				
20F2	3E		LD	A,10	
20F3	10				
20F4	77		LD	(HL),A	LOAD "GOOD" MESSAGE
20F5	23		INC	HL	IN DISPLAY ROUTINE'S
20F6	3E		LD	A,40	MEMORY.
20F7	40				
20F8	77		LD	(HL),A	
20F9	23		INC	HL	
20FA	77		LD	(HL),A	
20FB	23		INC	HL	

274

MEMORY INFORMATION			INSTRUCTION		COMMENT
ADDRESS	DATA	LABEL	OPCODE	OPERAND	
20FC	3E		LD	A,21	LOAD "RITE" MESSAGE
20FD	21				IN DISPLAY ROUTINE'S
20FE	77		LD	(HL),A	MEMORY.
20FF	23	END	INC	HL	
2100	3E		LD	A,79	
2101	79				
2102	77		LD	(HL),A	LOAD "15" DISPLAY CODE
2103	23		INC	HL	IN DISPLAY ROUTINE'S
2104	3E		LD	A,12	MEMORY FOR NEW GAME.
2105	12				
2106	77		LD	(HL),A	
2107	IE		LD	E,15	
2108	15				
2109	C9		RET		RETURN TO MAIN PROGRAM.
210A	21	LOST	LD	HL,2000	
210B	00				
210C	20				
210D	3E		LD	A,47	
210E	47				
210F	77		LD	(HL),A	
2110	23		INC	HL	
2111	3E		LD	A,40	
2112	40				LOAD "LOSE" MESSAGE
2113	77		LD	(HL),A	IN DISPLAY ROUTINE'S
2114	23		INC	HL	MEMORY.
2115	3E		LD	A,12	
2116	12				
2117	77		LD	(HL),A	
2118	23		INC	HL	
2119	3E		LD	A,06	
211A	06				
211B	77		LD	(HL),A	
211C	18		JR	END	JUMP TO END.
2110	EI				
211E					
211F					

PROJECT 48: ROTATING ONE BLANK LIGHT WITH CONTROLLING SPEED

For the remainder of the projects in this book you must use all of the hardware projects in Chapter 1. This program rotates one blank (OFF) LED back and forth on output port PA. The switches on input port PB are employed to control the speed of the rotating lights.

After the program has been properly executed the NO character will appear in the Address Field. Also, the LEDs connected to out port PA will begin rotating. You can vary the speed of the rotating blank LED by moving the switches on the DIP package.

MEMORY INFORMATION			INSTRUCTION		COMMENT
ADDRESS	DATA	LABEL	OPCODE	OPERAND	
2000	31		LD	SP,2390	SET STACK POINTER.
2001	90				
2002	23				
2003	B7		OR	A	CLEAR FLAGS.
2004	3E		LD	A,0F	
2005	0F				SET PORT 80 AS OUTPUT
2006	D3		OUT	(82),A	PORT.
2007	82				
2008	3E		LD	AFF	
2009	FF				
200A	17	LEFT	RLA		ROTATE LEFT.
200B	D3		OUT	(80),A	OUTPUT DATA TO LEDS.
200C	80				
200D	30		JR	NC,RIGHT	ROTATE RIGHT IF ALL LEDS
200E	05				ARE ON.
200F	CD		CALL	SUB	PAUSE BEFORE SHIFTING
2010	30				BLANK.
2011	20				
2012	18		JR	LEFT	CONTINUE.
2013	F6				
2014	1F	RIGHT	RRA		ROTATE RIGHT.
2015	D3		OUT	(80),A	OUTPUT DATA TO LEDS.
2016	80				
2017	30		JR	NC,LEFT	ROTATE LEFT IF ALL LEDS
2018	F1				ARE ON.
2019	CD		CALL	SUB	PAUSE BEFORE SHIFTING
201A	30				BLANK.
201B	20				
201C	18		JR	RIGHT	CONTINUE.
201D	F6				
2030	F5	SUB	PUSH	AF	STORE LED DISPLAY.
2031	2E		LD	L,00	
2032	00				
2033	DB		IN	A,(81)	GET DELAY TIME.
2034	81				
2035	67		LD	H,A	STORE DELAY TIME.
2036	CD		CALL	DELAY	
2037	52				
2038	06				
2039	F1		POP	AF	RESTORE DISPLAY.
203A	C9		RET		RETURN.

PROJECT 49: ROTATING LIGHTS (NO BLANKS) WITH CONTROLLING SPEED

This program rotates the LEDs on output port PA back and forth. The switches on input port PB are employed to control the speed of the rotating lights.

After the program has been properly executed, no character will appear in the Address Field. Also, one of the LEDs connected to out port PA will begin rotating. You can vary the speed of the rotating LED by moving the switches on the DIP package.

MEMORY INFORMATION			INSTRUCTION		COMMENT
ADDRESS	DATA	LABEL	OPCODE	OPERAND	
2000	31		LD	SP,2390	SET STACK POINTER.
2001	90				
2002	23				
2003	B7		OR	A	CLEAR FLAGS.
2004	3E		LD	A,OF	
2005	0F				SET PORT 80 AS OUTPUT PORT.
2006	D3		OUT	(82),A	
2007	82				
2008	3E		LD	A,01	
2009	01				
200A	17	LEFT	RLA		ROTATE LEFT.
200B	D3		OUT	(80),A	OUTPUT DATA.
200C	80				
200D	38		JR	C,RIGHT	ROTATE RIGHT IF ALL LEDS
200E	05				ARE OFF.
200F	CD		CALL	SUB	PAUSE BEFORE SHIFTING
2010	30				DISPLAY.
2011	20				
2012	18		JR	LEFT	CONTINUE.
2013	F6				
2014	1F	RIGHT	RRA		ROTATE RIGHT.
2015	D3		OUT	(80),A	OUTPUT DATA.
2016	80				
2017	38		JR	C,LEFT	ROTATE LEFT IF ALL LEDS ARE
2018	F1				OFF.
2019	CD		CALL	SUB	PAUSE BEFORE SHIFTING DISPLAY.
201A	30				
201B	20				
201C	18		JR	RIGHT	CONTINUE.
201D	F6				
2030	F5	SUB	PUSH	AF	STORE LED DISPLAY.
2031	2E		LD	L,00	
2032	00				
2033	DB		IN	A,(81)	GET DELAY TIME.
2034	81				
2035	67		LD	H,A	STORE DELAY TIME.
2036	CD		CALL	DELAY	
2037	52				
2038	06				
2039	F1		POP	AF	RESTORE DISPLAY.
203A	C9		RET		RETURN.

PROJECT 50: ROTATING LIGHTS (NO SPEED CONTROL)

This program rotates the LEDs on output port PA back and forth without employing speed control.

MEMORY INFORMATION			INSTRUCTION		COMMENT
ADDRESS	DATA	LABEL	OPCODE	OPERAND	
2000	31		LD	SP,2390	SET STACK POINTER.
2001	90				
2002	23				
2003	B7		OR	A	CLEAR FLAGS.
2004	3E		LD	A,0F	
2005	0F				
2006	D3		OUT	(82),A	SET PORT 80 AS OUTPUT PORT.
2007	82				
2008	3E		LD	A,01	
2009	01				
200A	17	LEFT	RLA		ROTATE LEFT.
200B	D3		OUT	(80),A	OUTPUT DATA.
200C	80				
200D	38		JR	C,RIGHT	ROTATE RIGHT IF ALL LEDS ARE
200E	05				OFF.
200F	CD		CALL	SUB	PAUSE BEFORE SHIFTING
2010	30				DISPLAY.
2011	20				
2012	18		JR	LEFT	CONTINUE.
2013	F6				
2014	1F	RIGHT	RRA		ROTATE RIGHT.
2015	D3		OUT	(80),A	OUTPUT DATA.
2016	80				
2017	38		JR	C,LEFT	ROTATE LEFT IF ALL LEDS ARE
2018	F1				OFF.
2019	CD		CALL	SUB	PAUSE BEFORE SHIFTING
201A	30				DISPLAY.
201B	20				
201C	18		JR	RIGHT	CONTINUE.
201D	F6				
2030	21	SUB	LD	HL,4000	SET TIME DELAY.
2031	00				
2032	40				
2033	CD		CALL	DELAY	
2034	52				
2035	06				
2036	C9		RET		RETURN.

PROJECT 51: ROTATING BLANK LIGHTS WITHOUT SPEED CONTROL

This program rotates the LEDs on output port PA back and forth with one blank LED without employing speed control.

MEMORY INFORMATION			INSTRUCTION		COMMENT
ADDRESS	DATA	LABEL	OPCODE	OPERAND	
2000	31		LD	SP,2390	SET STACK POINTER.
2001	90				
2002	23				
2003	B7		OR	A	CLEAR FLAGS.
2004	3E		LD	A,0F	
2005	0F				SET PORT 80 AS OUTPUT PORT.
2006	D3		OUT	(82),A	
2007	82				
2008	3E		LD	A,FF	
2009	FF				
200A	17	LEFT	RLA		ROTATE LEFT.
200B	D3		OUT	(80),A	OUTPUT DATA.
200C	80				
200D	30		JR	NC,RIGHT	ROTATE LEFT IF ALL LEDS ARE
200E	05				ON.
200F	CD		CALL	SUB	PAUSE BEFORE SHIFTING
2010	30				DISPLAY.
2011	20				
2012	18		JR	LEFT	CONTINUE.
2013	F6				
2014	1F	RIGHT	RRA		ROTATE RIGHT.
2015	D3		OUT	(80),A	OUTPUT DATA.
2016	80				
2017	30		JR	NC,LEFT	ROTATE LEFT IF ALL LED'S ARE
2018	F1				ON.
2019	CD		CALL	SUB	PAUSE BEFORE SHIFTING
201A	30				DISPLAY.
201B	20				
201C	18		JR	RIGHT	CONTINUE.
201D	F6				
2030	21	SUB	LD	HL,4000	SET TIME DELAY.
2031	00				
2032	40				
2033	CD		CALL	DELAY	
2034	52				
2035	06				
2036	C9		RET		RETURN.

PROJECT 52: DISPLAYING THE SEVEN SEGMENT WITH "ZILOG Z-80"

This program displays the phrase ZILOG Z-80 on the SD-Z80 Kit's seven segment display. The display codes for each letter to be displayed starts at location 2000 in memory. The display will rotate across the seven-segment display from right to left.

MEMORY INFORMATION			INSTRUCTION		COMMENT
ADDRESS	DATA	LABEL	OPCODE	OPERAND	
2000	24	Z			
2001	79	I			
2002	47	L			
2003	40	O			
2004	10	G			
2005	7F	BLANK			
2006	24	Z			
2007	3F	—			DATA TO BE DISPLAYED.
2008	00	8			
2009	40	0			
200A	7F	BLANK			
200B	7F	BLANK			
200C	7F	BLANK			
200D	7F	BLANK			
200E	7F	BLANK			
200F	7F	BLANK			
2010	31		LD	SP,2390	SET UP STACK POINTER.
2011	90				
2012	23				
2013	DB	START	IN	A,(80)	GET DISPLAY SPEED.
2014	80				
2015	47		LD	B,A	STORE SPEED.
2016	11	DISPLAY	LD	DE,2000	SET UP DISPLAY POINTER.
2017	00				
2018	20				
2019	1A		LD	A,(DE)	
201A	D3		OUT	(88),A	
201B	88				DISPLAY DATA IN MEMORY.
201C	3E		LD	A,20	LOCATION 2000 IN FIRST
201D	20				DISPLAY.
201E	D3		OUT	(8C),A	
201F	8C				
2020	13		INC	DE	ADVANCE POINTER.
2021	21		LD	HL,01FF	LOAD TIME DELAY.
2022	FF				
2023	01				
2024	CD		CALL	DELAY	
2025	52				
2026	06				
2027	1A		LD	A,(DE)	
2028	D3		OUT	(88),A	DISPLAY DATA IN MEMORY
2029	88				LOCATION 2001 IN SECOND
202A	3E		LD	A,10	DISPLAY.
202B	10				
202C	D3		OUT	(8C),A	
202D	8C				
202E	13		INC	DE	ADVANCE POINTER.
202F	21		LD	HL,01FF	LOAD TIME DELAY.
2030	FF				
2031	01				

MEMORY INFORMATION			INSTRUCTION		COMMENT
ADDRESS	DATA	LABEL	OPCODE	OPERAND	
2032	CD		CALL	DELAY	
2033	52				
2034	06				
2035	1A		LD	A,(DE)	
2036	D3		OUT	(88),A	
2037	88				DISPLAY DATA IN MEMORY
2038	3E		LD	A,08	LOCATION 2002 IN THIRD
2039	08				DISPLAY.
203A	D3		OUT	(8C),A	
203B	8C				
203C	13		INC	DE	ADVANCE POINTER.
203D	21		LD	HL,0IFF	RELOAD TIME DELAY.
203E	FF				
203F	01				
2040	CD		CALL	DELAY	
2041	52				
2042	06				
2043	1A		LD	A,(DE)	
2044	D3		OUT	(88),A	
2045	88				DISPLAY DATA IN MEMORY
2046	3E		LD	A,04	LOCATION 2003 IN FOURTH
2047	04				DISPLAY.
2048	D3		OUT	(8C),A	
2049	8C				
204A	13		INC	DE	ADVANCE POINTER.
204B	21		LD	HL,0IFF	RELOAD TIME DELAY.
204C	FF				
204D	01				
204E	CD		CALL	DELAY	
204F	52				
2050	06				
2051	1A		LD	A,(DE)	
2052	D3		OUT	(88),A	
2053	88				DISPLAY DATA IN MEMORY
2054	3E		LD	A,02	LOCATION 2004 IN FIFTH
2055	02				DISPLAY.
2056	D3		OUT	(8C),A	
2057	8C				
2058	13		INC	DE	ADVANCE POINTER.
2059	21		LD	HL,0IFF	RELOAD TIME DELAY.
205A	FF				
205B	01				
205C	CD		CALL	DELAY	
205D	52				
205E	06				
205F	1A		LD	A,(DE)	
2060	D3		OUT	(88),A	DISPLAY DATA IN MEMORY
2061	88				LOCATION 2005 IN LAST
2062	3E		LD	A,01	DISPLAY.
2063	01				

MEMORY INFORMATION			INSTRUCTION		COMMENT
ADDRESS	DATA	LABEL	OPCODE	OPERAND	
2064	D3		OUT	(8C),A	DISPLAY DATA IN MEMORY LO-
2065	8C				CATION 2005 IN LAST DISPLAY.
2066	21		LD	HL	RELOAD TIME DELAY.
2067	FF				
2068	01				
2069	CD		CALL	DELAY	
206A	52				
206B	06				
206C	05		DEC	B	
206D	20		JR	NZ,DISPLAY	CONTINUE WITH DISPLAY
206E	A7				UNTIL B IS EQUAL TO ZERO.
206F	0E		LD	C,0F	LOAD COUNTER.
2070	0F				
2071	11		LD	DE,2000	
2072	00				
2073	20				
2074	21		LD	HL,2001	LOAD POINTERS.
2075	01				
2076	20				
2077	1A		LD	A,(DE)	GET DATA IN MEMORY
2078	47		LD	B,A	LOCATION 2000 & SAVE IN B.
2079	7E	SHIFT	LD	A,(HL)	
207A	12		LD	(DE),A	MOVE DISPLAY DATA DOWN
207B	0D		DEC	C	ONE MEMORY LOCATION.
207C	28		JR	Z,END	CONTINUE SHIFTING DATA
207D	04				UNTIL COUNTER IS ZERO.
207E	13		INC	DE	EXAMPLE: MOVE DATA IN 2001 TO
207F	23		INC	HL	2000, 2002 TO 2001, . . . 200F TO
2080	18		JR	SHIFT	200E.
2081	F7				
2082	70	END	LD	(HL),B	MOVE IN REG. B TO ADD. 200F.
2083	18		JR	START	START PROGRAM OVER AGAIN.
2084	8E				

PROJECT 53: DISPLAYING THE SEVEN SEGMENT WITH "CHIP DISPLAY"

This program displays the phrase CHIP DISPLAY on the SD-Z80 Kit's seven segment display. The display codes for each letter to be displayed start at location 2000 in memory. The display will rotate across the seven-segment display from right to left.

MEMORY INFORMATION			INSTRUCTION		COMMENT
ADDRESS	DATA	LABEL	OPCODE	OPERAND	
2000	46	C			DATA TO BE DISPLAYED.
2001	09	H			
2002	79	I			
2003	0C	P			

MEMORY INFORMATION			INSTRUCTION		COMMENT
ADDRESS	DATA	LABEL	OPCODE	OPERAND	
2004	7F	BLANK			
2005	21	D			
2006	79	I			
2007	12	S			
2008	0C	P			DATA TO BE DISPLAYED.
2009	47	L			
200A	08	A			
200B	11	Y			
200C	7F	BLANK			
2010	31		LD	SP,2390	SET STACK POINTER.
2011	90				
2012	23				
2013	DB	START	IN	A,(80)	GET DISPLAY SPEED.
2014	80				
2015	57		LD	D,A	STORE SPEED.
2016	06	BEGIN	LD	B,20	SET DISPLAY POINTER.
2017	20				
2018	0E		LD	C,06	SET COUNTER.
2019	06				
201A	21		LD	HL,2000	SET DISPLAY DATA POINTER.
201B	00				
201C	20				
201D	7E	DISPLAY	LD	A,(HL)	
201E	D3		OUT	(88),A	
201F	88				
2020	78		LD	A,B	DISPLAY CHARACTER.
2021	D3		OUT	(8C),A	
2022	8C				
2023	E5		PUSH	HL	
2024	21		LD	HL,01FF	SET TIME DELAY.
2025	FF				
2026	01				
2027	CD		CALL	DELAY	PAUSE BETWEEN CHARACTERS.
2028	52				
2029	06				
202A	EI		POP	HL	
202B	CB		SRL	B	SHIFT DISPLAY POINTER RIGHT.
202C	38				
202D	23		INC	HL	ADVANCE DISPLAY DATA POINTER.
202E	0D		DEC	C	DECREMENT COUNTER.
202F	20		JR	NZ,DISPLAY	CONTINUE UNTIL COUNTER
2030	EC				IS ZERO.
2031	15		DEC	D	
2032	20		JR	NZ,BEGIN	CONTINUE WITH DISPLAY UNTIL
2033	E2				REG. D IS ZERO.
2034	0E		LD	C,0C	SET COUNTER.
2035	0C				
2036	11		LD	DE,2000	SET POINTERS.
2037	00				

MEMORY INFORMATION			INSTRUCTION		COMMENT
ADDRESS	DATA	LABEL	OPCODE	OPERAND	
2038	20		LD	HL,2001	SET POINTERS.
2039	21				
203A	01				
203B	20				
203C	1A		LD	A,(DE)	GET DATA IN MEMORY LOCATION
203D	47		LD	B,A	2000 AND STORE IN REG. B
203E	7E	SHIFT	LD	A,(HL)	
203F	12		LD	(DE),A	MOVE DISPLAY DATA DOWN ONE
2040	0D		DEC	C	MEMORY LOCATION. CONTINUE
2041	28		JR	Z,END	SHIFTING DATA UNTIL COUNTER
2042	04				IS ZERO. EXAMPLE: MOVE DATA
2043	13		INC	DE	IN 2001 TO 2000, 2002 TO 2001,. . .
2044	23		INC	HL	., 200C to 200B.
2045	18		JR	SHIFT	
2046	F7				
2047	70	END	LD	(HL),B	MOVE DATA IN REG. B TO ADD. 200C.
2048	18		JR	START	START PROGRAM OVER AGAIN.
2049	C9				

PROJECT 54: VOLTAGE COMPARATOR

This program takes an external voltage and compares it to a voltage which is coded in memory. If the external voltage is greater than the voltage coded in memory, the left-most LED on port PA lights. If the external voltage is less than the voltage in memory, the right-most LED on port PA lights. If the external voltage is equal to the voltage in memory, the middle two LEDs on port PA light. (The voltage in memory is written in hexadecimal format.)

MEMORY INFORMATION			INSTRUCTION		COMMENT
ADDRESS	DATA	LABEL	OPCODE	OPERAND	
2000					REFERENCE VOLTAGE LOCATION.
2010	31		LD	SP,2390	SET STACK POINTER.
2011	90				
2012	23				
2013	3E		LD	A,0F	
2014	0F				INITIALIZE PORT 80 AS
2015	D3		OUT	(82),A	OUTPUT PORT.
2016	82				
2017	21		LD	HL,2000	SET REFERENCE POINTER.
2018	00				
2019	20				
201A	DB	LOOP	IN	A,(81)	GET EXTERNAL VOLTAGE.
201B	81				
201C	BE		CP	(HL)	COMPARE WITH REFERENCE.

284

MEMORY INFORMATION			INSTRUCTION		COMMENT
ADDRESS	DATA	LABEL	OPCODE	OPERAND	
201D	CA		JP	Z,EQUAL	
201E	27				
201F	20				
2020	DA		JP	C,LESS	
2021	2B				
2022	20				
2023	3E		LD	A,80	TURN ON LEFT LED IF GREATER.
2024	80				
2025	18		JR	EXIT	
2026	06				
2027	3E	EQUAL	LD	A,18	TURN ON MIDDLE LEDS IF
2028	18				EQUAL.
2029	18		JR	EXIT	
202A	02				
202B	3E	LESS	LD	A,01	TURN ON RIGHT LED IF LESS.
202C	01				
202D	D3	EXIT	OUT	(80),A	
202E	80				
202F	18		JR	LOOP	CONTINUE WITH PROGRAM.
2030	E9				

PROJECT 55: COUNT THE NUMBER OF BITS IN THE HIGH STATE

This program counts the number of bits in the high ("1" or on) state for the number stored in location 2000. The total number of bits stored in the high state will be stored in location 2001.

MEMORY INFORMATION			INSTRUCTION		COMMENT
ADDRESS	DATA	LABEL	OPCODE	OPERAND	
2000		DATA			
2001		RESULT			
2010	21		LD	HL,2000	SET POINTER.
2011	00				
2012	20				
2013	AF		XOR	A	CLEAR COUNTER.
2014	4F		LD	C,A	
2015	06		LD	B,08	SET LOOP COUNTER.
2016	08				
2017	7E		LD	A,(HL)	GET THE NUMBER.
2018	CB	SHIFT	SLA	A	SHIFT BITS LIFT ONE POSITION
2019	27				TO CARRY FLAG.
201A	DA		JP	C,ADVANCE	TEST FOR HIGH BIT.
201B	24				
201C	20				
201D	05	DECREASE	DEC	B	DECREASE LOOP COUNTER.
201E	C2		JP	NZ,SHIFT	TEST FOR END OF LOOP.

MEMORY INFORMATION			INSTRUCTION		COMMENT
ADDRESS	DATA	LABEL	OPCODE	OPERAND	
201F	18				
2020	20				
2021	23		INC	HL	ADVANCE POINTER.
2022	71		LD	(HL),C	STORE RESULT.
2023	C7		RST	00	END OF PROGRAM.
2024	0C	ADVANCE	INC	C	ADVANCE BIT COUNTER.
2025	C3		JP	DECREASE	
2026	1D				
2027	20				

PROJECT 56: ADJUSTABLE RANDOM NUMBER GENERATOR

This program generates a random number between 00 and XX, where XX is in location 2001. To begin the program, press 200F, EXEC and the interrupt button.

MEMORY INFORMATION			INSTRUCTION		COMMENT
ADDRESS	DATA	LABEL	OPCODE	OPERAND	
2000		RESULT			
2001		LIMIT			
2002					DATA TO BE DISPLAYED WILL
2003					BE STORED HERE.
200F	31		LD	SP,2390	SET STACK POINTER.
2010	90				
2011	23				
2012	ED		IM	1	SET INTERRUPT MODE.
2013	56				
2014	FB		EI		ENABLE INTERRUPT.
2015	3A		LD	A,2001	GET LIMIT.
2016	01				
2017	20				
2018	47		LD	B,A	STORE LIMIT.
2019	AF	LIMIT	XOR	A	CLEAR FLAGS.
201A	11	GEN	LD	DE,2002	SET DISPLAY DATA POINTER.
201B	02				
201C	20				
201D	3C		INC	A	INCREASE NUMBER.
201E	B8		CP	B	LOOP BACK IF NUMBER IS
201F	20		JR	NZ,GEN	NOT EQUAL TO LIMIT.
2020	F9				
2021	18		JR	LIMIT	JUMP IF NUMBER HAS
2022	F6				REACHED LIMIT.
2023	32	SUB	LD	(2000),A	STORE RANDOM NUMBER.
2024	00				
2025	20				
2026	0E		LD	C,02	LOAD COUNTER.
2027	02				

MEMORY INFORMATION			INSTRUCTION		COMMENT
ADDRESS	DATA	LABEL	OPCODE	OPERAND	
2028	E6		AND	F0	MASK OUT LOW BYTE OF NO.
2029	F0				
202A	1F		RRA		
202B	1F		RRA		SHIFT HIGH BYTE TO LOW
202C	1F		RRA		BYTE.
202D	1F		RRA		
202E	DD	LOAD	LD	IX,2080	SET INDEX TABLE POINTER.
202F	21				
2030	80				
2031	20				
2032	21		LD	HL,07A6	SET DISPLAY CODE POINTER.
2033	A6				
2034	07				
2035	DD	LOOP	CP	(IX+d)	COMPARE NUMBER TO INDEX
2036	BE				TABLE.
2037	00				
2038	CA		JP	Z,CODE	JUMP WHEN A MATCH IS
2039	41				MADE.
203A	20				
203B	DD		INC	IX	
203C	23				ADVANCE POINTERS.
203D	23		INC	HL	
203E	C3		JP	LOOP	CONTINUE TO LOOP.
203F	35				
2040	20				
2041	7E	CODE	LD	A,(HL)	GET DISPLAY CODE.
2042	12		LD	(DE),A	STORE CODE.
2043	3A		LD	A,(2000)	GET RANDOM NUMBER.
2044	00				
2045	20				
2046	E6		AND	0F	MASK OUT HIGH BYTE.
2047	0F				
2048	13		INC	DE	ADVANCE DISPLAY DATA POINTER.
2049	0D		DEC	C	DECREMENT COUNTER.
204A	C2		JP	NZ,LOAD	JUMP IF COUNTER NOT ZERO.
204B	2E				
204C	20				
204D	0E		LD	C,30	RELOAD COUNTER.
204E	30				
204F	11	DISPLAY	LD	DE,2002	RESET DISPLAY DATA POINTER.
2050	02				
2051	20				
2052	1A		LD	A,(DE)	GET DISPLAY DATA.
2053	D3		OUT	(88),A	
2054	88				
2055	3E		LD	A,02	DISPLAY CHARACTER.
2056	02				
2057	D3		OUT	(8C),A	
2058	8C				
2059	CD		CALL	DELAY	

MEMORY INFORMATION			INSTRUCTION		COMMENT
ADDRESS	DATA	LABEL	OPCODE	OPERAND	
205A	4F				
205B	06				
205C	13		INC	DE	ADVANCE POINTER.
204D	1A		LD	A,(DE)	GET DATA.
205E	D3		OUT	(88),A	
205F	88				
2060	3E		LD	A,01	DISPLAY CHARACTER.
2061	01				
2062	D3		OUT	(8C),A	
2063	8C				
2064	CD		CALL	DELAY	
2065	4F				
2066	06				
2067	0D		DEC	C	DECREMENT COUNTER.
2068	C2		JP	NZ,DISPLAY	JUMP UNTIL COUNTER IS ZERO.
2069	4F				
206A	20				
206B	FB		EI		ENABLE INTERRUPT.
206C	3E		LD	A,7F	
206D	7F				TURN OFF DISPLAY.
206E	D3		OUT	(88),A	
206F	88				
2070	ED		RETI		RETURN TO MAIN PROGRAM.
2071	4D				
2080	00				
2081	01				
2082	02				
2083	03				
2084	04				
2085	05				
2086	06				INDEX TABLE.
2087	07				
2088	08				
2089	09				
208A	0A				
208B	0B				
208C	0C				
208D	0D				
208E	0E				
208F	0F				
23D3	C3		JP	SUB	
23D4	23				
23D5	20				

PROJECT 57: ELECTRONIC DICE 1

This program simulates the throwing of dice. Every time the interrupt button is pushed, a new roll of the dice will be displayed.

When the program is properly executed no character will appear in the Address Field. Pressing the intr. button will cause a two-digit number to be displayed in the Data Field. The two-digit number will have values between 11 and 66 that represent two die values. If a 24 appears in the Data Field, this value represents a dice throw of six. Pressing of the intr. button will randomly display other dice throws.

MEMORY INFORMATION			INSTRUCTION		COMMENT
ADDRESS	DATA	LABEL	OPCODE	OPERAND	
2000					DATA TO BE DISPLAYED
2001					STORED HERE.
2010	31		LD	SP,2390	SET STACK POINTER.
2011	90				
2012	23				
2013	ED		IM	1	SET INTERRUPT MODE.
2014	56				
2015	FB		EI		ENABLE INTERRUPT.
2016	06	LOAD	LD	B,05	SET LIMITS FOR THE DICE.
2017	05				
2018	0E	LOOP-2	LD	C,05	
2019	05				
201A	0D	LOOP	DEC	C	DECREMENT DIE.
201B	20		JR	NZ,LOOP	LOOP UNTIL ZERO.
201C	FD				
201D	05		DEC	B	DECREMENT DIE.
201E	20		JR	NZ,LOOP-2	LOOP UNTIL ZERO.
201F	F8				
2020	18		JR	LOAD	START OVER AGAIN.
2021	F4				
2022	11	DECODE	LD	DE,2000	SET DISPLAY DATA POINTER.
2023	00				
2024	20				
2025	04		INC	B	INCREMENT DICE SO NO.'S
2026	0C		INC	C	ARE BETWEEN 1 & 6.
2027	79		LD	A,C	MOVE DIE NO. TO ACC.
2028	0E		LD	C,02	SET COUNTER.
2029	02				
202A	DD	SET	LD	IX,2070	SET INDEX TABLE POINTER.
202B	21				
202C	70				
2020	20				
202E	21		LD	HL,07A6	SET DISPLAY CODE POINTER.
202F	A6				
2030	07				
2031	DD	COMPARE	CP	(1X+d)	LOOK FOR MATCH IN INDEX
2032	BE				TABLE.
2033	00				

MEMORY INFORMATION			INSTRUCTION		COMMENT
ADDRESS	DATA	LABEL	OPCODE	OPERAND	
2034	CA		JP	Z,GET	IF MATCH IS FOUND THEN
2035	3D				JUMP.
2036	20				
2037	DD		INC	IX	ADVANCE POINTER.
2038	23				
2039	23		INC	HL	ADVANCE POINTER.
203A	C3		JP	COMPARE	CONTINUE LOOKING FOR
203B	31				MATCH.
203C	20				
203D	7E	GET	LD	A,(HL)	GET DISPLAY CODE.
203E	12		LD	(DE),A	STORE CODE.
203F	78		LD	A,B	MOVE SECOND DIE TO ACC.
2040	13		INC	DE	ADVANCE POINTER.
2041	0D		DEC	C	DECREMENT COUNTER.
2042	C2		JP	NZ,SET	JUMP IF COUNTER IS NOT
2043	2A				ZERO.
2044	20				
2045	0E		LD	C,30	RESET COUNTER.
2046	30				
2047	11	DISPLAY	LD	DE,2000	RESET DISPLAY DATA POINTER.
2048	00				
2049	20				
204A	1A		LD	A,(DE)	GET DATA.
204B	D3		OUT	(88),A	
204C	88				
204D	3E		LD	A,02	DISPLAY DATA.
204E	02				
204F	D3		OUT	(8C),A	
2050	8C				
2051	CD		CALL	DELAY	PAUSE BEFORE DISPLAYING.
2052	4F				NEXT CHARACTER.
2053	06				
2054	13		INC	DE	ADVANCE POINTER.
2055	1A		LD	A,(DE)	GET DATA.
2056	D3		OUT	(88),A	
2057	88				
2058	3E		LD	A,01	DISPLAY DATA.
2059	01				
205A	D3		OUT	(8C),A	
205B	8C				
205C	CD		CALL	DELAY	PAUSE BEFORE CONTINUING
205D	4F				WITH DISPLAY ROUTINE.
205E	06				
205F	0D		DEC	C	DECREMENT COUNTER.
2060	C2		JP	NZ,DISPLAY	CONTINUE UNTIL COUNTER
2061	47				IS ZERO.
2062	20				
2063	FB		EI		ENABLE INTERRUPTS.
2064	3E		LD	A,7F	TURN OFF DISPLAY.
2065	7F				
2066	D3		OUT	(88),A	

MEMORY INFORMATION			INSTRUCTION		COMMENT
ADDRESS	DATA	LABEL	OPCODE	OPERAND	
2067	88				TURN OFF DISPLAY.
2068	ED		RETI		RETURN FROM INTERRUPT.
2069	4D				
2070	01				
2071	02				
2072	03				INDEX TABLE.
2073	04				
2074	05				
2075	06				
23D3	C3		JP	DECODE	JUMP IF THERE IS AN
23D4	22				INTERRUPT.
23D5	20				

PROJECT 58: D/A CONVERTER CIRCUIT—PLUS AND MINUS 15-VOLT POWER SUPPLY

The power supply that must be employed to furnish dc voltage to the D/A converter circuit is shown in Fig. 10-1. The complete parts list is shown on Fig. 10-1. The dc supply will furnish +15 V and −15 V at a very low current demand (about 50 mA) from the D/A converter circuit. The +5 V needed for the D/A converter circuit can be acquired from the SD-Z80 custom power supply shown in Project 1. The circuit components must be put together in a separate package.

This power supply is also employed in the projects of Chapter 12. The same voltages (+15 V, −15 V) are used at about a current demand of 100 mA. You should return to this section when you need a +15 V and −15 V dc supply in Chapter 12.

PROJECT 59: D/A CONVERTER CIRCUIT—HARDWARE FOR OSCILLOSCOPE DISPLAY

The circuit shown in Fig. 10-2 must be used to interface the SD-Z80 trainer with an oscilloscope in order to display a staircase voltage. The main program in Project 60 generates the staircase voltage, which is a software control led voltage waveform.

Two chips are needed for the hardware. Both are Motorola chips; MC 1408 and MC 1741. The 5 V power supply shown in Chapter 1 must be used in this D/A converter circuit.

To test the D/A converter circuit, connect pins 5 through 12 on the MC 1408 chip to +5 V (high). Then adjust the $10\,k\Omega$ potentiometer of the MC 1741 chip for an output of +5 V at pin 10 of the MC 1741 chip. In other words, turn the 10 kΩ potentiometer until you find the position when pin 10 of the MC 1741 chip reaches +5 V with respect to common (ground).

Next, remove the +5 V from pin 5 of the MC 1408 chip and connect pin 5 to common. If the output on pin 10 of the MC 1741 chip is + 2.5 V with respect to common, then the D/A circuit is operating properly. Now disconnect +5 V from pins 5 through 12 on the MC 1408 chip, and connect pins 5 through 12 to the proper connections on port 80 (PA) as indicated on Fig. 10-2.

If the procedure doesn't work as outlined, repeat the procedure once again to verify your first results. If +2.5 V is not measured at pin 10 of the MC 1741 chip the second time, then a wiring mistake may have been made, or one or both of the chips may not be operating properly.

PROJECT 60: D/A CONVERTER CIRCUIT—MAIN PROGRAM

The main program that generates a software-controlled voltage waveform (staircase voltage) is given below. The voltage can be displayed on the oscilloscope by employing Projects 58 and 59.

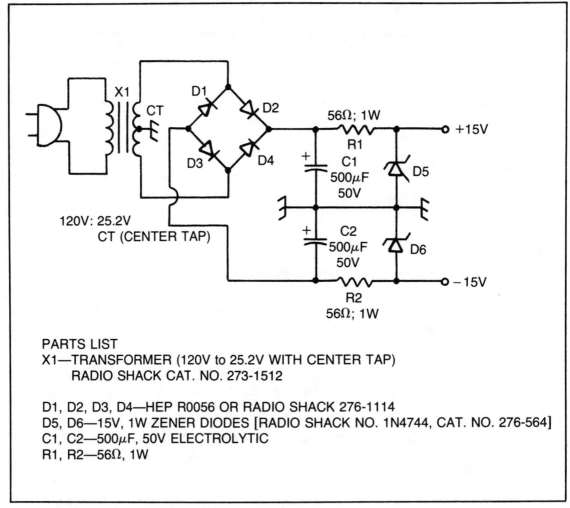

PARTS LIST
X1—TRANSFORMER (120V to 25.2V WITH CENTER TAP)
    RADIO SHACK CAT. NO. 273-1512

D1, D2, D3, D4—HEP R0056 OR RADIO SHACK 276-1114
D5, D6—15V, 1W ZENER DIODES [RADIO SHACK NO. 1N4744, CAT. NO. 276-564]
C1, C2—500μF, 50V ELECTROLYTIC
R1, R2—56Ω, 1W

Fig. 10-1. Power supply for D/A converter circuit.

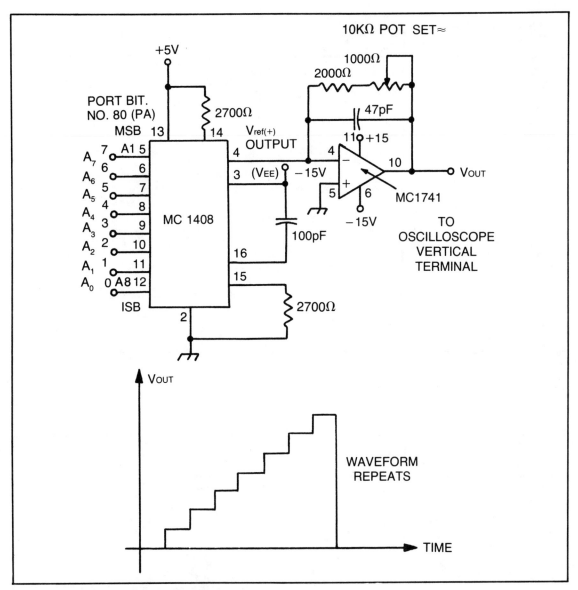

Fig. 10-2. D/A converter hardware and output voltage.

MEMORY INFORMATION			INSTRUCTION		COMMENT
ADDRESS	DATA	LABEL	OPCODE	OPERAND	
2000	31		LD	SP,2390	INITIALIZE STACK POINTER.
2001	90				
2002	23				
2003	3E		LD	A,0F	INITIALIZE PORT 80 AS
2004	0F				OUTPUT PORT.

293

MEMORY INFORMATION			INSTRUCTION		COMMENT
ADDRESS	DATA	LABEL	OPCODE	OPERAND	
2005	D3		OUT	(82), A	INITIALIZE PORT 80 AS
2006	82				OUTPUT PORT.
2007	3E	START	LD	A,C8	
2008	C8				OUTPUT DATA TO D/A
2009	D3		OUT	(80),A	
200A	80				
200B	21	LOOP	LD	HL,0107	
200C	07				
200D	01				PAUSE BEFORE DISPLAYING
200E	CD		CALL	DELAY	NEXT BYTE OF DATA.
200F	52				
2010	06				
2011	3D		DEC	A	DECREMENT DATA.
2012	FE		CP	32	CHECK FOR END OF RAMP.
2013	32				
2014	D3		OUT	(80),A	OUTPUT DATA.
2015	80				
2016	20		JR	NZ,LOOP	JUMP IF RAMP IS NOT COMPLETE.
2017	F3				
2018	18		JR	START	START NEW RAMP.
2019	ED				

PROJECT 61: MEMORY RESET FOR EXPANSION RAM

This program will zero the expansion RAM.

MEMORY INFORMATION			INSTRUCTION		COMMENT
ADDRESS	DATA	LABEL	OPCODE	OPERAND	
2010	21		LD	HL,2400	SET MEMORY POINTER.
2011	00				
2012	24				
2013	06		LD	B,00	
2014	00				
2015	48		LD	C,B	SET COUNTER.
2016	70	LOOP	LD	(HL),B	PUT ZERO IN MEMORY.
2017	23		INC	HL	ADVANCE POINTER.
2018	0C		INC	C	ADVANCE COUNTER.
2019	20		JR	NZ,LOOP	CONTINUE UNTIL COUNTER IS
201A	FB				ZERO.
201B	C7		RST	00	RETURN TO MONITOR.

PROJECT 62: BINARY TO HEXADECIMAL NUMBER CONVERSION

This program will convert the binary input on the DIP switch at port PB into a hexidecimal number, which will be displayed in the Data Field. If the first four LEDs of port PB are lit and the program is executed properly, then OF should appear in the Data Field.

294

MEMORY INFORMATION			INSTRUCTION		COMMENT
ADDRESS	DATA	LABEL	OPCODE	OPERAND	
2000					} DATA TO BE DISPLAYED.
2001					
2010	11	START	LD	DE,2000	SET DATA DISPLAY POINTER.
2011	00				
2012	20				
2013	31		LD	SP,2390	SET STACK POINTER.
2014	90				
2015	23				
2016	DB		IN	A,(80)	GET DATA FROM SWITCHES.
2017	80				
2018	47		LD	B,A	STORE DATA.
2019	0E		LD	C,02	SET COUNTER.
201A	02				
201B	E6		AND	F0	MASK OUT LOW BYTE.
201C	F0				
201D	1F		RRA		} MOVE HIGH BYTE TO LOW.
201E	1F		RRA		BYTE.
201F	1F		RRA		
2020	1F		RRA		
2021	DD	SET	LD	IX,2060	SET INDEX TABLE POINTER.
2022	21				
2023	60				
2024	20				
2025	21		LD	HL,07A6	SET DISPLAY CODE POINTER.
2026	A6				
2027	07				
2028	DD	LOOP	CP	(IX+d)	LOOK FOR A MATCH IN INDEX
2029	BE				TABLE.
202A	00				
202B	CA		JP	Z,LOAD	JUMP WHEN A MATCH IS
202C	34				FOUND.
202D	20				
202E	DD		INC	IX	} ADVANCE POINTERS.
202F	23				
2030	23		INC	HL	
2031	C3		JP	LOOP	CONTINUE TO SEARCH.
2032	28				
2033	20				
2034	7E	LOAD	LD	A,(HL)	GET DISPLAY CODE.
2035	12		LD	(DE),A	STORE CODE.
2036	78		LD	A,B	GET DATA FROM STORAGE.
2037	E6		AND	0F	MASK OUT HIGH BYTE.
2038	0F				
2039	13		INC	DE	ADVANCE POINTER.
203A	0D		DEC	C	DECREMENT COUNTER.
203B	C2		JP	NZ,SET	JUMP IF COUNTER ISN'T
203C	21				ZERO.
203D	20				
203E	11		LD	DE,2000	RESET POINTER.

MEMORY INFORMATION			INSTRUCTION		COMMENT
ADDRESS	DATA	LABEL	OPCODE	OPERAND	
203F	00				
2040	20				
2041	1A		LD	A,(DE)	GET DATA.
2042	D3		OUT	(88),A	
2043	88				
2044	3E		LD	A,02	DISPLAY DATA.
2045	02				
2046	D3		OUT	(8C),A	
2047	8C				
2048	CD		CALL	DELAY	
2049	4F				
204A	06				
204B	13		INC	DE	ADVANCE POINTER.
204C	1A		LD	A,(DE)	GET DATA.
204D	D3		OUT	(88),A	
204E	88				
204F	3E		LD	A,01	DISPLAY DATA.
2050	01				
2051	D3		OUT	(8C),A	
2052	8C				
2053	CD		CALL	DELAY	
2054	4F				
2055	06				
2056	C3		JP	START	START OVER AGAIN.
2057	10				
2058	20				
2060	00		206A	0A	INDEX TABLE.
2061	01		206B	0B	
2062	02		206C	0C	
2063	03		206D	0D	
2064	04		206E	0E	
2065	05		206F	0F	
2066	06				
2067	07				
2068	08				
2069	09				

PROJECT 63: THE GREATEST COMMON DIVISOR

The program shown below takes a number stored in location 2000, compares it with a number stored in location 2001, and determines which number is the greatest common divisor. The answer is stored in location 2002. You must first put the numbers in locations 2000 and 2001.

MEMORY INFORMATION			INSTRUCTION		COMMENT
ADDRESS	DATA	LABEL	OPCODE	OPERAND	
2000		NO.1			
2001		NO.2			
2002		RESULT			
2010	21		LD	HL,2000	SET POINTER.
2011	00				
2012	20				
2013	7E		LD	A,(HL)	GET FIRST NUMBER.
2014	23		INC	HL	ADVANCE POINTER.
2015	46		LD	B,(HL)	GET SECOND NUMBER.
2016	B8	LOOP	CP	B	COMPARE NUMBERS.
2017	28		JR	Z,EXIT	EXIT IF NO.'S ARE EQUAL.
2018	0C				
2019	30		JR	NC,SUB	JUMP IF SECOND NO. IS LESS
201A	07				THAN FIRST.
201B	4F		LD	C,A	MOVE A INTO C.
201C	78		LD	A,B	MOVE B INTO A.
201D	91		SUB	C	SUBTRACT FIRST NO. FROM SECOND.
201E	47		LD	B,A	MOVE A TO B.
201F	79		LD	A,C	MOVE C TO A.
2020	18		JR	LOOP	CONTINUE WITH PROGRAM.
2021	F4				
2022	90	SUB	SUB	B	SUBTRACT SECOND NO. FROM FIRST.
2023	18		JR	LOOP	CONTINUE WITH PROGRAM.
2024	F1				
2025	23	EXIT	INC	HL	ADVANCE POINTER.
2026	77		LD	(HL),A	STORE RESULT.
2027	C7		RST	00	RETURN TO MONITOR.

Chapter 11

Teletypewriter Projects

PROJECT 64: PURCHASE OF A TTY

We purchased used teletypewriters (TTY) for one-fifth the cost of a printer or new teletypewriter. They are in perfect working order and have served us for the past four years without any need for repair. The teletypewriters we purchased were Teletype Corporation Model 33. You can purchase this from RCA data communication service groups, which have offices in every large city throughout the United States, or by calling their toll free number:(800) 257-7784.A Teletypewriter can be purchased for a few hundred dollars and can be used as a printer or an input keyboard to a microcomputer system.

We recommend the purchase of any of the following Model 33s: 33 216 JA, 33 216 JE, 33 203 JE, 33 205 JA, and 33 205 JB. You will probably find other Model 33s that will operate satisfactorily in addition to the models listed above.

PROJECT 65: CONSTRUCTION OF INTERFACE CIRCUITS CONNECTING THE TTY AND THE SD-Z80 KIT

In order to interface the TTY with the SD-Z80 Kit, you must construct the circuits shown in Fig. 11-1. All the parts can be purchased at your favorite electronics store.

PROJECT 66: INTERFACING THE TTY WITH THE SD-Z80 KIT

The TTY custom dc power supply (− 10 V) shown in Project 7, Fig. 1-11 must be connected to the circuits

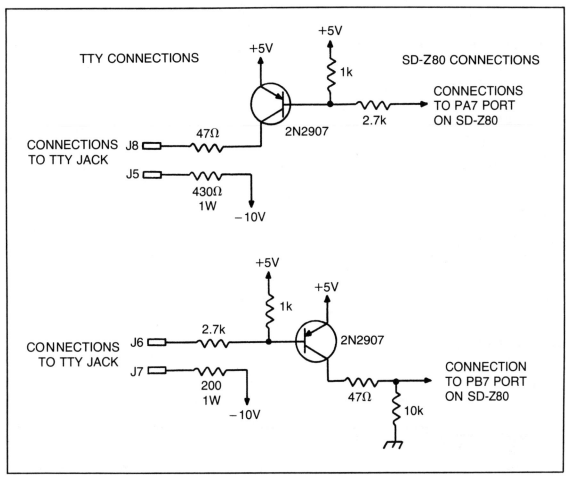

Fig. 11-1. Interface circuits.

shown in Fig. 11-1. Look at Fig. 11-1 and connect the −10 V dc supply to the terminals in the two circuits labeled −10 V. Of course the other side of the dc supply is connected to common on the SD-Z80 Kit. Also, the +5 V supply of the SD-Z80 Kit must be connected to the two circuits in Fig. 11-1 as indicated.

The output of the two circuits in Fig. 11-1 is connected to the SD-Z80 trainer at the ports labeled PA7 and PB7 as shown in Fig. 11-1.

Figure 11-2 illustrates the connections to be made from the jack of the back of the TTY to the input of the interface circuits in Fig. 11-1. *CAUTION:* DO NOT TURN ON the TTY until the following programs are loaded into memory and executed on the SD-Z80 Kit.

- Call Out TTY (Project 67)
- Carriage Return (Project 68)
- Call IN TTY (Project 69)
- Any program in this chapter or any programs you may develop.

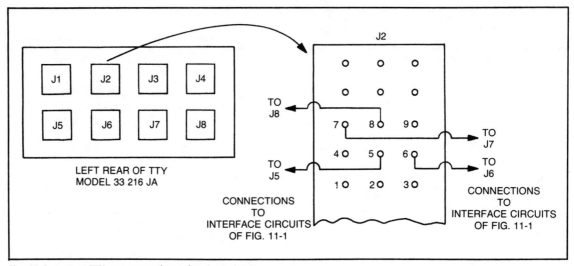

Fig. 11-2. Jack of TTY and connection to interface circuit.

If you don't follow these instructions, the TTY carriage may continually move without control.

PROJECT 67: CALL OUT TTY

The program listed below allows the SD-Z80 Kit to move data from the SD-Z80 Kit to the TTY. This program must be loaded in the SD-Z80 Kit before the TTY is turned on.

MEMORY INFORMATION			INSTRUCTION		COMMENT
ADDRESS	DATA	LABEL	OPCODE	OPERAND	
2040	C5	OUT-TTY	PUSH	BC	SAVE REGISTERS ON STACK.
2041	E5		PUSH	HL	
2042	3E		LO	A,80	LOAD START BIT.
2043	80				
2044	06		LD	B,08	SET BIT COUNTER.
2045	08				
2046	D3	LOOP-1	OUT	(80),A	SEND BIT.
2047	80				
2048	21		LD	HL,0561	SET TIME DELAY.
2049	61				
204A	05				
204B	CD		CALL	DELAY	DELAY FOR 1 BIT.
204C	52				
204D	06				
204E	79		LD	A,C	MOVE CHAR. TO ACC.
204F	IF		RRA		ROTATE BIT TO BE SENT INTO CARRY.
2050	4F		LD	C,A	SAVE REMAINDER.
2051	IF		RRA		ROTATE BIT BACK INTO ACC.
2052	2F		CPL	A	COMPLEMENT BIT.

MEMORY INFORMATION			INSTRUCTION		COMMENT
ADDRESS	DATA	LABEL	OPCODE	OPERAND	
2053	05		DEC	B	DECREMENT BIT COUNTER.
2054	20		JR	NZ,LOOP-1	JUMP UNTIL ALL BITS HAVE BEEN SENT.
2055	F0				
2056	AF		XOR	A	LOAD STOP BIT.
2057	D3		OUT	(80),A	SEND STOP BIT.
2058	80				
2059	21		LD	HL,09C4	SET DELAY TIME.
205A	C4				
205B	09				
205C	CD		CALL	DELAY	DELAY FOR 2 BITS.
205D	52				
205E	06				
205F	E1		POP	HL	} RESTORE REGISTERS.
2060	C1		POP	BC	
2061	C9		RET		RETURN TO MAIN PROGRAM

PROJECT 68: CARRIAGE RETURN

The program listed below allows the SD-Z80 to control the return of the carriage on the TTY. This program must be loaded in the SD-Z80 Kit before the TTY is turned on.

MEMORY INFORMATION			INSTRUCTION		COMMENT
ADDRESS	DATA	LABEL	OPCODE	OPERAND	
2062	0E	CR	LD	C,0D	LOAD CARRIAGE RETURN CHAR.
2063	0D				
2064	CD		CALL	CHECK	
2065	68				
2066	20				
2067	C9		RET		
2068	41	CHECK	LD	B,C	MOVE CHARACTER INTO B REG.
2069	3E		ID	A,1B	LOAD ESC. CHAR. INTO ACC.
206A	1B				
206B	B8		CP	B	CHECK FOR ESC. CHAR.
206C	20		JR	NZ,OUT	IF NOT ESC. JUMP.
206D	02				
206E	0E		LD	C,24	LOAD $ CHAR.
206F	24				
2070	CD	OUT	CALL	OUT-TTY	OUTPUT TO TTY.
2071	40				
2072	20				
2073	3E		LD	A,0D	} CHECK FOR CR.
2074	0D				
2075	B8		CP	B	
2076	20		JR	NZ,EXIT	IF NOT JUMP TO EXIT.
2077	05				
2078	0E		LD	C,0A	LOAD LINE FEED CHAR.

MEMORY INFORMATION			INSTRUCTION		COMMENT
ADDRESS	DATA	LABEL	OPCODE	OPERAND	
2079	0A				OUTPUT TO TTY.
207A	CD		CALL	OUT-TTY	
207B	40				
207C	20				RESTORE REGISTER.
207D	48	EXIT	LD	C,B	
207E	C9		RET		

PROJECT 69: CALL IN TTY

The program below allows the SD-Z80 to move data from the TTY into the SD-Z80 Kit. This program must be loaded in the SD-Z80 Kit before the TTY is turned on.

MEMORY INFORMATION			INSTRUCTION		COMMENT
ADDRESS	DATA	LABEL	OPCODE	OPERAND	
207F	C5	IN-TTY	PUSH	BC	SAVE REGISTERS.
2080	E5		PUSH	HL	
2081	DB	BACK	IN	A,(81)	
2082	81				
2083	E6		AND	80	
2084	80				
2085	17		RLA		WAIT FOR START BIT.
2086	38		JR	C,BACK	
2087	F9				
2088	21		LD	HL,0330	SET DELAY TIME.
2089	30				
208A	03				
208B	CD		CALL	DELAY	DELAY FOR ½ BIT.
208C	52				
208D	06				
208E	01		LD	BC,0008	SET BIT COUNTER & CLEAR,
208F	08				CHARACTER REGISTER.
2090	00				
2091	21	GET	LD	HL,0561	SET DELAY TIME.
2092	61				
2093	05				
2094	CD		CALL	DELAY	DELAY FOR 1 BIT.
2095	52				
2096	06				
2097	DB		IN	A,(81)	GET BIT.
2098	81				
2099	E6		AND	80	
209A	80				
209B	17		RLA		PACK BIT IN CHARACTER.
209C	78		LD	A,B	REGISTER.
209D	1F		RRA		
209E	47		LD	B,A	
209F	0D		DEC	C	DECREMENT BIT COUNTER.

MEMORY INFORMATION			INSTRUCTION		COMMENT
ADDRESS	DATA	LABEL	OPCODE	OPERAND	
20A0	20		JR	NZ,GET	JUMP IF MORE LEFT.
20A1	EF				
20A2	21		LD	HL,0561	SET TIME DELAY.
20A3	61				
20A4	05				
20A5	CD		CALL	DELAY	DELAY FOR 1 BIT.
20A6	52				
20A7	06				
20A8	78		LD	A,B	GET RESULT.
20A9	E1		POP	HL	⎫ RESTORE REGISTERS.
20AA	C1		POP	BC	⎬
20AB	C9		RET		⎭

PROGRAM LOADING INSTRUCTIONS

Before you try to load and execute the programs given in this chapter, the following instructions must be followed if you want the programs to run correctly.

1. Read the first six sections of this chapter carefully and follow the instructions exactly.

2. You can load any of the programs that remain in this chapter with the TTY off. Once the program is loaded into memory, then press the beginning address of the program, and then press EXEC. CAUTION: Once the program is executed DO NOT PRESS the RESET button at the top of the SD-Z80 Kit, or the TTY carriage will continually move without control.

If you want to stop the program, press the MON (monitor) key. The same program can be rerun by repeating the above procedure, or a new program can be loaded into memory.

3. After you have followed instructions 1 and 2 above, you can turn on the TTY without deleterious effects. The procedure listed above needs to be followed oniy once for the initial program. However, if the SD-Z80 Kit is ever turned off or loses power, the entire procedure must be repeated.

PROJECT 70: TTY PRINTING FROM SD-Z80 MEMORY

You must read the "Program Loading Instructions" above before you load this program, which takes data stored in the SD-Z80 memory and displays it on a TTY.

MEMORY INFORMATION			INSTRUCTION		COMMENT
ADDRESS	DATA	LABEL	OPCODE	OPERAND	
2000	31		LD	SP,2390	
2001	90				

MEMORY INFORMATION			INSTRUCTION		COMMENT
ADDRESS	DATA	LABEL	OPCODE	OPERAND	
2002	23				
2003	21		LD	HL,2400	POINT TO START OF MESSAGE.
2004	00				
2005	24				
2006	3E		LD	A,OF	
2007	0F				
2008	D3		OUT	(82),A	SET PORT 80 AS OUTPUT PORT.
2009	82				
200A	AF		XOR	A	
200B	D3		OUT	(80),A	SEND OUT STOP BIT.
200C	80				
200D	3E	LOOP	LD	A,0D	
200E	0D				GET CHARACTER AND CHECK
200F	4E		LD	C,(HL)	FOR CARRIAGE RETURN (CR).
2010	B9		CP	C	
2011	28		JR	Z,EXIT	IF IT IS A CR JUMP TO EXIT.
2012	06				
2013	CD		CALL	OUT-TTY	SEND CHARACTER TO TTY.
2014	40				
2015	20				
2016	23		INC	HL	POINT TO NEXT CHARACTER.
2017	18		JR	LOOP	
2018	F4				
2019	CD	EXIT	CALL	CR	OUTPUT A CR AND LINE FEED.
201A	62				
201B	20				
201C	C7		RST	00	RETURN TO MONITOR.
2400	48	45 4C	4C		
2404	4F	20 54	48		
2408	45	52 45	20		
240C	46	52 41	4E		
2410	4B	2C 20	48		
2414	4F	57 20	41		
2418	52	45 20	59		SAMPLE MESSAGE.
241C	4F	55 20	54		
2420	4F	44 41	59		
2424	20	42 4F	42		
2428	3F	0D			

PROJECT 71: SEND DATA INTO THE SD-Z80 AND PLAY BACK TO THE TTY

You must read the "Program Loading Instructions" before you load this program, which will read a line from the TTY into the SD-Z80. Once a character is entered, it will display that character on the TTY.

MEMORY INFORMATION			INSTRUCTION		COMMENT
ADDRESS	DATA	LABEL	OPCODE	OPERAND	
2000	31		LD	SP,2390	

MEMORY INFORMATION			INSTRUCTION		COMMENT
ADDRESS	DATA	LABEL	OPCODE	OPERAND	
2001	90				
2002	23				
2003	21		LD	HL,2400	POINT TO MESSAGE STORAGE.
2004	00				
2005	24				
2006	3E		LD	A,0F	
2007	0F				SET PORT 80 AS OUTPUT PORT.
2008	D3		OUT	(82),A	
2009	82				
200A	AF		XOR	A	
200B	D3		OUT	(80),A	
200C	80				SEND OUT STOP BIT.
200D	CD	REPEAT	CALL	IN-TTY	GET CHARACTER FROM TTY.
200E	7F				
200F	20				
2010	E6		AND	7F	TURN INTO ASCII.
2011	7F				
2012	77		LD	(HL),A	STORE IT.
2013	23		INC	HL	ADVANCE POINTER.
2014	FE		CP	0D	
2015	0D				CHECK FOR CR. IF NOT
2016	20		JR	NZ,REPEAT	GET NEXT CHARACTER.
2017	F5				
2018	21		LD	HL,2400	RESET POINTER.
2019	00				
201A	24				
201B	3E	LOOP	LD	A,0D	
201C	0D				CHECK FOR CR.
201D	4E		LD	C,(HL)	
201E	B9		CP	C	JUMP TO EXIT IF IT IS CR.
201F	28		JR	Z,EXIT	
2020	06				
2021	CD		CALL	OUT-TTY	SEND CHARACTER TO TTY.
2022	40				
2023	20				
2024	23		INC	HL	ADVANCE POINTER.
2025	18		JR	LOOP	
2026	F4				
2027	CD	EXIT	CALL	CR	OUTPUT CR & LINE FEED.
2028	62				
2029	20				
202A	C7		RST	00	

PROJECT 72: TTY ECHO AND PLAYBACK

This program will get a character from the TTY, echo it, then display the whole message when the C/R key is pressed on the TTY. You must read the "Program Loading Instructions" above before you load this program.

MEMORY INFORMATION			INSTRUCTION		COMMENT
ADDRESS	DATA	LABEL	OPCODE	OPERAND	
2000	31		LD	SP,2390	
2001	90				
2002	23				
2003	21		LD	HL,2400	POINT TO MESSAGE STORAGE.
2004	00				
2005	24				
2006	3E		LD	A,OF	
2007	0F				SET PORT 80 AS OUTPUT PORT.
2008	D3		OUT	(82),A	
2009	82				
200A	AF		XOR	A	
200B	D3		OUT	(80),A	SEND STOP BIT.
200C	80				
200D	CD	AGAIN	CALL	IN-TTY	GET CHARACTER FROM TTY.
200E	7F				
200F	20				
2010	E6		AND	7F	TURN INTO ASCII.
2011	7F				
2012	77		LD	(HL),A	STORE IT.
2013	3E		LD	A,0D	
2014	0D				CHECK FOR CR.
2015	4E		LD	C,(HL)	
2016	B9		CP	C	
2017	28		JR	Z,EXIT	
2018	06				
2019	CD		CALL	OUT-TTY	SEND CHARACTER TO TTY.
201A	40				
201B	20				
201C	23		INC	HL	ADVANCE POINTER.
201D	18		JR	AGAIN	
201E	EE				
201F	CD	EXIT	CALL	CR	OUTPUT CR AND LINE FEED.
2020	62				
2021	20				
2022	21		LD	HL,2400	POINT TO START OF MESSAGE.
2023	00				
2024	24				
2025	3E	LOOP	LD	A,OD	
2026	0D				CHECK AGAIN FOR CR.
2027	4E		LD	C,(HL)	
2028	B9		CP	C	
2029	28		JR	Z,END	
202A	06				
202B	CD		CALL	OUT-TTY	SEND CHARACTER TO TTY.
202C	40				
202D	20				
202E	23				
202F	18		INC	HL	ADVANCE POINTER.
2030	F4		JR	LOOP	

MEMORY INFORMATION			INSTRUCTION		COMMENT
ADDRESS	DATA	LABEL	OPCODE	OPERAND	
2031	CD	END	CALL	CR	SEND CR & LINE FEED.
2032	62				
2033	20				
2034	C7		RST	00	

PROJECT 73: TTY MESSAGE SHOWN ON THE SD-Z80 SEVEN-SEGMENT DISPLAY

This program takes characters from the TTY and displays them on the seven segment of the SD-Z80. Read the "Program Loading Instructions" before you load this program.

MEMORY INFORMATION			INSTRUCTION		COMMENT
ADDRESS	DATA	LABEL	OPCODE	OPERAND	
2000	31		LD	SP,2390	
2001	90				
2002	23				
2003	3E		LD	A,0F	
2004	0F				SET PORT 80 AS OUTPUT PORT.
2005	D3		OUT	(82),A	
2006	82				
2007	AF		XOR	A	
2008	D3		OUT	(80), A	SEND STOP BIT.
2009	80				
200A	CD	START	CALL	IN-TTY	GET CHARACTER FROM TTY.
200B	7F				
200C	20				
200D	E6		AND	7F	CONVERT TO ASCII.
200E	7F				
200F	D6		SUB	30	
2010	30				TEST NO. IF LESS THAN 30.
2011	38		JR	C,START	JUMP TO START.
2012	F7				
2013	FE		CP	0A	
2014	0A				
2015	38		JR	C,DISPLAY	TEST NO. IF BETWEEN 0 & 9
2016	06				THEN DISPLAY IT.
2017	D6		SUB	07	
2018	07				
2019	FE		CP	10	TEST NO. IF BETWEEN 9 & F THEN
201A	10				DISPLAY IT.
201B	30		JR	NC,START	
201C	ED				
201D	DD	DISPLAY	LD	IX,07A6	SET DISPLAY CODE POINTER.
201E	21				
201F	A6				
2020	07				

MEMORY INFORMATION			INSTRUCTION		COMMENT
ADDRESS	DATA	LABEL	OPCODE	OPERAND	
2021	32		LD	(2026),A	USE NO. AS OFFSET.
2022	26				
2023	20				
2024	DD		LD	A,(1X+d)	GET DISPLAY CODE.
2025	7E				
2026	00				
2027	D3		OUT	(88),A	
2028	88				
2029	3E		LD	A,01	DISPLAY NUMBER.
202A	01				
202B	D3		OUT	(8C),A	
202C	8C				
202D	C3		JP	START	CONTINUE WITH PROGRAM.
202E	0A				
202F	20				

PROJECT 74: TTY LOOK-UP TABLE

This program will take a hexadecimal number between 0 and F from the TTY and display it on the seven-segment display and then output a look up value on the TTY. The new data format and the previous data format are both shown below so that you can compare them. You must read the "Program Loading Instructions" before you load the program.

MEMORY INFORMATION			INSTRUCTION		COMMENT
ADDRESS	DATA	LABEL	OPCODE	OPERAND	
2000	31		LD	SP,2390	
2001	90				
2002	23				
2003	3E		LD	A,OF	
2004	0F				SET PORT 80 AS OUTPUT PORT.
2005	D3		OUT	(82),A	
2006	82				
2007	AF		XOR	A	
2008	D3		OUT	(80),A	SEND OUT STOP BIT.
2009	80				
200A	CD	START	CALL	IN-TTY	GET CHARACTER FROM TTY.
200B	7F				
200C	20				
200D	E6		AND	7F	CONVERT TO ASCII.
200E	7F				
200F	D6		SUB	30	
2010	30				TEST TO SEE IF NO. IS LESS
2011	38		JR	C,START	THAN 30.
2012	F7				

308

MEMORY INFORMATION			INSTRUCTION		COMMENT
ADDRESS	DATA	LABEL	OPCODE	OPERAND	
2013	FE		CP	0A	
2014	0A				
2015	38		JR	C,DISPLAY	
2016	06				TEST IF NO. IS 0 THROUGH 9.
2017	D6		SUB	07	
2018	07				
2019	FE		CP	10	
201A	10				TEST TO SEE IF BETWEEN
201B	30		JR	NC,START	9 AND F.
201C	ED				
201D	DD	DISPLAY	LD	IX,07A6	SET DISPLAY CODE POINTER.
201E	21				
201F	A6				
2020	07				
2021	32		LD	(2027),A	USE NO. AS OFFSET.
2022	27				
2023	20				
2024	F5		PUSH	PSW	SAVE NO.
2025	DD		LD	A,(1X+d)	GET DISPLAY CODE.
2026	7E				
2027	00				
2028	D3		OUT	(88),A	
2029	88				
202A	3E		LD	A,01	DISPLAY NUMBER.
202B	01				
202C	D3		OUT	(8C),A	
202D	8C				
202E	F1		POP	PSW	RESTORE NO. TO ACC.
202F	FD		LD	1Y,20B0	SET LOOK-UP TABLE POINTER.
2030	21				
2031	B0				
2032	20				
2033	32		LD	(2038),A	USE NO. AS OFFSET.
2034	38				
2035	20				
2036	FD		LD	C,(1Y+d)	GET VALUE FROM TABLE.
2037	4E				
2038	00				
2039	CD		CALL	OUT-TTY	SEND VALUE TO TTY.
203A	40				
203B	20				
203C	C3		JP	START	
203D	0A				
203E	20				

ADDRESS	DATA	LABEL	OPCODE	OPERAND	COMMENT
					MEMORY INFORMATION / **INSTRUCTION**
20B0	41				
20B1	42				
20B2	43				
20B3	44				
20B4	45				
20B5	46				
20B6	47				
20B7	48				LOOK-UP TABLE DATA.
20B8	49				
20B9	4A				
20BA	4B				
20BB	4C				
20BC	4D				
20BD	4E				
20BE	4F				
20BF	50				

PROJECT 75: TTY PRINTING—MAIN PROGRAM

This program will get data starting at location 2400. If the data represents a ASCII character it will be printed. The Data Design, Project 76, used as an example will display Z-80 on the TTY. The data starts at location 2400 and ends at location 24C4. You must read the "Program Loading Instructions" before you load the programs in this section.

Begin ADDR.	DATA(SIXTEEN ADDR: FROM BEGIN ADDR. TO NEXT BEGIN ADDR.)
2400	86 5A 5A 5A 5A 5A 5A 5A 5A 5A 5A 5A 97 38 38 38
2410	38 38 8B 30 30 30 0D 90 5A 95 38 38 85 38 38 87
2420	30 30 83 30 30 0D 8F 5A 95 38 89 38 85 30 87 30
2430	0D 8E 5A 96 38 89 38 84 30 89 30 0D 8D 5A 97 38
2440	89 38 83 30 8B 30 0D 8C 5A 99 38 38 85 38 38 84
2450	30 8B 30 0D 8B 5A 89 2D 2D 2D 2D 2D 2D 2D 2D 2D
2460	2D 2D 2D 2D 86 38 38 38 38 38 86 30 8B 30 0D 8A
2470	5A 9B 38 38 85 38 38 84 30 8B 30 0D 89 5A 9B 38
2480	89 38 83 30 8B 30 0D 88 5A 9C 38 89 38 84 30 89
2490	30 0D 87 5A 9D 38 89 38 85 30 87 30 0D 86 5A 9F
24A0	38 38 85 38 38 87 30 30 83 30 30 0D 86 5A 5A 5A
24B0	5A 5A 5A 5A 5A 5A 5A 5A 97 38 38 38 38 38 8B 30
24C0	30 30 0D 00

Fig. 11-3. Data addresses for *data design* "Z80."

MEMORY INFORMATION			INSTRUCTION		COMMENT
ADDRESS	DATA	LABEL	OPCODE	OPERAND	
2000	31		LD	SP,2390	
2001	90				
2002	23				
2003	21		LD	HL,2400	POINT TO DATA STORAGE.
2004	00				
2005	24				
2006	3E		LD	A,0F	
2007	0F				
2008	D3		OUT	(82),A	SET PORT 80 AS OUTPUT PORT.
2009	82				
200A	AF		XOR	A	
200B	D3		OUT	(80),A	SEND STOP BIT.
200C	80				
200D	AF	START	XOR	A	SET ACC. TO ZERO.
200E	4E		LD	C,(HL)	GET DATA.
200F	23		INC	HL	ADVANCE POINTER.
2010	B9		CP	C	TEST FOR END OF DATA.
2011	28		JR	Z,EXIT	
2012	24				IF SO, JUMP.
2013	CB		RL	C	
2014	11				CHECK MSB. FOR TAB.
2015	38		JR	C,TAB	IF SO, JUMP.
2016	10				
2017	CB		RR	C	RESTORE DATA.
2018	19				
2019	79		LD	A,C	
201A	FE		CP	0D	CHECK FOR CR.
201B	0D				
201C	28		JR	Z,CRET	IF SO, JUMP.
201D	05				
201E	CD		CALL	OUT-TTY	PRINT CHARACTER.
201F	40				
2020	20				
2021	18		JR	START	GET NEXT CHARACTER.
2022	EA				
2023	CD	CRET	CALL	CR	OUTPUT CARRIAGE RETURN
2024	62				AND LINE FEED.
2025	20				
2026	18		JR	START	GET NEXT CHARACTER.
2027	E5				
2028	CB	TAB	RR	C	RESTORE DATA.
2029	19				
202A	CB		RES	7,C	RESET MSB.
202B	B9				
202C	59		LD	E,C	PUT NO. OF LOOPS IN E REG.
202D	0E		LD	C,20	LOAD SPACE CODE.
202E	20				
202F	CD	LOOP	CALL	OUT-TTY	OUTPUT SPACE.
2030	40				
2031	20				

MEMORY INFORMATION			INSTRUCTION		COMMENT
ADDRESS	DATA	LABEL	OPCODE	OPERAND	
2032	1D		DEC	E	DECREMENT NO. OF LOOPS.
2033	20		JR	NZ,LOOP	CONTINUE UNTIL COUNTER IS
2034	FA				ZERO.
2035	18		JR	START	GET NEXT CHARACTER.
2036	D6				
2037	C7	EXIT	BST	00	RETURN TO MONITOR.

PROJECT 76: TTY PRINTING—DATA DESIGN

The data given in Fig. 11-3 will produce the Data Design Z-80 on the TTY employing the characters Z, 0, and 8. The data is represented by a new data format explained in Fig. 11-3. This new format is used to save space and writing for the programmer. (See Fig. 11-4.)

```
ZZZZZZZZZZZ                       88888           000
          Z                     88     88         00   00

         Z                     8         8     0       0

        Z                      8         8    0         0
       Z                       8         8   0           0
      Z                         88     88    0           0
     Z         -------------      88888      0           0
    Z                           88     88    0           0
   Z                           8         8   0           0
  Z                            8         8    0         0
 Z                             8         8     0       0
Z                               88     88       00   00
ZZZZZZZZZZZ                       88888           000
```

Fig. 11-4. Graph of data design "Z80."

Chapter 12

Oscilloscope Projects

PROJECT 77: D/A CONVERTER CIRCUITS FOR VERTICAL AND HORIZONTAL INPUTS OF THE OSCILLOSCOPE

Figure 12-1 shows the circuit needed to interface the SD-Z80 Kit with an oscilloscope to display the projects of this chapter on the CRT of the oscilloscope. The vertical and horizontal inputs of the D/A converters go directly to the vertical and horizontal inputs of most oscilloscopes. The ground of the oscilloscope, the D/A converters, and the SD-Z80 Kit MUST be tied to a common point.

The power supplies for the D/A converter circuits are shown in earlier chapters. The 5 V power supply circuit is given in Chapter 1, and the plus and minus 15 V power supply circuit is given in Chapter 10.

PROJECT 78: STATIONARY DISPLAY WITHOUT SWITCH CONTROL DELAY—MAIN PROGRAM

This program displays on the CRT of the oscilloscope the program given in Project 79, the Data Design "Z-80." The D/A converter circuit must be connected to the oscilloscope and the SD-Z80 Kit as indicated in Project 77.

The data design, which is stored in the SD-Z80 memory, is displayed on the CRT by fast-moving dots generated by the CRT electron beam. Since the electron beam is flashing the dots one at a time on the CRT at a very high speed, the data design appears to be a solid design to the observer.

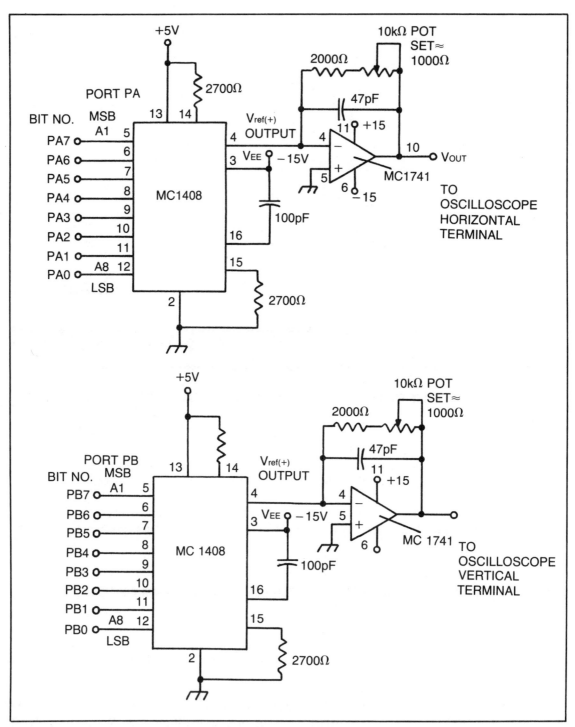

Fig. 12-1. D/A converter circuit. To check proper D/A circuit operation, refer to Chapter 10, Project #58 before operating the above circuit.

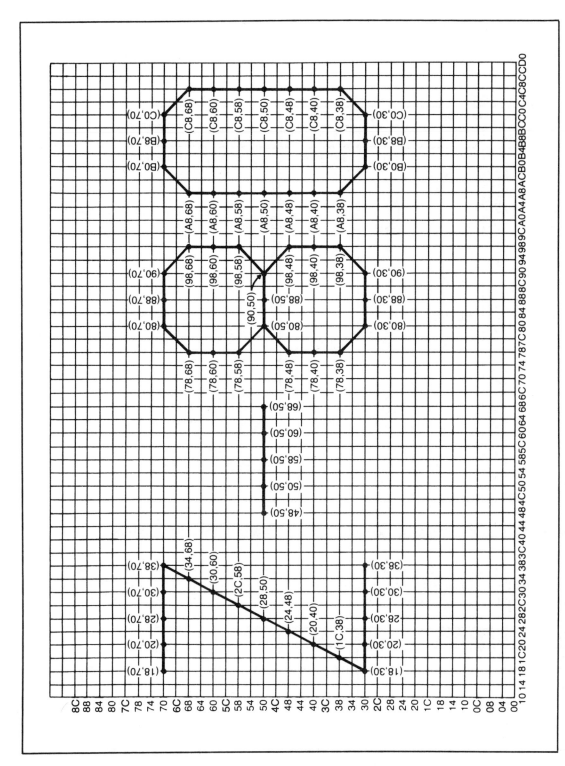

Fig. 12-2. Oscilloscope display, data design "Z80."

315

The dots to be displayed on the CRT have their coordinates stored in memory starting at location 2400. The x coordinates are stored in the even number memory locations and the y coordinates are stored in the odd number memory locations. Figure 12-2 shows a graph of the dots indicating the position each dot should have in the data design "Z80."

MEMORY INFORMATION			INSTRUCTION		COMMENT
ADDRESS	DATA	LABEL	OPCODE	OPERAND	
2000	31		LD	SP,2390	INITIALIZE STACK POINTER
2001	90				
2002	23				
2003	3E		LD	A,0F	
2004	0F				INITIALIZE PORTS 80 AND 81 AS
2005	D3		OUT	(82),A	OUTPUT PORTS.
2006	82				
2007	D3		OUT	(83),A	
2008	83				
2009	21	START	LD	HL,2400	SET POINTER TO FIRST
200A	00				DATA LOCATION.
200B	24				
200C	7E	OUTPUT	LD	A,(HL)	GET HORIZONTAL POSITION.
200D	B7		OR	A	CHECK FOR END OF DISPLAY.
200E	28		JR	Z,START	IF DONE START OVER AGAIN.
200F	F9				
2010	D3		OUT	(80),A	OUTPUT HORIZONTAL POSITION.
2011	80				
2012	23		INC	HL	ADVANCE POINTER.
2013	7E		LD	A,(HL)	GET VERTICAL POSITION.
2014	D3		OUT	(81),A	OUTPUT VERTICAL POSITION.
2015	81				
2016	23		INC	HL	ADVANCE POINTER.
2017	C3		JP	OUTPUT	CONTINUE TO DISPLAY DATA.
2018	0C				
2019	20				

PROJECT 79: STATIONARY DISPLAY WITHOUT SWITCH CONTROL DELAY—DATA DESIGN

The following program is for the design "Z80." The data is stored in the SD-Z80 memory as digital information, then is converted to analog information through the D/A converter circuit. The data will then appear on the CRT of the oscilloscope.

MEMORY INFORMATION			INSTRUCTION		COMMENT
ADDRESS	DATA	LABEL	OPCODE	OPERAND	
2400	18				DATA FOR Z80 DESIGN. THE POSITION
2401	70				THE DATA WILL APPEAR ON THE CRT IS
2402	20				SHOWN IN THE LAST PAGE OF THIS PRO-
2403	70				JECT.
2404	28				

MEMORY INFORMATION			INSTRUCTION		COMMENT
ADDRESS	DATA	LABEL	OPCODE	OPERAND	
2405	70				
2406	30				
2407	70				
2408	38				
2409	70				
240A	34				
240B	68				
240C	30				
240D	60				
240E	2C				
240F	58				
2410	28				
2411	50				
2412	24				
2413	48				
2414	20				
2415	40				
2416	1C				
2417	38				
2418	18				
2419	30				
241A	20				
241B	30				
241C	28				
241D	30				
241E	30				
241F	30				
2420	38				
2421	30				
2422	48				
2423	50				
2424	50				
2425	50				
2426	58				
2427	50				
2428	60				
2429	50				
242A	68				
242B	50				
242C	78				
242D	58				
242E	78				
242F	60				
2430	78				
2431	68				
2432	80				
2433	70				
2434	88				
2435	70				
2436	90				

MEMORY INFORMATION			INSTRUCTION		COMMENT
ADDRESS	DATA	LABEL	OPCODE	OPERAND	
2437	70				
2438	98				
2439	68				
243A	98				
243B	60				
243C	98				
243D	58				
243E	90				
243F	50				
2440	88				
2441	50				
2442	80				
2443	50				
2444	78				
2445	48				
2446	78				
2447	40				
2448	78				
2449	38				
244A	80				
244B	30				
244C	88				
244D	30				
244E	90				
244F	30				
2450	98				
2451	38				
2452	98				
2453	40				
2454	98				
2455	48				
2456	A8				
2457	48				
2458	A8				
2459	50				
245A	A8				
245B	58				
245C	A8				
245D	60				
245E	A8				
245F	68				
2460	B0				
2461	70				
2462	B8				
2463	70				
2464	C0				
2465	70				
2466	C8				
2467	68				
2468	C8				

MEMORY INFORMATION			INSTRUCTION		COMMENT
ADDRESS	DATA	LABEL	OPCODE	OPERAND	
2469	60				
246A	C8				
246B	58				
246C	C8				
246D	50				
246E	C8				
246F	48				
2470	C8				
2471	40				
2472	C8				
2473	38				
2474	C0				
2475	30				
2476	B8				
2477	30				
2478	B0				
2479	30				
247A	A8				
247B	38				
247C	A8				
247D	40				
247E	00				

PROJECT 80: MOVING PICTURE DISPLAY—MAIN PROGRAM

This main program displays on the CRT of the oscilloscope the program in Project 81, the Data Design for a tank. In fact, this program will make the tank move across the CRT. The D/A converter circuit must be connected to the oscilloscope and the SD-Z80 trainer as indicated in Project 77 of this chapter.

The data design, which is stored in the SD-Z80 memory, is displayed on the CRT by fast-moving dots generated by the CRT electron beam. Since the electron beam is flashing the dots one at a time on the CRT at a very high speed, the data design appears to be a solid design to the observer. The data design will first appear stationary, then after a short pause the data design will move off the CRT. This procedure keeps repeating.

The dots to be displayed on the CRT have their coordinates stored in memory starting at location 2400. The x coordinates are stored in the even number memory locations, and the y coordinates are stored in the odd number memory locations. At the end of this section there is a graph of the dots indicating the position each dot should have in the Data Design of the Tank. Figure 12-3 shows a graph of the data design as it will appear on the CRT screen.

MEMORY INFORMATION			INSTRUCTION		COMMENT
ADDRESS	DATA	LABEL	OPCODE	OPERAND	
2000	31		LD	SP,2390	INITIALIZE STACK POINTER.
2001	90				
2002	23				

MEMORY INFORMATION			INSTRUCTION		COMMENT
ADDRESS	DATA	LABEL	OPCODE	OPERAND	
2003	3E		LD	A,0F	
2004	0F				INITIALIZE PORTS 80 AND 81
2005	D3		OUT	(82),A	AS OUTPUT PORTS.
2006	82				
2007	D3		OUT	(83),A	
2008	83				
2009	21	START	LD	HL,2400	SET POINTER TO FIRST DATA
200A	00				LOCATION.
200B	24				
200C	04		INC	B	ADVANCE POSITION OFFSET.
200D	7E	OUTPUT	LD	A,(HL)	GET HORIZONTAL POSITION.
200E	B7		OR	A	CHECK FOR END OF DISPLAY.
200F	28		JR	Z,START	IF ENDED JUMP TO "START."
2010	F8				
2011	80		ADD	A,B	ADD POSITION OFFSET.
2012	D3		OUT	(80),A	OUTPUT HORIZONTAL POSITION.
2013	80				
2014	23		INC	HL	ADVANCE POINTER.
2015	7E		LD	A,(HL)	GET VERTICAL POSITION.
2016	D3		OUT	(81),A	OUTPUT VERTICAL POSITION.
2017	81				
2018	23		INC	HL	ADVANCE POINTER.
2019	DB		IN	A,(94)	GET VALUE FOR DELAY.
201A	94				
201B	57		LD	D,A	
201C	CD		CALL	DELAY	PAUSE BEFORE DISPLAYING
201D	30				NEXT DOT.
201E	20				
201F	C3		JP	OUTPUT	CONTINUE WITH DISPLAY.
2020	0D				
2021	20				
2030	15	LOOP	DEC	D	
2031	20		JR	NZ,LOOP	DELAY ROUTINE.
2032	FD				
2033	C9		RET		

PROJECT 81: MOVING PICTURE DISPLAY—DATA DESIGN FOR THE TANK

The following program is for the tank design. The data are stored in the SD-Z80 memory as digital information, then converted to analog information through the D/A converter circuit, before appearing on the CRT of the oscilloscope. The tank will first appear stationary, then after a pause it will move off the CRT.

MEMORY INFORMATION			INSTRUCTION		COMMENT
ADDRESS	DATA	LABEL	OPCODE	OPERAND	
2400	6E				DATA FOR TANK DESIGN. THE POSITION
2401	60				THE DATA WILL APPEAR ON THE OSCIL-
2402	60				LOSCOPE IS SHOWN ON THE LAST PAGE
					OF THIS PROJECT.

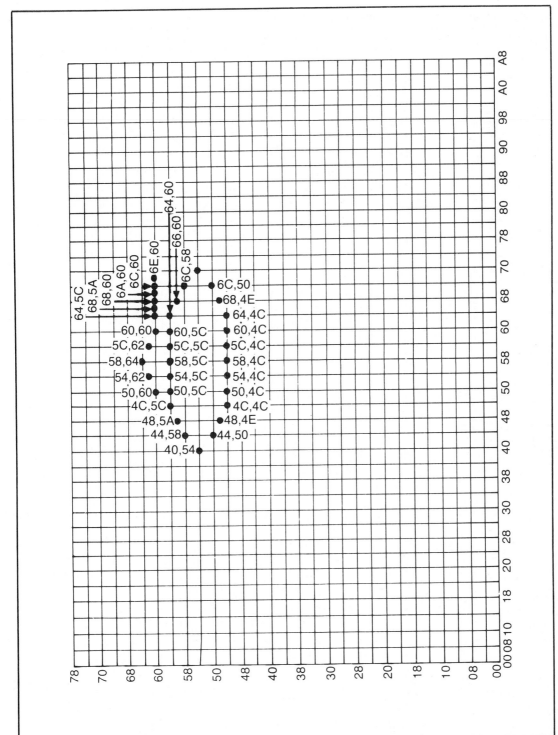

Fig. 12-3. Graph of CRT display for data design "TANK."

321

MEMORY INFORMATION			INSTRUCTION		COMMENT
ADDRESS	DATA	LABEL	OPCODE	OPERAND	
2403	60				
2404	6A				
2405	60				
2406	68				
2407	60				
2408	66				
2409	60				
240A	64				
240B	60				
240C	60				
240D	60				
240E	5C				
240F	62				
2410	58				
2411	64				
2412	54				
2413	62				
2414	50				
2415	60				
2416	4C				
2417	5C				
2418	48				
2419	5A				
241A	44				
241B	58				
241C	40				
241D	54				
241E	44				
241F	50				
2420	48				
2421	4E				
2422	4C				
2423	4C				
2424	50				
2425	4C				
2426	54				
2427	4C				
2428	58				
2429	4C				
242A	5C				
2428	4C				
242C	60				
242D	4C				
242E	64				
242F	4C				
2430	68				
2431	4E				
2432	6C				
2433	50				
2434	70				
2435	54				

ADDRESS	DATA	LABEL	OPCODE	OPERAND	COMMENT
2436	6C				
2437	58				
2438	68				
2439	5A				
243A	64				
243B	5C				
243C	60				
243D	5C				
243E	5C				
243F	5C				
2440	58				
2441	5C				
2442	54				
2443	5C				
2444	50				
2445	5C				
2446	00				

PROJECT 82: MOVING LETTERS PICTURE DISPLAY—MAIN PROGRAM

For an explanation of the main program see Project 80. Instead of the Tank design the design for this program is CSU, given in Project 83. Figure 12-4 shows a graph of the CRT display for the data design, "CSU."

ADDRESS	DATA	LABEL	OPCODE	OPERAND	COMMENT
2000	31		LD	SP,2390	INITIALIZE STACK POINTER.
2001	90				
2002	23				
2003	3E		LD	A,0F	
2004	0F				INITIALIZE PORTS 80 AND 81
2005	D3		OUT	(82),A	AS OUTPUT PORTS.
2006	82				
2007	D3		OUT	(83),A	
2008	83				
2009	21	START	LD	HL,2400	SET POINTER TO FIRST DATA
200A	00				LOCATION.
200B	24				
200C	04		INC	B	ADVANCE POSITION OFFSET.
200D	7E	OUTPUT	LD	A,(HL)	GET HORIZONTAL POSITION.
200E	B7		OR	A	CHECK FOR END OF DISPLAY.
200F	28		JR	Z,START	IF ENDED JUMP TO "START."
2010	F8				
2011	80		ADD	A,B	ADD POSITION OFFSET.
2012	D3		OUT	(80),A	OUTPUT HORIZONTAL POSITION.
2013	80				

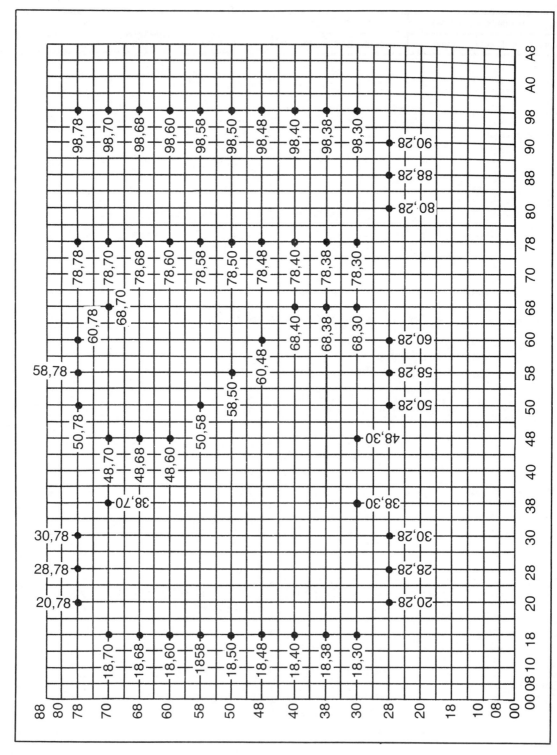

Fig. 12-4. Graph of CRT display for data design "CSU."

MEMORY INFORMATION			INSTRUCTION		COMMENT
ADDRESS	DATA	LABEL	OPCODE	OPERAND	
2014	23		INC	HL	ADVANCE POINTER.
2015	7E		LD	A,(HL)	GET VERTICAL POSITION.
2016	D3		OUT	(81),A	OUTPUT VERTICAL POSITION.
2017	81				
2018	23		INC	HL	ADVANCE POINTER.
2019	DB		IN	A,(94)	GET VALUE FOR DELAY.
201A	94				
201B	57		LD	D,A	PAUSE BEFORE DISPLAYING
201C	CD		CALL	DELAY	NEXT DOT.
201D	30				
201E	20				
201F	C3		JP	OUTPUT	CONTINUE WITH DISPLAY.
2020	0D				
2021	20				
2030	15	LOOP	DEC	D	
2031	20		JR	NZ,LOOP	DELAY ROUTINE.
2032	FD				
2033	C9		RET		

PROJECT 83: MOVING LETTERS PICTURE DISPLAY—DATA DESIGN FOR CSU

MEMORY INFORMATION			INSTRUCTION		COMMENT
ADDRESS	DATA	LABEL	OPCODE	OPERAND	
2400	38				DATA FOR C.S.U. DESIGN. THE POSITION
2401	70				THE DATA WILL APPEAR ON THE OSCIL-
2402	30				LOSCOPE IS SHOWN ON THE LAST PAGE
2403	78				OF THIS PROJECT.
2404	28				
2405	78				
2406	20				
2407	78				
2408	18				
2409	70				
240A	18				
240B	68				
240C	18				
240D	60				
240E	18				
240F	58				
2410	18				
2411	50				
2412	18				
2413	48				
2414	18				
2415	40				
2416	18				
2417	38				

MEMORY INFORMATION			INSTRUCTION		COMMENT
ADDRESS	DATA	LABEL	OPCODE	OPERAND	
2418	18				
2419	30				
241A	20				
241B	28				
241C	28				
241D	28				
241E	30				
241F	28				
2420	38				
2421	30				
2422	48				
2423	30				
2424	50				
2425	28				
2426	58				
2427	28				
2428	60				
2429	28				
242A	68				
242B	30				
242C	68				
242D	38				
242E	68				
242F	40				
2430	60				
2431	48				
2432	58				
2433	50				
2434	50				
2435	58				
2436	48				
2437	60				
2438	48				
2439	68				
243A	48				
243B	70				
243C	50				
243D	78				
243E	58				
243F	78				
2440	60				
2441	78				
2442	68				
2443	70				
2444	78				
2445	78				
2446	78				
2447	70				
2448	78				
2449	68				

MEMORY INFORMATION			INSTRUCTION		COMMENT
ADDRESS	DATA	LABEL	OPCODE	OPERAND	
244A	78				
244B	60				
244C	78				
244D	58				
244E	78				
244F	50				
2450	78				
2451	48				
2452	78				
2453	40				
2454	78				
2455	38				
2456	78				
2457	30				
2458	80				
2459	28				
245A	88				
245B	28				
245C	90				
245D	28				
245E	98				
245F	30				
2460	98				
2461	38				
2462	98				
2463	40				
2464	98				
2465	48				
2466	98				
2467	50				
2468	98				
2469	58				
246A	98				
246B	60				
246C	98				
246D	68				
246E	98				
246F	70				
2470	98				
2471	78				
2472	00				

PROJECT 84: CONTROLLING SPEED OF MOVING PICTURE DISPLAY—MAIN PROGRAM

For an explanation of the main program see Projects 80 and 81. Instead of a tank, the design for this program is "BOOM." The design is programmed to move across the CRT, the speed at which it moves being varied by merely adjusting the DIP switches at port PB. You will enjoy watching the BOOM design moving at different speeds across the CRT as you adjust the switches at port PB. Figure 12-5 shows a graph of the CRT display for the data design, "BOOM."

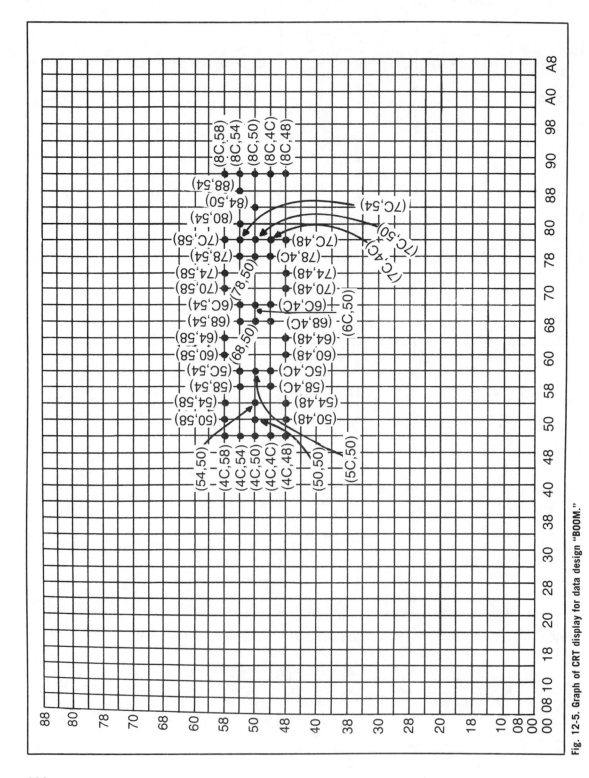

Fig. 12-5. Graph of CRT display for data design "BOOM."

328

MEMORY INFORMATION			INSTRUCTION		COMMENT
ADDRESS	DATA	LABEL	OPCODE	OPERAND	
2000	31		LD	SP,2390	INITIALIZE STACK POINTER.
2001	90				
2002	23				
2003	3E		LD	A,0F	
2004	0F				
2005	D3		OUT	(82),A	INITIALIZE PORTS 80 AND 81
2006	82				AS OUTPUT PORTS.
2007	D3		OUT	(83),A	
2008	83				
2009	DB	START	IN	A,(94)	GET SPEED OF DISPLAY.
200A	94				
200B	80		ADD	A,B	
200C	47		LD	B,A	
200D	21		LD	HL,2400	SET POINTER TO FIRST DATA
200E	00				LOCATION.
200F	24				
2010	7E	OUTPUT	LD	A,(HL)	GET HORIZONTAL POSITION.
2011	B7		OR	A	IF DATA IS 00 THEN START
2012	28		JR	Z,START	OVER.
2013	F5				
2014	80		ADD	A,B	ADD OFFSET.
2015	D3		OUT	(80),A	OUTPUT HORIZONTAL POSITION.
2016	80				
2017	23		INC	HL	ADVANCE POINTER.
2018	7E		LD	A,(HL)	GET VERTICAL POSITION.
2019	D3		OUT	(81),A	OUTPUT VERTICAL POSITION.
201A	81				
201B	23		INC	HL	ADVANCE POINTER.
201C	DB		IN	A,(95)	GET VALUE FOR DELAY.
201D	95				
201E	57		LD	D,A	PAUSE BEFORE DISPLAYING
201F	CD		CALL	DELAY	NEXT DOT.
2020	30				
2021	20				
2022	C3		JP	OUTPUT	CONTINUE WITH DISPLAY.
2023	10				
2024	20				
2030	15	LOOP	DEC	D	DELAY ROUTINE.
2031	20		JR	NZ,LOOP	
2032	FD				
2033	C9		RET		

PROJECT 85: CONTROLLING SPEED OF MOVING PICTURE DISPLAY—DATA DESIGN FOR BOOM

MEMORY INFORMATION			INSTRUCTION		COMMENT
ADDRESS	DATA	LABEL	OPCODE	OPERAND	
2400	4C				DATA FOR BOOM DESIGN. THE POSITION
2401	48				THE DATA WILL APPEAR ON THE OSCIL-
2402	4C				LOSCOPE IS SHOWN ON THE LAST PAGE
					OF THIS PROJECT.

MEMORY INFORMATION			INSTRUCTION		COMMENT
ADDRESS	DATA	LABEL	OPCODE	OPERAND	
2403	4C				
2404	4C				
2405	50				
2406	4C				
2407	54				
2408	4C				
2409	58				
240A	50				
240B	58				
240C	54				
240D	58				
240E	58				
240F	54				
2410	54				
2411	50				
2412	50				
2413	50				
2414	58				
2415	4C				
2416	54				
2417	48				
2418	50				
2419	48				
241A	5C				
241B	4C				
241C	5C				
241D	50				
241E	5C				
241F	54				
2420	60				
2421	58				
2422	64				
2423	58				
2424	68				
2425	54				
2426	68				
2427	50				
2428	68				
2429	4C				
242A	64				
242B	48				
242C	60				
242D	48				
242E	70				
242F	48				
2430	6C				
2431	4C				
2432	6C				
2433	50				
2434	6C				
2435	54				

330

MEMORY INFORMATION			INSTRUCTION		COMMENT
ADDRESS	DATA	LABEL	OPCODE	OPERAND	
2436	70				
2437	58				
2438	74				
2439	58				
243A	78				
243B	54				
243C	78				
243D	50				
243E	78				
243F	4C				
2440	74				
2441	48				
2442	7C				
2443	48				
2444	7C				
2445	4C				
2446	7C				
2447	50				
2448	7C				
2449	54				
244A	7C				
244B	58				
244C	80				
244D	54				
244E	84				
244F	50				
2450	88				
2451	54				
2452	8C				
2453	58				
2454	8C				
2455	54				
2456	8C				
2457	50				
2458	8C				
2459	4C				
245A	8C				
245B	48				
245C	00				

PROJECT 86: SPACE SHUTTLE MOVING DISPLAY—MAIN PROGRAM

For the explanation of the main program see Projects 80 and 81. Instead of the tank, the design for this program is a space shuttle. The design is programmed to move across the CRT, with the speed being controlled by merely adjusting the DIP switches at Port PB. Figure 12-6 shows a graph of the CRT display for the space shuttle data design.

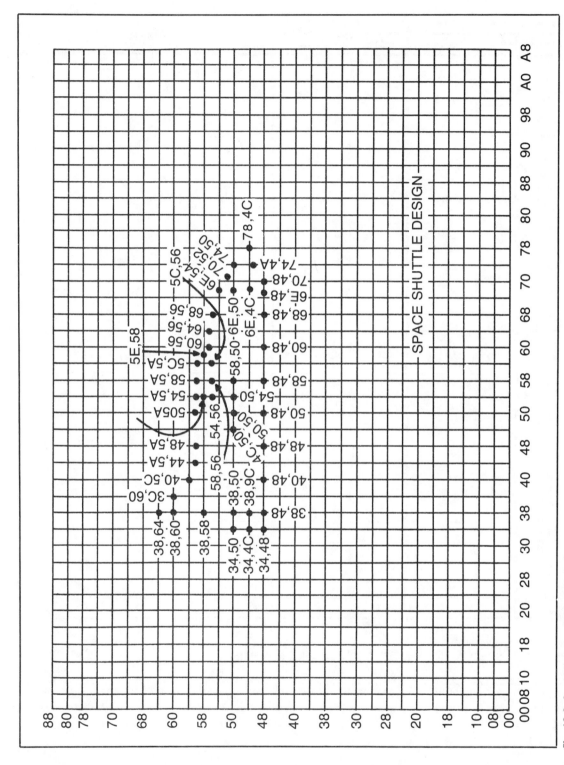

Fig. 12-6. Graph of space shuttle data design.

332

MEMORY INFORMATION			INSTRUCTION		COMMENT
ADDRESS	DATA	LABEL	OPCODE	OPERAND	
2000	31		LD	SP,2390	INITIALIZE STACK POINTER.
2001	90				
2002	23				
2003	3E		LD	A,0F	
2004	0F				INITIALIZE PORTS 80 AND 81
2005	D3		OUT	(82),A	AS OUTPUT PORTS.
2006	82				
2007	D3		OUT	(83),A	
2008	83				
2009	21	START	LD	HL,2400	SET POINTER TO FIRST DATA
200A	00				LOCATION.
200B	24				
200C	04		INC	B	ADVANCE POSITION OFFSET.
200D	7E	OUTPUT	LD	A,(HL)	GET HORIZONTAL POSITION.
200E	B7		OR	A	CHECK FOR END OF DISPLAY.
200F	28		JR	Z,START	IF ENDED JUMP TO "START."
2010	F8				
2011	80		ADD	A,B	ADD POSITION OFFSET.
2012	D3		OUT	(80), A	OUTPUT HORIZONTAL POSITION.
2013	80				
2014	23		INC	HL	ADVANCE POINTER.
2015	7E		LD	A,(HL)	GET VERTICAL POSITION.
2016	D3		OUT	(81),A	OUTPUT VERTICAL POSITION.
2017	81				
2018	23		INC	HL	ADVANCED POINTER.
2019	DB		IN	A,(94)	GET VALUE FOR DELAY.
201A	94				
201B	57		LD	D,A	PAUSE BEFORE DISPLAYING
201C	CD		CALL	DELAY	NEXT DOT.
201D	30				
201E	20				
201F	C3		JP	OUTPUT	CONTINUE WITH DISPLAY.
2020	0D				
2021	20				
2030	15	LOOP	DEC	D	DELAY ROUTINE.
2031	20		JR	NZ,LOOP	
2032	FD				
2033	C9		RET		

PROJECT 87: SPACE SHUTTLE MOVING DISPLAY—DATA DESIGN

MEMORY INFORMATION			INSTRUCTION		COMMENT
ADDRESS	DATA	LABEL	OPCODE	OPERAND	
2400	78				DATA FOR SPACE SHUTTLE.
2401	4C				
2402	74				
2403	50				

MEMORY INFORMATION			INSTRUCTION		COMMENT
ADDRESS	DATA	LABEL	OPCODE	OPERAND	
2404	70				
2405	52				
2406	6E				
2407	54				
2408	6E				
2409	50				
240A	6E				
240B	4C				
240C	6E				
240D	48				
240E	68				
240F	48				
2410	60				
2411	48				
2412	58				
2413	48				
2414	50				
2415	48				
2416	58				
2417	50				
2418	54				
2419	50				
241A	50				
241B	50				
241C	40				
241D	50				
241E	48				
241F	48				
2420	40				
2421	48				
2422	38				
2423	48				
2424	34				
2425	48				
2426	34				
2427	4C				
2428	34				
2429	50				
242A	38				
242B	50				
242C	38				
242D	4C				
242E	38				
242F	58				
2430	38				
2431	60				
2432	38				
2433	64				
2434	3C				
2435	60				
2436	40				

MEMORY INFORMATION			INSTRUCTION		COMMENT
ADDRESS	DATA	LABEL	OPCODE	OPERAND	
2437	5C				
2438	44				
2439	5A				
243A	48				
243B	5A				
243C	50				
243D	5A				
243E	54				
243F	5A				
2440	58				
2441	5A				
2442	5C				
2443	5A				
2444	5E				
2445	58				
2446	60				
2447	56				
2448	5C				
2449	56				
244A	58				
244B	56				
244C	54				
244D	56				
244E	54				
244F	58				
2450	64				
2451	56				
2452	68				
2453	56				
2454	70				
2455	48				
2456	74				
2457	4A				
2458	00				

Chapter 13

Miscellaneous Projects

PROJECT 88: ONE-HERTZ SQUARE WAVE GENERATOR AND TIME DELAY CIRCUIT

The two circuits shown in Fig. 13-1 are needed to execute the programs for Projects 89, 90, and 91. The time delay circuit (Fig. 13-1B) is employed for the three projects. The one-Hertz square wave generator is used for Project 91, but it must be connected to the time delay circuit (see Fig. 13-1B). The interrupt button must be employed with the time delay circuit as shown in Fig. 13-1B to properly execute Projects 89 and 90.

PROJECT 89: ELECTRONIC DICE

The program begins by punching in the machine-language instructions for the main program and the interrupt service routine. First, set the program counter at location 2000, and then execute the program with the key sequence of Reset, 2, 0, 0, and 0. Then press the Exec. key.

The program continually loops until the V interrupt button is pressed. At this time, the value of two dice is output at port 80 in binary coded decimal (BCD) in the form shown in Table 13-1.

When the interrupt button is pressed the second time, the output port is zeroed and the die values are removed. Additional keystrokes on the interrupt button will produce further die values.

You must connect the interrupt button to the time delay circuit of Project 88 and connect the output of the time delay circuit to $\overline{INT}$ on the wire-wrap area of the SD-Z80 kit.

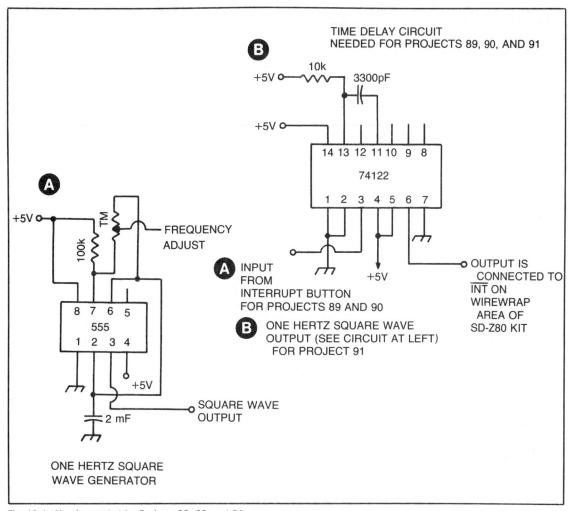

Fig. 13-1. Circuits needed for Projects 89, 90, and 91.

Port 80 Bit Number	BCD Number	
0	BCD 1	First
1	BCD 2	Die
2	BCD 4	Value
3	BCD 8	
4	BCD 1	Second
5	BCD 2	Die
6	BCD 4	Value
7	BCD 8	

Table 13-1. BCD Output
Port Codes for Dice Game.

MEMORY INFORMATION			INSTRUCTION		COMMENT
ADDRESS	DATA	LABEL	OPCODE	OPERAND	
2000	31		LD	SP,2390	SET STACK POINTER.
2001	90				
2002	23				
2003	ED		IM	1	SET INTERRUPT MODE.
2004	56				
2005	3E		LD	A,0F	SET PORT 80 AS AN OUTPUT
2006	0F				PORT.
2007	D3		OUT	(82), A	
2008	82				
2009	AF		XOR	A	CLEAR FLAGS.
200A	FB		EI		ENABLE INTERRUPTS.
200B	21	LOOP-1	LD	HL,2030	SET MEMORY POINTER.
200C	30				
200D	20				
200E	06		LD	B,23	SET LOOP COUNTER.
200F	23				
2010	30	LOOP-2	JR	NC,CONT.	
2011	01				
2012	76		HALT		WAIT FOR INTERRUPT.
2013	23	CONT.	INC	HL	ADVANCE POINTER.
2014	05		DEC	B	DECREMENT COUNTER.
2015	20		JR	NZ,LOOP-2	
2016	F9				
2017	18		JR	LOOP-1	
2018	F2				
2019	38	SUB	JR	C,RESET	
201A	08				
201B	7E		LD	A,(HL)	GET DICE VALUE.
201C	D3		OUT	(80),A	OUTPUT TO PORT 80.
201D	80				
201E	AF		XOR	A	RESET FLAGS.
201F	37		SCF		SET CARRY FLAG.
2020	FB	BACK	EI		ENABLE INTERRUPTS.
2021	ED		RETI		RETURN FROM INTERRUPT.
2022	4D				
2023	AF	RESET	XOR	A	CLEAR FLAGS AND CANCEL
2024	D3		OUT	(80), A	DICE VALUE AT PORT 80.
2025	80				
2026	18		JR	BACK	
2027	F8				
23D3	C3		JP	SUB	
23D4	19				
23D5	20				
2030	11				
2031	12				
2032	13				NOTE:
2033	14				THESE NUMBERS ARE ALL
2034	15				THE POSSIBILITIES OF 2 DIE.
2035	16				

MEMORY INFORMATION			INSTRUCTION		COMMENT
ADDRESS	DATA	LABEL	OPCODE	OPERAND	
2036	21				
2037	22				
2038	23				
2039	24				
203A	25				
203B	26				
203C	31				
203D	32				
203E	33				
203F	34				
2040	35				
2041	36				
2042	41				
2043	42				
2044	43				NOTE: THESE NUMBERS ARE ALL THE POSSIBILITIES OF 2 DIE.
2045	44				
2046	45				
2047	46				
2048	51				
2049	52				
204A	53				
204B	54				
204C	55				
204D	56				
204E	61				
204F	62				
2050	63				
2051	64				
2052	65				
2053	66				

PROJECT 90: RANDOM NUMBER GENERATOR

The program begins by punching in the machine-language instructions into the SD-Z80. The program is operated by positioning the program counter at location 2000 and executing the program with the key sequence of Reset, 2, 0, 0 and 0. Then the Exec. key is pressed.

Port 80 Bit Number	BCD Number	
0	BCD 1	Least Significant Digit of Random Number
1	BCD 2	
2	BCD 4	
3	BCD 8	
4	BCD 1	Most Significant Digit of Random Number
5	BCD 2	
6	BCD 4	
7	BCD 8	

Table 13-2. BCD Output Port Codes for Random Number Generator.

The program continually loops until the interrupt button is pressed. At this time the decimal value of the loop counter is output at port 80 in binary coded decimal (BCD) in the form shown in Table 13-2.

When the interrupt button is pressed the second time, the output port is zeroed.

See Project 88 for the connection of the interrupt button.

MEMORY INFORMATION			INSTRUCTION		COMMENT
ADDRESS	DATA	LABEL	OPCODE	OPERAND	
2000	31		LD	SP,2390	SET STACK POINTER.
2001	90				
2002	23				
2003	ED		IM	1	SET INTERRUPT MODE.
2004	56				
2005	3E		LD	A,0F	SET PORT 80 AS AN OUTPUT
2006	0F				PORT.
2007	D3		OUT	(82),A	
2008	82				
2009	AF		XOR	A	RESET FLAGS.
200A	FB		EI		ENABLE INTERRUPTS.
200B	06	START	LD	B,09	BOUNDS OF RANDOM NUMBER
200C	09				FOR: 0-9 LOAD 09, 0-99 LOAD 63.
200D	30	LOOP	JR	NC,CONT.	
200E	01				
200F	76		HALT		WAIT FOR 2ND INTERRUPT.
2010	05	CONT.	DEC	B	DECREMENT COUNTER.
2011	20		JR	NZ,LOOP	
2012	FA				
2013	18		JR	START	
2014	F6				
2015	F3	SUB	DI		
2016	38		JR	C,RESET	
2017	0A				
2018	AF		XOR	A	CLEAR FLAGS.
2019	78		LD	A,B	LOAD NO. IN LOOP COUNTER TO ACC.
201A	27		DAA		CONVERT TO DECIMAL.
201B	D3		OUT	(80),A	OUTPUT NO. TO PORT 80.
201C	80				
201D	AF		XOR	A	CLEAR FLAGS.
201E	37		SCF		SET CARRY FLAG.
201F	FB	BACK	EI		ENABLE INTERRUPTS.
2020	ED		RETI		RETURN FROM INTERRUPT.
2021	4D				
2022	AF	RESET	XOR	A	RESET FLAGS.
2023	D3		OUT	(80),A	CANCEL NO. AT PORT 80.
2024	80				
2025	18		JR	BACK	
2026	F8				
23D3	C3		JP	SUB	
23D4	15				
23D5	20				

PROJECT 91: TWENTY-FOUR HOUR CLOCK—MAIN PROGRAM

The circuits in Fig. 13-1, Project 88, are used with this project. The machine-language instructions are put into the memory locations, and the circuits in Project 88 is used for interrupt. To set the time (given in military time), the current time is put into memory locations 200A, 200B, and 200C employing the Memory Exam key. For example, if the time is 2:23 P.M. the keystrokes used to set the time are as follows:

- Reset 2, 0, 0, A. Memory Exam, 1, 4 and Next. (This keystroke increments to memory location 200B, the minutes location of this program.)
- 2, 3, Next. (This keystroke increments to memory location 200C, the seconds memory location.
- 0, 0.

Once the preset time is loaded, operation of the clock is started with the following sequence:

- Reset, 2, 0, 1, 0, Exec.

MEMORY INFORMATION			INSTRUCTION		COMMENT
ADDRESS	DATA	LABEL	OPCODE	OPERAND	
2000		10's OF	HOURS	DIGIT	MEMORY LOCATIONS OF
2001		UNIT	HOURS	DIGIT	DISPLAY CODES OF THE
2002		10's OF	MINUTES	DIGIT	TIME TO BE DISPLAYED.
2003		UNIT	MINUTES	DIGIT	
2004		10's OF	SECONDS	DIGIT	
2005		UNIT	SECONDS	DIGIT	
200A		HOURS			LOCATION OF CURRENT
200B		MINUTES			TIME.
200C		SECONDS			
2010	31		LD	SP,2390	INITIALIZE STACK POINTER.
2011	90				
2012	23				
2013	ED		IM	1	SET INTERRUPT MODE 1.
2014	56				
2015	FB		EI		ENABLE INTERRUPT.
2016	06	START	LD	B,20	SET DISPLAY POINTER.
2017	20				
2018	0E		LD	C,06	SET LOOP COUNTER.
2019	06				
201A	11		LD	DE,2000	SET DISPLAY CODE POINTER.
201B	00				
201C	20				
201D	1A	LOOP	LD	A,(DE)	GET DATA AND DISPLAY
201E	D3		OUT	(88),A	IT.
201F	88				
2020	78		LD	A,B	
2021	D3		OUT	(8C),A	
2022	8C				
2023	21		LD	HL,01FF	SET TIME DELAY.
2024	FF				
2025	01				
2026	CD		CALL	DELAY	
2027	52				
2028	06				
2029	CB		SRL	B	POINTER TO NEXT DISPLAY.

MEMORY INFORMATION			INSTRUCTION		COMMENT
ADDRESS	DATA	LABEL	OPCODE	OPERAND	
202A	38				ADVANCE POINTER.
202B	13		INC	DE	
202C	0D		DEC	C	DECREMENT LOOP COUNTER.
202D	20		JR	NZ,LOOP	CONTINUE UNTIL COUNTER
202E	EE				IS ZERO.
202F	18		JR	START	START OVER AGAIN.
2030	E5				

PROJECT 92: TWENTY-FOUR-HOUR CLOCK—UPDATE ROUTINE

MEMORY INFORMATION			INSTRUCTION		COMMENT
ADDRESS	DATA	LABEL	OPCODE	OPERAND	
2031	F3	UP-DATE	DI		DISABLE INTERRUPTS.
2032	F5		PUSH	AF	
2033	C5		PUSH	BC	SAVE REGISTERS ON
2034	D5		PUSH	DE	STACK.
2035	E5		PUSH	HL	
2036	21		LD	HL,200C	POINT TO CURRENT TIME.
2037	0C				
2038	20				
2039	11		LD	DE,2005	POINT TO UNIT SECONDS DISPLAY
203A	05				CODE LOCATION.
203B	20				
203C	7E		LD	A,(HL)	GET CURRENT SECONDS.
203D	B7		OR	A	CLEAR FLAGS.
203E	3C		INC	A	ADVANCE TIME
203F	27		DAA		CONVERT TO DECIMAL.
2040	FE		CP	60	TEST FOR 60 SECONDS.
2041	60				
2042	28		JR	Z,MINUTES	JUMP IF 60 SECONDS.
2043	06				
2044	77		LD	(HL),A	STORE SECONDS.
2045	CD		CALL	SUB	GET DISPLAY CODE.
2046	90				
2047	20				
2048	18		JR	EXIT	JUMP TO EXIT.
2049	36				
204A	3E	MINUTES	LD	A,00	RESET CURRENT SECONDS TO
204B	00				ZERO.
204C	77		LD	(HL),A	
204D	2B		DEC	HL	POINT TO CURRENT MINUTES.
204E	3E		LD	A,40	LOAD DISPLAY CODE FOR ZERO.
204F	40				IN 10's AND ONE's UNIT MEMORY
2050	12		LD	(DE),A	LOCATION OF SECONDS.
2051	1B		DEC	DE	
2052	12		LD	(DE),A	
2053	1B		DEC	DE	
2054	7E		LD	A,(HL)	GET CURRENT MINUTES.
2055	3C		INC	A	ADVANCE TIME.
2056	27		DAA		CONVERT TO DECIMAL.

MEMORY INFORMATION			INSTRUCTION		COMMENT
ADDRESS	DATA	LABEL	OPCODE	OPERAND	
2057	FE		CP	60	TEST FOR 60 MINUTES.
2058	60				
2059	28		JR	Z,HORUS	JUMP IF 60 MINUTES.
205A	06				
205B	77		LD	(HL),A	STORE MINUTES.
205C	CD		CALL	SUB	GET DISPLAY CODE
205D	90				
205E	20				
205F	18		JR	EXIT	JUMP TO EXIT.
2060	1F				
2061	3E	HOURS	LD	A,00	RESET CURRENT MINUTES TO
2062	00				ZERO.
2063	77		LD	(HL),A	
2064	2B		DEC	HL	POINT TO CURRENT HOURS.
2065	3E		LD	A,40	LOAD DISPLAY CODE FOR ZERO.
2066	40				IN 10's AND 1's UNIT MEMORY.
2067	12		LD	(DE),A	LOCATION OF MINUTES.
2068	1B		DEC	DE	
2069	12		LD	(DE),A	
206A	1B		DEC	DE	
206B	7E		LD	A,(HL)	GET CURRENT HOURS.
206C	3C		INC	A	ADVANCE TIME.
206D	27		DAA		CONVERT TO DECIMAL.
206E	FE		CP	24	TEST FOR 24 HOURS.
206F	24				
2070	28		JR	Z,MIDNITE	JUMP IF 24 HOURS.
2071	06				
2072	77		LD	(HL),A	STORE HOURS.
2073	CD		CALL	SUB	GET DISPLAY CODE.
2074	90				
2075	20				
2076	18		JR	EXIT	JUMP TO EXIT.
2077	08				
2078	3E	MIDNITE	LD	A,00	RESET CURRENT HOURS TO
2079	00				ZERO.
207A	77		LD	(HL),A	
207B	3E		LD	A,40	STORE DISPLAY CODE FOR ZERO
207C	40				IN 10's AND 1's UNIT MEMORY.
207D	12		LD	(DE),A	LOCATION OF HOURS.
207E	1B		DEC	DE	
207F	12		LD	(DE),A	
2080	E1	EXIT	POP	HL	RESTORE REGISTERS.
2081	D1		POP	DE	
2082	C1		POP	BC	
2083	F1		POP	AF	
2084	FB		EI		ENABLE INTERRUPT.
2085	ED		RETI		RETURN TO MAIN PROGRAM.
2086	4D				

PROJECT 93: TWENTY-FOUR-HOUR CLOCK—DISPLAY CODE ROUTINE

MEMORY INFORMATION			INSTRUCTION		COMMENT
ADDRESS	DATA	LABEL	OPCODE	OPERAND	
2090	0E	SUB	LD	C,02	SET COUNTER.
2091	02				
2092	DD		LD	IX,07A6	LOAD DISPLAY CODE POINTER.
2093	21				
2094	A6				
2095	07				
2096	E6	LOOP	AND	OF	MASK OUT HIGH BYTE.
2097	OF				
2098	32		LD	(209D),A	USE AS OFFSET FOR POINTER
2099	9D				
209A	20				
209B	DD		LD	A,(1X+d)	GET DISPLAY CODE.
209C	7E				
209D	00				
209E	12		LD	(DE),A	STORE DISPLAY CODE.
209F	0D		DEC	C	DECREMENT COUNTER.
20A0	28		JR	Z,END	JUMP IF COUNTER IS ZERO.
20A1	08				
20A2	7E		LD	A,(HL)	GET NUMBER.
20A3	1F		RRA		
20A4	1F		RRA		MOVE HIGH BYTE TO LOW
20A5	1F		RRA		BYTE.
20A6	1F		RRA		
20A7	1B		DEC	DE	
20A8	18		JR	LOOP	JUMP BACK.
20A9	EC				
20AA	C9	END	RET		RETURN TO SERVICE ROUTINE.
23D3	C3		JP	UP-DATE	JUMP TO UP-DATE ROUTINE.
23D4	31				
23D5	20				

PROJECT 94: METRONOME—EXPLANATION AND MAIN PROGRAM

To operate the metronome, follow these steps:

1. Connect the sound effect amplifier shown in Project 97 to the SD-Z80 Kit.

2. Put the machine-language instructions in the memory of the SD-Z80 Kit. That is, put three programs into memory: the main program, (below), the keyboard scan routine (Project 95), and the store display routine (Project 96).

3. The following keystrokes operate the metronome:

   • RESET, 2, 0, 1, 0, Exec.

4. To load in the beats per minute keystroke 1, 2, 0, for 120 beats per minute. CAUTION: Hold in each number until the seven-segment display blanks out the number you are keystroking. Once all the numbers

representing the beats per minute you desire, the displays will flash the beats per minute which will be heard for the metronome program.

The software is designed to output 60 to 240 beats per minute in 10 beat increments (e.g., 60, 70, 80, etc.). The LED display indicates the number of beats per minute being outputed. Trying to enter a number outside the range of 60 to 240 beats per minute or a number not an integer increment of 10 beats per minute will cause the display to indicate "Err" and the processor will beat at the previous setting. The second keystroke shown in the preceding paragraph is employed to load the desired beats per minute. For example, 60 beats/min would be loaded as 0, 6, 0, and 70 beats/min. would be loaded as 0, 7, 0.

MEMORY INFORMATION			INSTRUCTION		COMMENT
ADDRESS	DATA	LABEL	OPCODE	OPERAND	
2000					LOCATION OF DATA TO
2001					BE DISPLAYED.
2002					
2010	31		LD	SP,2390	
2011	90				
2012	23				
2013	3E		LD	A,0F	DEFINE PORT 80 AS
2014	0F				OUTPUT PORT.
2015	D3		OUT	(82),A	
2016	82				
2017	AF		XOR	A	STORE ZER DIGIT COUNTER
2018	ED		LD	I,A	
2019	47				
201A	01	START	LD	BC,2003	LOAD DISPLAY POINTER AND,
201B	03				LOOP COUNTER.
201C	20				
201D	11		LD	DE,2000	LOAD DISPLAY DATA POINTER
201E	00				
201F	20				
2020	1A	LOOP	LD	A,(DE)	GET DATA.
2021	D3		OUT	(88),A	SEND TO DISPLAY.
2022	88				
2023	78		LD	A,B	POINT TO DISPLAY THAT DATA
2024	D3		OUT	(8C),A	WILL BE SENT TO.
2025	8C				
2026	21		LD	HL,01FF	SET DELAY TIME.
2027	FF				
2028	01				
2029	CD		CALL	DELAY	
202A	52				
202B	06				
202C	CB		SRL	B	POINT TO NEXT DISPLAY.
202D	38				
202E	13		INC	DE	POINT TO NEXT DATA.
202F	0D		DEC	C	DECREMENT LOOP COUNTER.
2030	20		JR	NZ,LOOP	LOOP BACK UNTIL DONE.
2031	EE				
2032	CD		CALL	KEY-SCAN	SCAN KEY BOARD FOR NO.
2033	50				
2034	20				

MEMORY INFORMATION			INSTRUCTION		COMMENT
ADDRESS	DATA	LABEL	OPCODE	OPERAND	
2035	3E		LD	A,01	TURN ON SPEAKER.
2036	01				
2037	D3		OUT	(80),A	
2038	80				
2039	2A		LD	HL,(2008)	
203A	08				GET TIME DELAY.
203B	20				
203C	CD		CALL	DELAY	
203D	52				PAUSE BEFORE RESETTING
203E	06				SPEAKER.
203F	AF		XOR	A	
2040	D3		OUT	(80),A	
2041	80				TURN OFF SPEAKER.
2042	2A		LD	HL,(2008)	
2043	08				GET TIME DELAY.
2044	20				
2045	CD		CALL	DELAY	
2046	52				PAUSE BEFORE CONTINUING.
2047	06				WITH PROGRAM.
2048	C3		JP	START	
2049	1A				
204A	20				
2004					
2005					THESE LOCATIONS ARE USED AS TEMPORARY STORAGE FOR FIRST TWO DIGITS LOADED FROM KEYBOARD.
2008	00				DATA STORED IN THESE LOCATIONS WILL BE USED IN DELAY ROUTINE IN MAIN PROGRAM.
2009	00				NOTE: PRELOAD LOCATIONS TO ZERO.

PROJECT 95: METRONOME—KEYBOARD SCAN ROUTINE

MEMORY INFORMATION			INSTRUCTION		COMMENT
ADDRESS	DATA	LABEL	OPCODE	OPERAND	
2050	3E		LD	A,7F	TURN OFF DISPLAY.
2051	7F				
2052	D3		OUT	(88),A	
2053	88				
2054	3E		LD	A,3F	OUTPUT ALL ROWS LOW.
2055	3F				
2056	D3		OUT	(8C),A	
2057	8C				
2058	DB		IN	A,(90)	GET DATA FROM KEYBOARD.
2059	90				
205A	E6		AND	1F	MASK OUT UNWANTED INPUTS
205B	1F				

MEMORY INFORMATION			INSTRUCTION		COMMENT
ADDRESS	DATA	LABEL	OPCODE	OPERAND	
205C	FE		CP	1F	ANY KEY DOWN?
205D	1F				
205E	C8		RET	Z	NO, RETURN TO MAIN PROGRAM
205F	CD		CALL	DELAY	DEBOUNCE KEYS.
2060	4F				
2061	06				
2062	06		LD	B,01	
2063	01				
2064	78	LOOP-1	LD	A,B	PLACE SELECTED ROW
2065	D3		OUT	(8C),A	LOW.
2066	8C				
2067	DB		IN	A,(90)	INPUT DATA.
2068	90				
2069	E6		AND	1F	MASK OUT UNWANTED INPUTS.
206A	1F				
206B	FE		CP	IF	IS KEY DOWN?
206C	1F				
206D	20		JR	NZ,LOAD	YES, DECODE KEY.
206E	04				
206F	CB		RLC	B	NO, SELECT NEXT ROW.
2070	00				
2071	18		JR	LOOP-1	LOOP BACK
2072	F1				
2073	0E	LOAD	LD	C,00	
2074	00				
2075	0D	DEC	DEC	C	
2076	CB		SRL	B	
2077	38				
2078	20		JR	NZ,DEC	CONTINUE WHEN ZERO.
2079	FB				
207A	CB		SLA	C	
207B	21				
207C	CB		SLA	C	
207D	21				
207E	CB		SLA	C	
207F	21				
2080	CB		SLA	C	SHIFT NO. TO HIGH NIBBLE.
2081	21				
2082	81		ADD	A,C	ADD NO. TO ACC.
2083	21		LD	HL,07B9	SET POINTER TO KEYVALUE.
2084	B9				LOOK-UP TABLE.
2085	07				
2086	BE	LOOP-2	CP	(HL)	IS ACC. EQUAL TO TABLE VALUE?
2087	28		JR	Z,Loop-3	YES, JUMP AHEAD.
2088	04				
2089	23		INC	HL	ADVANCE POINTERS.
208A	04		INC	B	
208B	18		JR	LOOP-2	LOOP BACK.
208C	F9				

MEMORY INFORMATION			INSTRUCTION		COMMENT
ADDRESS	DATA	LABEL	OPCODE	OPERAND	
208D	DB	LOOP-3	IN	A,(90)	
208E	90		1F		
208F	E6		AND	1F	CHECK FOR KEY RELEASE.
2090	1F				
2091	FE		CP	1F	
2092	1F				
2093	20		JR	NZ,LOOP-3	LOOP BACK TILL KEY UP.
2094	F8				
2095	CD		CALL	DELAY	DEBOUNCE KEY.
2096	4F				
2097	06				
2098	78		LD	A,B	GET KEY VALUE

PROJECT 96: METRONOME—STORE DISPLAY ROUTINE

MEMORY INFORMATION			INSTRUCTION		COMMENT
ADDRESS	DATA	LABEL	OPCODE	OPERAND	
2099	DD		LD	IX,07A6	SET DISPLAY CODE POINTER.
209A	21				
209B	A6				
209C	07				
209D	32		LD	(20AB),A	USES NO. AS OFFSET.
209E	AB				
209F	20				
20A0	FD		LD	1Y,2000	POINT TO STORAGE LOCATION
20A1	21				OF DISPLAY CODE.
20A2	00				
20A3	20				
20A4	ED		LD	A,I	GET VALUE FROM DIGIT COUNTER.
20A5	57				
20A6	32		LD	(20AE),A	USE AS AN OFFSET.
20A7	AE				
20A8	20				
20A9	DD		LD	A,(1X+d)	GET DISPLAY CODE.
20AA	7E				
20AB	00				
20AC	FD		LD	(1Y+d),A	STORE DISPLAY CODE.
20AD	77				
20AE	00				
20AF	ED		LD	A,I	GET DIGIT COUNT.
20B0	57				
20B1	3C		INC	A	INCREMENT COUNT.
20B2	ED		LD	I,A	STORE COUNT.
20B3	47				
20B4	FE		CP	03	IS COUNT EQUAL TO 3?
20B5	03				
20B6	28		JR	Z,ANSWER	YES, FORM ANSWER.
20B7	07				
20B8	21		LD	HL,2003	NO, FORM STORAGE LOCATION
20B9	03				FOR KEY NO. PRESSED.

MEMORY INFORMATION			INSTRUCTION		COMMENT
ADDRESS	DATA	LABEL	OPCODE	OPERAND	
20BA	20				NO, FORM STORAGE LOCATION
20BB	85		ADD	L	FOR KEY NO. PRESSED.
20BC	6F		LD	L,A	
20BD	70		LD	(HL),B	STORE KEY NO.
20BE	C9		RET		
20BF	21	ANSWER	LD	HL,2005	POINT TO LOCATION OF DATA
20C0	05				
20C1	20				
20C2	7E		LD	A,(HL)	GET DATA.
20C3	17		RAL		
20C4	17		RAL		
20C5	17		RAL		SHIFT NO. TO HIGH NIBBLE
20C6	17		RAL		
20C7	B0		OR	B	FORM NO.
20C8	4F		LD	C,A	STORE NO.
20C9	2B		DEC	HL	POINT TO NEXT DATA.
20CA	46		LD	B,(HL)	GET DATA.
20CB	21		LD	HL,2110	POINT TO LOOK UP TABLE FOR
20CC	10				METRONOME.
20CD	21				
20CE	16		LD	D,00	CLEAR REGISTER.
20CF	00				
20D0	3E		LD	A,60	
20D1	60				
20D2	B9	FIND	CP	C	IS NO. EQUAL TO NO. IN ACC?
20D3	28		JR	Z,CHECK	YES, CHECK NO. IN REG B.
20D4	23				
20D5	C6	ADD	ADD	10	NO, ADD 10 TO NO. IN ACC.
20D6	10				
20D7	27		DAA		DECIMAL ADJUST NO.
20D8	30		JR	NC,ADVANCE	
20D9	01				
20DA	14		INC	D	
20DB	23	ADVANCE	INC	HL	ADVANCE POINTER.
20DC	F5		PUSH	AF	
20DD	7D		LD	A,L	CHECK TO SEE IF AT END
20DE	FE		CP	23	OF TABLE.
20DF	23				
20E0	C2		JP	NZ,LOOP-4	NO, CONTINUE WITH LOOP.
20E1	F4				
20E2	20				
20E3	21		LD	HL,2000	
20E4	00				
20E5	20				
20E6	3E		LD	A,06	
20E7	06				YES, LOAD "ERR" MESSAGE
20E8	77		LD	(HL),A	FOR DISPLAY ROUTINE.
20E9	23		INC	HL	
20EA	3E		LD	A,2F	
20EB	2F				

MEMORY INFORMATION			INSTRUCTION		COMMENT
ADDRESS	DATA	LABEL	OPCODE	OPERAND	
20EC	77		LD	(HL),A	YES, LOAD "ERR" MESSAGE
20ED	23		INC	HL	FOR DISPLAY ROUTINE.
20EE	77		LD	(HL),A	
20EF	AF	EXIT	XOR	A	ZERO DIGIT COUNTER.
20F0	ED		LD	I,A	
20F1	47				
20F2	F1		POP	AF	
20F3	C9		RET		RETURN TO MAIN PROGRAM.
20F4	F1	LOOP-4	POP	AF	
20F5	C3		JP	FIND	
20F6	D2				
20F7	20				
20F8	F5	CHECK	PUSH	AF	
20F9	7A		LD	A,D	
20FA	B8		CP	B	IS NO. IN B-A.
20FB	C2		JP	NZ,LOOP-5	NO, CONTINUE.
20FC	05				
20FD	21				
20FE	7E		LD	A,(HL)	YES, GET VALUE FROM TABLE.
20FF	32		LD	(2009),A	STORE VALUE.
2100	09				
2101	20				
2102	C3		JP	EXIT	
2103	EF				
2104	20				
2105	F1	LOOP-5	POP	AF	
2106	C3		JP	ADD	
2107	D5				
2108	20				
		BEATS/	MINUTE		LOOK UP TABLE FOR THE METRONOME.
2110	F0	60			
2111	CC	70			
2112	B4	80			
2113	A0	90			
2114	90	100			
2115	84	110			
2116	78	120			
2117	70	130			
2118	67	140			
2119	60	150			CORRESPONDING BEATS PER MINUTE.
211A	5A	160			
211B	55	170			
211C	50	180			
211D	4B	190			
211E	48	200			
211F	45	210			
2120	42	220			
2121	3F	230			
2122	3C	240			

PROJECT 97: METRONOME—SOUND EFFECT AMPLIFIER

Figure 13-2 shows the circuit for the amplifier used to simulate the sound of a metronome. It must be connected to the SD-Z80 as indicated.

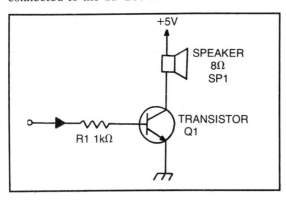

Fig. 13-2. From bit No. "0" output port 80.

Parts List

Q1: Transistor, 2N2222
SP1: Speaker, 8Ω miniature (Radio Shack Catalog No. 40-247)
R1: Resistor, 1kΩ, ¼ W

PROJECT 98: PARALLEL DATA OUTPUT OR MEMORY DUMP TO LINE PRINTER

This program sends 200 characters per second to a printer. The program displays the output to the printer on the LEDs connected on port 80.

MEMORY INFORMATION			INSTRUCTION		COMMENT
ADDRESS	DATA	LABEL	OPCODE	OPERAND	
2000	31		LD	SP,2390	SET STACK POINTER.
2001	90				
2002	23				
2003	ED		IM	2	SET INTERRUPT MODE.
2004	5E				
2005	3E		LD	A,20	LOAD INTERRUPT REGISTER
2006	20				WITH HIGH 8-BITS OF INTERRUPT
2007	ED		LD	1,A	SERVICE ROUTINE. STARTING
2008	47				ADDRESS TABLE.
2009	3E		LD	A,0F	SET PORTS 80 PLUS 81 AS
200A	0F				
200B	D3		OUT	(82),A	OUTPUT PORTS.
200C	82				
200D	D3		OUT	(83),A	
200E	83				
200F	3E		LD	A,40	LOAD INTERRUPT VECTOR FOR
2010	40				PORT 80.

MEMORY INFORMATION			INSTRUCTION		COMMENT
ADDRESS	DATA	LABEL	OPCODE	OPERAND	
2011	D3		OUT	(82),A	LOAD INTERRUPT VECTOR FOR
2012	82				PORT 80
2013	3E		LD	A,87	
2014	87				ENABLE PORT 80 INTERRUPTS.
2015	D3		OUT	(82),A	
2016	82				
2017	21		LD	HL,2400	POINT TO DATA TO BE SENT.
2018	00				
2019	24				
201A	0E		LD	C,00	SET COUNTER.
201B	00				
201C	FB	BACK	EI		ENABLE INTERRUPTS.
201D	76		HALT		WAIT FOR INTERRUPTS.
201E	23		INC	HL	ADVANCE POINTER.
201F	0D		DEC	C	DECREMENT COUNTER.
2020	20		JR	NZ,BACK	JUMP BACK IF ALL DATA NOT
2021	FA				SENT.
2022	C7		RST	00	RETURN TO MONITOR.
2030	7E	SUB	LD	A,(HL)	GET DATA.
2031	D3		OUT	(80),A	OUTPUT DATA TO INTERRUPTING
2032	80				DEVICE.
2033	D3		OUT	(81),A	OUTPUT DATA TO LED's.
2034	81				
2035	ED		RETI		
2036	4D				
2040	30		LOWER	8-BITS	INTERRUPT SERVICE ROUTINE.
2041	20		HIGHER	8-BITS	STARTING ADDRESS TABLE.

PROJECT 99: SD-Z80 USED AS A TRANSMITTER

This program runs at a 110 baud rate transmitting data to another SD-Z80 Kit. The PA7 line is employed as the output for data transmission. The data to be transferred begins at location 2400. The words are sent out using even parity.

MEMORY INFORMATION			INSTRUCTION		COMMENT
ADDRESS	DATA	LABEL	OPCODE	OPERAND	
2000	31		LD	SP,2390	SET STACK POINTER.
2001	90				
2002	23				
2003	21		LD	HL,2400	POINT TO DATA TO BE TRANSMITTED.
2004	00				
2005	24				
2006	3E		LD	A,CF	
2007	CF				INITIALIZE PORT 80 IN MODE
2008	D3		OUT	(82),A	3.
2009	82				
200A	3E		LD	A,7F	DEFINE BIT 7 TO BE AN
200B	7F				OUTPUT BIT. ALL OTHER BITS
200C	D3		OUT	(82),A	AS INPUTS.
200D	82				

MEMORY INFORMATION			INSTRUCTION		COMMENT
ADDRESS	DATA	LABEL	OPCODE	OPERAND	
200E	AF	START	XOR	A	ZERO ACC.
200F	06		LD	B,08	SET BIT COUNTER.
2010	08				
2011	D3		OUT	(80),A	SEND START BIT.
2012	80				
2013	E5		PUSH	HL	
2014	21		LD	HL,0561	SET DELAY TIME.
2015	61				
2016	05				
2017	CD		CALL	DELAY	DELAY FOR 1 BIT.
2018	52				
2019	06				
201A	E1		POP	HL	
201B	4E		LD	C,(HL)	GET CHARACTER.
201C	79	LOOP	LD	A,C	MOVE IT TO ACC.
201D	1F		RRA		ROTATE BIT TO BE SENT INTO CARRY.
201E	4F		LD	C,A	SAVE REMAINDER.
201F	1F		RRA		ROTATE BIT BACK INTO ACC.
2020	D3		OUT	(80),A	SEND BIT.
2021	80				
2022	E5		PUSH	HL	
2023	21		LD	HL,0561	SET DELAY TIME.
2024	61				
2025	05				
2026	CD		CALL	DELAY	DELAY FOR 1 BIT.
2027	52				
2028	06				
2029	E1		POP	HL	
202A	05		DEC	B	DECREMENT BIT COUNTER.
202B	20		JR	NZ,LOOP	JUMP IF ALL BITS HAVEN'T BEEN SENT.
202C	EF				
202D	3E		LD	A,80	SEND STOP BIT.
202E	80				
202F	D3		OUT	(80),A	
2030	80				
2031	E5		PUSH	HL	
2032	21		LD	HL,09C4	SET DELAY TIME.
2033	C4				
2034	09				
2035	CD		CALL	DELAY	DELAY FOR 2 BITS.
2036	52				
2037	06				
2038	E1		POP	HL	
2039	7E		LD	A,(HL)	CHECK FOR ESC. CHARACTER.
203A	FE		CP	1B	
203B	1B				
203C	28		JR	Z,END	
203D	03				
203E	23		INC	HL	ADVANCE POINTER.

MEMORY INFORMATION			INSTRUCTION		COMMENT
ADDRESS	DATA	LABEL	OPCODE	OPERAND	
203F	18		JR	START	
2040	CD				RETURN TO MONITOR.
2041	C7	END	RST	00	

PROJECT100: SD-Z80 USED AS A RECEIVER

This program receives series data from another SD-Z80 Kit using the PB7 line to input the data. The words brought into the Kit are stored sequentially starting at location 2400. When an odd parity is detected the parity error routine writes EE in location 2043. The program stops receiving once an ESC character code is received.

MEMORY INFORMATION			INSTRUCTION		COMMENT
ADDRESS	DATA	LABEL	OPCODE	OPERAND	
2000	31		LD	SP,2390	SET STACK POINTER.
2001	90				
2002	23				
2003	21		LD	HL,2400	POINT TO DATA STORAGE.
2004	00				
2005	24				
2006	AF		XOR	A	ZERO ACC. & CLEAR FLAGS.
2007	32		LD	(2043),A	CLEAR ERROR MESSAGE.
2008	43				
2009	20				
200A	01	START	LD	BC,0008	SET BIT COUNTER AND CLEAR
200B	08				CHARACTER REGISTER.
200C	00				
200D	DB	BACK	IN	A,(81)	
200E	81				
200F	E6		AND	80	
2010	80				WAIT FOR START BIT.
2011	17		RLA		
2012	38		JR	C,BACK	
2013	F9				
2014	E5		PUSH	HL	
2015	21		LD	HL,0792	SET DELAY TIME.
2016	92				
2017	07				
2018	CD		CALL	DELAY	DELAY FOR 1½ BITS.
2019	52				
201A	06				
201B	E1		POP	HL	
201C	DB	READ	IN	A,(81)	GET BIT.
201D	81				
201E	E6		AND	80	
201F	80				
2020	17		RLA		PACK BIT IN CHARACTER REGISTER.

MEMORY INFORMATION			INSTRUCTION		COMMENT
ADDRESS	DATA	LABEL	OPCODE	OPERAND	
2021	78		LD	A,B	PACK BIT IN CHARACTER
2022	1F		RRA		REGISTER.
2023	47		LD	B,A	
2024	E5		PUSH	HL	
2025	21		LD	HL,0561	SET DELAY TIME.
2026	61				
2027	05				
2028	CD		CALL	DELAY	DELAY FOR 1 BIT.
2029	52				
202A	06				
202B	E1		POP	HL	
202C	OD		DEC	C	DECREMENT BIT COUNTER.
202D	20		JR	NZ,READ	
202E	ED				
202F	70		LD	(HL),B	STORE 8-BIT CHARACTER.
2030	B0		OR	B	
2031	E4		CALL	P0,ERROR	CHECK PARITY IF ODD CALL
2032	3D				"ERROR" MESSAGE.
2033	20				
2034	7E		LD	A,(HL)	
2035	FE		CP	1B	CHECK FOR ESC. CHARACTER.
2036	1B				
2037	28		JR	Z,END	
2038	03				JUMP IF LAST CHAR. RECEIVED.
2039	23		INC	HL	ADVANCE POINTER.
203A	18		JR	START	
203B	CE				
203C	C7	END	RST	00	RETURN TO MONITOR.
203D	3E	ERROR	LD	A,EE	
203E	EE				
203F	32		LD	(2043),A	STORE ERROR MESSAGE.
2040	43				
2041	20				
2042	C9		RET		
2043					LOCATION OF ERROR MESSAGE.

PROJECT 101: SD-Z80 TRANSMITTING-RECEIVING CONNECTIONS

The diagram shown below shows the connections that must be made between two SD-Z80 Kits so that the kits may communicate with one another.

PB7	PA7
PA7	PB7
GROUND	GROUND

Now either can be used as a transmitter or receiver.

1. Start the Receive Program.
2. Start the Transmit Program.
3. Check memory locations starting at 2400 to see if "message" was received.
4. Check location 2043 to make sure no parity error occurs. (No. EE there).
5. Modify one character of your message in the transmitter by giving it odd parity.
6. Do parts (1) and (2) above again.
7. Check to see that your error detection routine has written an "EE" in location 2043.

Index